Principles of Circuit Synthesis

McGRAW-HILL ELECTRICAL AND ELECTRONIC ENGINEERING SERIES

Frederick Emmons Terman, *Consulting Editor*

W. W. Harman, Hubert Heffner, and J. G. Truxal, *Associate Consulting Editors*

AHRENDT AND SAVANT   Servomechanism Practice
ANGELO   Electronic Circuits
ASELTINE   Transform Method in Linear System Analysis
ATWATER   Introduction to Microwave Theory
BAILEY AND GAULT   Alternating-current Machinery
BERANEK   Acoustics
BRENNER AND JAVID   Analysis of Electric Circuits
BROWN   Analysis of Linear Time-invariant Systems
BRUNS AND SAUNDERS   Analysis of Feedback Control Systems
CAGE   Theory and Application of Industrial Electronics
CAUER   Synthesis of Linear Communication Networks
CHEN   The Analysis of Linear Systems
CHEN   Linear Network Design and Synthesis
CHIRLIAN AND ZEMANIAN   Electronics
CLEMENT AND JOHNSON   Electrical Engineering Science
COTE AND OAKES   Linear Vacuum-tube and Transistor Circuits
CUCCIA   Harmonics, Sidebands, and Transients in Communication Engineering
CUNNINGHAM   Introduction to Nonlinear Analysis
EASTMAN   Fundamentals of Vacuum Tubes
EVANS   Control-system Dynamics
FEINSTEIN   Foundations of Information Theory
FITZGERALD AND HIGGINBOTHAM   Basic Electrical Engineering
FITZGERALD AND KINGSLEY   Electric Machinery
FRANK   Electrical Measurement Analysis
FRIEDLAND, WING, AND ASH   Principles of Linear Networks
GEPPERT   Basic Electron Tubes
GHOSE   Microwave Circuit Theory and Analysis
GREINER   Semiconductor Devices and Applications
HAMMOND   Electrical Engineering
HANCOCK   An Introduction to the Principles of Communication Theory
HAPPELL AND HESSELBERTH   Engineering Electronics
HARMAN   Fundamentals of Electronic Motion
HARMAN   Principles of the Statistical Theory of Communication
HARMAN AND LYTLE   Electrical and Mechanical Networks
HARRINGTON   Introduction to Electromagnetic Engineering
HARRINGTON   Time-harmonic Electromagnetic Fields
HAYT   Engineering Electromagnetics
HILL   Electronics in Engineering
HUELSMAN   Circuits, Matrices, and Linear Vector Spaces
JAVID AND BRENNER   Analysis, Transmission, and Filtering of Signals
JAVID AND BROWN   Field Analysis and Electromagnetics
JOHNSON   Transmission Lines and Networks
KOENIG AND BLACKWELL   Electromechanical System Theory
KRAUS   Antennas
KRAUS   Electromagnetics

PRINCIPLES OF
CIRCUIT SYNTHESIS

Ernest S. Kuh

Donald O. Pederson

ASSOCIATE PROFESSORS OF ELECTRICAL ENGINEERING
UNIVERSITY OF CALIFORNIA, BERKELEY

McGRAW-HILL BOOK COMPANY, INC.

New York   Toronto   London

1959

PRINCIPLES OF CIRCUIT SYNTHESIS

III

35608

THE MAPLE PRESS COMPANY, YORK, PA.

PREFACE

Undergraduate electrical engineering curriculums are being increasingly modified and modernized to include fundamental rather than restricted or specialized subject matter. This trend is illustrated by the sequence of courses outlined below, which has been adopted by the University of California at Berkeley.

In linear circuit theory the first of two courses may deal with the fundamentals of circuit analysis in both the time and the frequency domains, i.e., with regard to both the transient and the steady state. Often, in this course, the students are introduced to the complex-frequency variable. Of course, the importance of the sinusoidal steady state, which constituted the entire content of the former courses in linear circuit theory, is not minimized. But the subject is now placed in a better perspective in the whole scheme of circuit analysis and application. The second course may then be a more advanced one in linear systems or circuit analysis. Here the important concept is the impedance or system function concept. Functions of complex-variable and the Fourier and Laplace transforms are introduced. The students become familiar with the complex-frequency plane, poles and zeros, and the relationship between the time and frequency responses for electrical, mechanical, and electromechanical circuits.

Much of the material in the two courses just described was formerly included in more advanced courses. But, as more and more engineering teachers gained a thorough understanding of the advanced material, the fundamental aspects were seen to be introducible with advantage in the earlier courses. As has been pointed out by others, the students had no more difficulty in learning the new material than the old. They are, in fact, quick to realize that the new material is broader and more basic.

The principles that apply to the teaching of circuit analysis also apply to the teaching of network synthesis. The undergraduate course in the principles and design of communication circuits need not be restricted to the elementary aspects of classical image filter or artificial line theory. With a basic and broad background in circuit analysis, it is possible to introduce the principles of modern circuit synthesis. Such a course enables students to handle and appreciate a much greater range of problems than the limited application of image filter theory. In particular, linear circuits, communication circuits, and control circuits can be designed to realize prescribed specifications in the time and frequency domains. In addition, the graduating students acquire a sufficient background to study the current technical literature individually. For those students going on to graduate work, more time is available to study advanced topics of importance.

The present book constitutes a text for a second-semester senior course in communication circuits, of which the prerequisite is a semester course in linear circuit and systems analysis. The aim of the course and the book is to introduce the principles of modern circuit synthesis together with the key aspects of classical filter theory. Modern circuit synthesis is esoteric and filled with detail. In many of its aspects it is an area of applied mathematics. However, the fundamentals of the modern approximation and realization problems can be introduced in an unsophisticated manner by a physical approach. These principles can then be used in a vast number of practical problems and applications.

The book has been developed and used over a period of several years. From the inception of the course, it has been enthusiastically received by the students. It has purposely been prepared in a concise form. A concise text with a minimum of verbiage permits the reader to grasp more readily the step-by-step, brick-upon-brick evolution of synthesis theory from the basis of circuit analysis. Experience has shown that the individual student and reader can, with the proper background and with diligence, work and think through the developments and reconstruct the illustrations. In a formal course the student has an advantage in that the teacher of such a course will undoubtedly be well versed in modern circuit synthesis; the teacher will be able to amplify and extend the text material as students demand. For the teacher, fortunately, there are now available many books on synthesis at the graduate level.

The plan of the book is as follows:

Chapter 1 introduces the reader to certain representative system applications, in which a key aspect is the proper design or synthesis of communication and control circuits. Chapter 2 is a review of the salient features of circuit analysis in the time and frequency domains. Of particular importance are the concepts of natural frequencies, stability conditions, and network or system functions. A restriction is made to circuits with lumped, linear, and time-invariant elements. The remainder of the book deals with four major topics: the approximation problem, 2-port characterization and description, realization by the removal technique, and the building-block synthesis technique.

Chapter 3 presents the approximation problem through a discussion of ideal transmission, which leads naturally, on the one hand, to the definition of the delay function and the maximally flat delay approximation and, on the other hand, to the development of the maximally flat and equal-ripple approximations to a constant magnitude over a passband. It is shown that the former approximation is most applicable to time-domain transmission problems, the latter to filtering in the frequency domain. Finally, an approximation to an arbitrary magnitude characteristic is made with simple poles and zeros on the negative real axis. These approximation methods are illustrated through the design of circuits with simple configurations, which makes possible realization by the method of equating coefficients. Also included is the important technique of frequency and magnitude normalization.

Chapters 4, 5, 13, and 14 cover the characterization and description of 2-ports. Chapter 4 introduces the open-circuit impedance and short-circuit admittance descriptions through the derivation of Thévenin's and Norton's theorems. Equivalent circuits in terms of 2-port parameters are discussed together with the relationships of these parameters to over-all network functions. The difference between reciprocal and nonreciprocal 2-ports is explained. Chapter 5 is an introduction to matrix algebra. The other conventional 2-port parameters are then concisely presented along with the interrelations between sets of parameters. The over-all characterization of the combinations of 2-ports is derived. Finally, the properties and importance of unilateral 2-ports are stressed. Chapters 13 and 14 introduce the image parameters and the scattering parameters.

Chapters 6 to 11 deal with the realization procedure by the removal technique. Of paramount importance in these chapters is the concept of the necessary and sufficient conditions that a network function must satisfy to achieve a realization. For driving-point functions, the positive real criterion is developed from stability and power considerations. From this criterion Chaps. 6 and 10 derive the necessary and sufficient conditions of driving-point functions for networks containing only two kinds of elements. From these conditions realization procedures are established. The formal and general realization procedures for 1-port networks containing R, L, and C are deliberately omitted as proper topics for a graduate or second course in synthesis. Chapters 7, 9, and 11 develop the necessary and sufficient properties and realization procedures for 2-port ladder networks. The realization procedure is again the removal technique stemming from a driving-point function. The zero-shifting technique may be necessary to achieve the desired transmission zeros. Chapter 8 introduces the conventional low-pass to high-pass and low-pass to bandpass transformations. The properties and use of ideal and practical transformers are illustrated for bandpass circuits.

The final major topic, which is covered in Chaps. 12 and 13, is the building-block synthesis procedure. In this procedure basic configurations are cascaded on an image-matched basis. Constant-resistance structures such as the bridged-T and the symmetric lattice networks are introduced first. Next comes the characterization of a 2-port in terms of image parameters and the general image-match concept. Application is then made to constant-K, m-derived, and lattice configurations.

Two appendixes are included. The first deals with simple continuants, useful in the analysis of ladder networks. The second is a presentation of energy considerations in a 1-port network. A list of selected references is included at the end of the book.

In the one-semester senior course at the University of California certain portions of the text are covered lightly in order to concentrate on fundamental matter. For example, Chaps. 10 and 11 on RC networks are treated only briefly, since the basic ideas and procedures are covered in Chaps. 6 and 7. In addition, the material in Chaps. 9 and 14 can be discussed in general terms only with no loss in developing the principles of circuit synthesis.

The authors wish to acknowledge the stimulation, encouragement, and editorial help received from Dr. T. R. Bashkow and Dr. C. A. Desoer. The senior and graduate students in the authors' courses at the University of California have also been of invaluable aid. The support of Dr. J. R. Whinnery in the preparation of the manuscript is greatly appreciated. Finally, the authors are very grateful to Mrs. Gayle Taylor for her excellent work in typing the manuscript.

Ernest S. Kuh
Donald O. Pederson

CONTENTS

CHAPTER 1

NETWORKS IN TRANSMISSION AND CONTROL SYSTEMS

1.1 Introduction. The performance of a given electrical system, such as a radio system for transmitting intelligence or a control system for regulating the flow or conversion of energy, can often be analyzed. Mathematical analysis may spare the expense of building and testing an actual system to ascertain whether it will meet requirements. Those parts of the system which are linear and constant with time can be described by a set of linear differential equations. The solutions of the equations needed to determine performance can be obtained readily by the use of existing mathematical techniques, such as the Laplace transform. For those parts of the system which are nonlinear, the analysis is not straightforward, and an exact solution, indicating performance and providing other information, may not be obtainable. Approximate descriptions based on series expansions or piecewise linear techniques may often suffice.

The converse problem, the synthesis problem, is that of designing a system or a component of a system to meet the required specifications. In general, the synthesis problem is much more difficult than the analysis problem. For nonlinear parts of a system, repeated approximate analysis may be used together with extensive experimentation. For the linear parts of a system, the parameters of which are constant with time, there again exists a body of applicable concepts and mathematical techniques that may aid in partly or fully achieving the desired synthesis. It is the purpose of this book to serve as an introduction to the body of concepts and techniques pertaining to the synthesis of linear and lumped electrical networks, i.e., those parts of a system which consist of components such as inductors, capacitors, resistors, transformers, and linear active devices.

In the succeeding sections of this chapter, several representative systems are discussed. These examples should illustrate the use of electrical networks in various over-all systems and indicate the types of requirements and specifications that must be satisfied.

1.2 A Typical Transmission System. A multichannel communication system illustrates the problems presented and the requirements that must be satisfied in transmitting intelligence through a medium between two points. The transatlantic coaxial submarine telephone system is chosen as a specific example.*

The undersea portion of this system consists of two coaxial cables, each approximately 2,000 miles long. One cable is for transmission from east to west and the other from west to east. The frequency band utilized is from 20 to 164 kc; it is divided into 36 telephone channels, each with a bandwidth of 4 kc. Because of copper and dielectric losses in the cable, the signals are attenuated. For the highest channel, the cable loss over the 2,000-mile length is approximately 3,200 db. Accordingly, if a 1-volt signal at the highest-channel frequency is applied at the North American shore, the signal will have a magnitude of 10^{-160} volt at the Great Britain end. Clearly, there is a need for amplification; it is supplied by 50 amplifiers located every 40 miles along the cable, each furnishing 64 db of gain

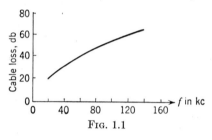

FIG. 1.1

at 164 kc. The loss of the cable is not constant but decreases with a decrease of frequency, as shown in Fig. 1.1. The loss in decibels varies approximately as the one-half power of frequency. The total loss for the lowest channel is approximately 1,100 db. Each amplifier, then, must supply only 22 db at 20 kc. Thus the individual amplifier not only must provide amplification but also must equalize the frequency distortion of the transmission medium.

The over-all amplifier-equalizer is called a repeater and has the block diagram shown in Fig. 1.2. The input and output coupling networks

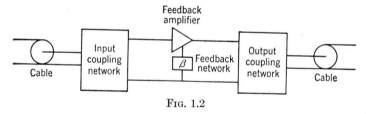

FIG. 1.2

provide part of the necessary equalization and also provide impedance matches to the cable. The remaining equalization required is supplied by the feedback amplifier—in particular, by the network in the series feedback path. The need for precise synthesis of the various networks of the repeater is shown by the effect of imperfect equalization on the over-all system. If the repeaters have an error of equalization of $\frac{1}{2}$ db

---

* *Bell System Tech. J.*, January, 1957.

(5 per cent) at a particular frequency, the over-all system error at this frequency is 25 db after transmission through 50 repeaters. Such a large over-all error is of course prohibitive. Usually, the allowable deviation is 0.1 db per repeater. Specifications of this kind require exact synthesis methods.

The synthesis procedure consists of two steps. First, a mathematical function must be determined which approximates within the allowable error the desired specifications and which is compatible with the transmission characteristics of a physical network. Usually, as in the case at hand, the specification is in the form of a graph or other description. Second, a design procedure starting from the above mathematical function and leading to network configurations together with element values must be followed. The first step is called the *approximation problem* and the second step is called the *realization problem*. The solution of both problems requires a thorough understanding of the properties of physical networks, to which, consequently, a significant portion of this book is devoted.

Needed first, in addition to inband equalization and amplification, is outband filtering in the repeaters. That is, spurious signals outside the band, such as noise, must be attenuated and not amplified and transmitted. The second major job of filtering occurs at the terminal ends of the system. Located here are the channel filters, which combine or separate various channels without interaction. Each channel filter must pass only the frequency spectrum in its 4-kc bandwidth and sharply reject the frequency components of adjacent channels. The inband requirements of filters are usually to preserve the frequency spectrum of the signals of the desired channel.

If in a similar coaxial system television signals are transmitted, not only the loss characteristic of the cable but also the distortion of the phase characteristic with frequency must be equalized. In practice, tandem networks are used; one network equalizes the loss characteristic, the other network equalizes the phase characteristic.

1.3 Pulse Data-transmission Systems. Transmission systems such as that discussed in the last section are called frequency multiplex systems. Another type of communication system uses time multiplexing. Intelligence in these systems is transmitted by using pulses, e.g., by relying on the presence or absence of a pulse, as in PCM (pulse code modulation).* The time multiplexing is accomplished by assigning to successive information channels successive intervals of time, as shown in Fig. 1.3.

* H. S. Black, "Modulation Theory," pp. 299–327, D. Van Nostrand Company, Inc., Princeton, N.J., 1953; F. E. Terman, "Electronic and Radio Engineering," 4th ed., McGraw-Hill Book Company, Inc., New York, 1955.

In these pulse data-transmission systems, the pulses undergo attenuation caused by the medium and are also distorted in shape. A typical repeater consists of a preamplifier, a postamplifier, and a pulse regenerator, as shown in Fig. 1.4. The preamplifier is an equalizer-amplifier comparable to the one discussed in the last section; however, only a coarse equalization is necessary. The pulse regenerator is a triggered nonlinear electronic circuit, e.g., a blocking oscillator. The postamplifier is the transmitter-amplifier. The output of the preamplifier for a particular time interval of one channel is either a distorted pulse in the presence of noise or the absence of a pulse with noise. The distorted pulse is sufficient to trigger the regenerator, and the output pulse of the regenerator

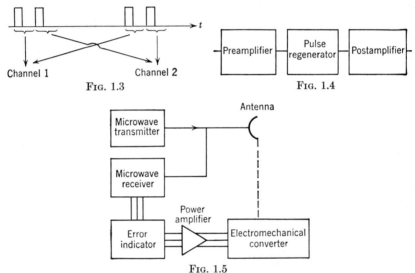

Fig. 1.3   Fig. 1.4

Fig. 1.5

is precise in time and in shape. The function of the postamplifier is to amplify the pulse and to preserve pulse shape and timing. Thus the requirements of the networks of the repeater lie in the time domain rather than in the frequency domain. The synthesis of transmission networks to obtain desired output pulse shapes is called time-domain synthesis and is more difficult than synthesis in the frequency domain. It is often possible for simple time-domain requirements to be translated into the frequency domain.

1.4 Networks in Control Systems. Electromechanical control systems constitute another area where precisely designed networks are needed. As an illustration, a tracking radar, shown in Fig. 1.5, is discussed.* The control system consists of the loop including the antenna, parts of the receiver, the power amplifier, the electromechanical converter,

* Terman, *op. cit.*, pp. 781–805.

and the mechanical coupling. In the output of the receiver there are three signals corresponding to the position coordinates of the target. The error indicator converts these signals into error signals which are proportional to the deviation between the antenna's position and that which is necessary to bring it "on target." These error signals are amplified and converted into a mechanical drive for the antenna.

The key problems are the stability and the speed of response of the system. The various time and frequency characteristics of the components of the control system may be such that the antenna will hunt or oscillate about the desired position, and the response may be so slow as to lag behind a moving target, thereby giving incorrect position data. The properties and characteristics of the components of the control system can be modified and corrected by the use of transmission networks in the loop, called control networks. From the properties of the given system and a description of the desired performance, specifications are obtained which must be satisfied by the control networks.

From this point, the synthesis of the control networks follows the pattern described in the preceding sections, with one major exception. This exception is that inductances can seldom be used. The pertinent frequencies of interest are on the order of cycles per second. Therefore the values of any required inductances are extremely large. The realization of these inductances is impractical, because of the large physical sizes and the unavoidable copper loss. Control networks therefore consist only of resistors, capacitors, and active devices. As in information transmission systems, some or all of the control networks are associated with the amplifier of the system.

CHAPTER 2

PROPERTIES OF NETWORK FUNCTIONS

2.1 Introduction. The transmission and control systems discussed in the last chapter illustrate the need for transmission networks and the general requirements that must be satisfied. As indicated, it is necessary to have a firm knowledge of the properties and descriptions of the networks. The networks to be discussed in this book are restricted to those having linear, lumped, and time-invariant elements.* The description that is pertinent here is the network function, which is a function of the complex-frequency variable. Its derivation is reviewed in this chapter, along with certain basic aspects of functions of a complex variable.

2.2 The Natural Frequencies of a Network. The electric behavior of a network can be described by a set of linear simultaneous integrodifferential equations with constant coefficients. For example, the nodal equations of a network which has n node pairs and which includes only one current source are of the following form. The current source $i_1(t)$ is assumed to occur across the node pair described by the voltage $v_1(t)$.

$$
\begin{aligned}
\alpha_{11}v_1 + \alpha_{12}v_2 + \cdots + \alpha_{1n}v_n &= i_1(t) \\
\alpha_{21}v_1 + \alpha_{22}v_2 + \cdots + \alpha_{2n}v_n &= 0 \\
\cdots \cdots \cdots \cdots \cdots \cdots \cdots \cdots \cdots \cdots \\
\alpha_{n1}v_1 + \alpha_{n2}v_2 + \cdots + \alpha_{nn}v_n &= 0
\end{aligned}
\tag{2.1}
$$

where
$$
\alpha_{jk} = G_{jk} + C_{jk}\frac{d}{dt} + \Gamma_{jk}\int dt
\tag{2.2}
$$

G_{jk} is either the self-conductance of a node pair for $j = k$ or the mutual conductance between node pairs for $j \neq k$. C_{jk} is the self- or mutual capacitance, and Γ_{jk} is the self- or mutual reciprocal inductance. The solution of these equations to determine the behavior of any one of the dependent variables $v_k(t)$ is easily accomplished through the use of the Laplace transformation. By taking the direct Laplace transform of each of the equations, one obtains a set of algebraic equations which are func-

---

* This particular type of electrical network is termed simply *network* in the remainder of the book.

6

tions of the complex-transform variable $p = (\sigma + j\omega)$. For the above equations the result is

$$a_{11}V_1 + a_{12}V_2 + \cdots + a_{1n}V_n = I_1{}^i + I_1(p)$$
$$a_{21}V_1 + a_{22}V_2 + \cdots + a_{2n}V_n = I_2{}^i \qquad (2.3)$$
$$\cdots \cdots \cdots \cdots \cdots \cdots \cdots \cdots \cdots \cdots \cdots$$
$$a_{n1}V_1 + a_{n2}V_2 + \cdots + a_{nn}V_n = I_n{}^i$$

where $$a_{jk} = G_{jk} + C_{jk}p + \frac{\Gamma_{jk}}{p} \qquad (2.4)$$

$a_{jk}(p)$ is the mutual admittance for $j \neq k$ and the self-admittance for $j = k$. $V_k(p)$ is the transform of the dependent variable $v_k(t)$; $I_1(p)$ is the transform of the source function $i_1(t)$; and the $I_j{}^i(p)$ are contributions from the initial values of voltages of the capacitances and from the sum of initial currents in the inductances leaving the jth node $i_{Lj}\,(0+)$.

$$I_j{}^i(p) = \sum_k [C_{jk}v_k(0+)] - \frac{i_{Lj}(0+)}{p} \qquad (2.5)$$

The solution for one of the dependent variables V_k can be written

$$V_k(p) = \frac{\Delta_{1k}}{\Delta} I_1(p) + \sum_{j=1}^{n} \frac{\Delta_{jk}}{\Delta} I_j{}^i(p) \qquad (2.6)$$

Δ is the determinant of (2.3) and is of the form

$$\Delta(p) = \frac{1}{p^r} P(p) \qquad (2.7)$$

$P(p)$ in (2.7) is a polynomial of degree $m \leq 2n$ with real coefficients, since G_{jk}, C_{jk}, and Γ_{jk} are real. Δ_{jk} is the cofactor of the a_{jk} obtained from Δ by deleting the jth row and the kth column and multiplying by $(-1)^{j+k}$. If the excitation is zero, the first term of the right-hand side of (2.6) is absent and the resulting function is referred to as the *free-response function*.

$$V_k(p)|_{\text{free}} = \sum_{j=1}^{n} \frac{\Delta_{jk}}{\Delta} I_j{}^i(p) \qquad (2.8)$$

Equation (2.8) can also be expressed in terms of a partial fraction expansion.

$$V_k(p)|_{\text{free}} = \sum_{i=1}^{r_1} \frac{k_{1i}}{(p - p_1)^i} + \sum_{i=1}^{r_2} \frac{k_{2i}}{(p - p_2)^i} + \cdots + \sum_{i=1}^{r_j} \frac{k_{ji}}{(p - p_j)^i}$$
$$+ \cdots \quad (2.9)$$

Using the inverse Laplace transform, one obtains the free response in the time domain.

$$v_k(t)\big|_{\text{free}} = \sum_{i=1}^{r_1} \frac{1}{(i-1)!} k_{1i} t^{i-1} e^{p_1 t} + \cdots + \sum_{i=1}^{r_j} \frac{1}{(i-1)!} k_{ji} t^{i-1} e^{p_j t} + \cdots$$

$$(2.10)$$

Except for the possible p_j at the origin, the p_j are the zeros of the determinant Δ, or from (2.7) the zeros of $P(p)$. The multiplicity of p_j is r_j, an integer. Clearly, the p_j are dependent only upon the values of the elements and the configuration of the network and not upon the source and the initial state of the network. Since the p_j have the dimensions of frequency and describe the free or natural response of the network, they are called the *natural frequencies* or the natural modes of vibration. The values of k_{ji} are dependent upon the element values, the configuration, and the initial state.

The nature of the contribution of each term of (2.10) depends upon the value of p_j, or its location if plotted in the complex-frequency plane, and also upon the multiplicity r_j. For natural frequencies which are real (i.e., which lie on the real axis of the complex plane), $p_j = \sigma_j(\sigma_j \text{ real})$. The contribution to the time response is

$$\sum_{i=1}^{r_j} \frac{k_{ji}}{(i-1)!} t^{i-1} e^{\sigma_j t}$$

$$(2.11)$$

If the natural frequencies lie on the imaginary axis, they must be accompanied by a conjugate set of the same multiplicity. In addition, the respective coefficients in (2.10) must be conjugates. This follows because the elements, as given in (2.4), in the determinant have coefficients which are real. The contribution in the time domain due to the natural frequencies occurring at $p_j = j\omega_j$ and the conjugates $\bar{p}_j = -j\omega_j$ can be written as

$$\sum_{i=1}^{r_j} \frac{2|k_{ji}|}{(i-1)!} t^{i-1} \cos(\omega_j t + \phi_{ji})$$

$$(2.12)$$

where
$$k_{ji} = |k_{ji}| e^{j\phi_{ji}}$$
$$(2.13)$$

Finally, if the natural frequencies are complex ($p_j = \sigma_j + j\omega_j$), the contributions due to the p_j and the conjugates are

$$\sum_{i=1}^{r_j} \frac{2|k_{ji}|}{(i-1)!} t^{i-1} e^{\sigma_j t} \cos(\omega_j t + \phi_{ji})$$

$$(2.14)$$

Notice in (2.11), (2.12), and (2.14) that time-response contributions which are bounded as t grows indefinitely are obtained for only two conditions:

(a) Natural frequencies lie in the left half plane (LHP) with any multiplicity.

(b) Natural frequencies lie on the $j\omega$ axis with unity multiplicity.

A network that without excitation has such a bounded free response is called a *stable network*. The conditions (a) and (b) are referred to as the *stability conditions*. For many electronic-circuit applications, unstable networks are important. However, for the purposes of this book a restriction is made to stable networks.

2.3 The Network Function. The response of the network due to the excitation only is called the *forced response*. In the transform or complex-frequency domain from (2.6)

$$V_k(p)|_{\text{forced}} = \frac{\Delta_{1k}}{\Delta} I_1(p) \tag{2.15}$$

The forced-response function $V_k(p)$ is the product of two functions. One function Δ_{1k}/Δ is due to the network alone and is called the *network function*. The other is due to the excitation alone and is called the *excitation function*.

$$\frac{\text{Response}}{\text{function}} = \left(\frac{\text{network}}{\text{function}}\right)\left(\frac{\text{excitation}}{\text{function}}\right) \tag{2.16}$$

The network function is a concept of major importance, and from (2.15) and (2.16)

$$\frac{\text{Network}}{\text{function}} = N(p) = \frac{\text{response function}}{\text{excitation function}}$$

$$= \frac{\Delta_{1k}}{\Delta} \tag{2.17}$$

The network function alone is sufficient to determine what effect the network produces upon the characteristics of an arbitrary excitation. From (2.7) and (2.17) it is seen that $N(p)$ is a rational function of p, i.e., a ratio of two polynomials.*

$$N(p) = \frac{a_n p^n + a_{n-1} p^{n-1} + \cdots + a_0}{b_m p^m + b_{m-1} p^{m-1} + \cdots + b_0} \tag{2.18}$$

The coefficients a_i and b_i are real numbers, as noted in the last section. The numerator and denominator polynomials of (2.18) can be written in factored form.

$$N(p) = H \frac{(p - z_1)(p - z_2) \cdots (p - z_n)}{(p - p_1)(p - p_2) \cdots (p - p_m)} \tag{2.19}$$

* In the following equations, n (the degree of the numerator polynomial) does not pertain to the number of nodal equations of Sec. 2.2.

The p_j are the poles of $N(p)$ and are the zeros of the denominator polynomial. The z_i are the zeros of $N(p)$. Since a_i and b_i are real, the poles and zeros, if complex, occur in conjugate pairs. Clearly, the values of the poles and zeros or their location, if plotted in the complex plane, completely specify the network function, except for the constant multiplier H.

In comparing (2.8) and (2.17), it is seen that the determinant Δ appears in the denominator of each expression. Since zeros of Δ are the natural frequencies of the circuit, the natural frequencies are usually the poles of $N(p)$. However, there may be natural frequencies which are not poles of $N(p)$. A cancellation of zeros of the cofactor and zeros of the determinant, i.e., a pole-zero cancellation, can occur. Conversely, there may be poles of $N(p)$ which are not natural frequencies. There are two basic instances of this condition.

First, if a branch is in series with the current source or if a branch is in shunt with the voltage source, as shown in Fig. 2.1, the impedance of

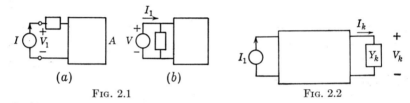

(a) (b)

FIG. 2.1   FIG. 2.2

either branch need not be included in the circuit determinant of network A. Hence neither branch affects the natural frequencies of A. However, the network function—V_1/I for the first case or I_1/V for the second case—is a function of the branch impedance. Any poles of the impedance (admittance) of the series (shunt) branch are also poles of the network function. The remaining poles of these network functions are the natural frequencies of network A.

For the second possibility, the desired network function may be either the ratio of two voltage functions or the ratio of two current functions. As an example, consider the situation shown in Fig. 2.2, where the excitation is a current source $I_1(p)$. From a nodal analysis one obtains

$$V_k(p) = \frac{\Delta_{1k}}{\Delta} I_1(p) \tag{2.20}$$

If the desired response is the current flowing through the branch Y_k

$$I_k(p) = V_k(p) Y_k \tag{2.21}$$

The network function in this case is

$$N(p) = \frac{I_k(p)}{I_1(p)} = \frac{\Delta_{1k}}{\Delta} Y_k \tag{2.22}$$

Here, as above, the poles of Y_k, if any, appear as poles of $N(p)$ and are not natural frequencies of the circuit.

Restrictions on the pole locations can be obtained for a stable network. On the basis of conclusions drawn in the last section, the following theorem can be stated:

The poles of all network functions must lie in the left half plane. If the poles lie on the boundary, the imaginary axis ($j\omega$ axis), they must be simple.

If the poles of the network function all lie in the interior of the left half plane, the denominator polynomial of $N(p)$ is known mathematically as a Hurwitz polynomial. This kind of polynomial plays an important part in network theory and control systems. In a later chapter a simple test procedure is derived in order to determine whether or not a given polynomial is Hurwitz.

It is to be emphasized that for a given network and given type of source the natural frequencies of the network are invariants. Furthermore, the natural frequencies are identical with the poles of any ratio of voltage or current response function to the given current or voltage excitation function, respectively.*

In general, no restriction such as is made for poles in the above theorem can be made about the locations of the zeros of $N(p)$. An exception occurs where $N(p)$ is a driving-point function. That is, the excitation and the response occur at the same pair of terminals, and $N(p)$ is either a driving-point impedance or admittance function. If the excitation is a current source, the network function is the driving-point impedance function.

$$Z(p) = \frac{V_1}{I_1} = \frac{Q(p)}{D(p)} \tag{2.23}$$

The zeros of $D(p)$ are the natural frequencies for this situation. Alternately, the excitation can be a voltage source, in which case the network function is the driving-point admittance function.

$$Y(p) = \frac{I_1}{V_1} = \frac{1}{Z(p)} = \frac{D(p)}{Q(p)} \tag{2.24}$$

Hence the natural frequencies are the zeros of $Q(p)$. Since the natural frequencies can be either the poles or the zeros of $Z(p)$ or $Y(p)$, depending upon the type of excitation, both the zeros and the poles of a driving-point function must either lie in the left half plane or be simple on the $j\omega$ axis.

2.4 The Transient and Steady-state Responses. In general, the total time response can be obtained from (2.6) and written

$$v_k(t) = v_k(t)|_{\text{free}} + v_k(t)|_{\text{forced}} \tag{2.25}$$

* With the exceptions mentioned previously.

$v_k(t)$ can also be separated into two other components:

$$v_k(t) = v_k(t)|_{\substack{\text{transient} \\ \text{response}}} + v_k(t)|_{\substack{\text{steady-state} \\ \text{response}}} \tag{2.26}$$

The transient response for a stable network includes those terms which vanish as $t \to \infty$. The steady-state response includes those terms which are either constants or undamped sinusoids. Both the free and the forced components can contribute to both the transient and the steady-state responses.

In this book the interest is in the response of a network to a given, arbitrary excitation. Hence only the forced response is considered, while the response due to the initial state of the network is ignored. This step is justified, since the network is linear and superposition holds. That is, the free response can always be added if desired. Often the given excitation is sinusoidal. The term in the steady-state response that has the same frequency as the excitation is called the *sinusoidal steady-state component*.

2.5 Mathematical Properties of Network Functions. Because the network function $N(p)$ is a rational function of a complex variable, it has certain implicit properties. Certain of the basic properties are of key importance in this book. The first is that $N(p)$ can always be written in terms of the sum of real and imaginary components.

$$N(p) = N(\sigma + j\omega) = U(\sigma,\omega) + jV(\sigma,\omega) \tag{2.27}$$

$U(\sigma,\omega)$ is the real part of $N(p)$; $jV(\sigma,\omega)$ is the imaginary part of $N(p)$; and U and V are real functions of the two real variables σ and ω. If $N(p)$ is analytic at a particular point, the real and imaginary parts are related by the famous Cauchy-Riemann conditions.*

$$\frac{\partial U}{\partial \sigma} = \frac{\partial V}{\partial \omega} \qquad \frac{\partial U}{\partial \omega} = -\frac{\partial V}{\partial \sigma} \tag{2.28}$$

The network function can also be separated in another manner; i.e., it can be separated into its even and odd parts. These components are obtained as follows. The numerator and denominator polynomials can be written as the sums of even and odd polynomials:

$$N(p) = \frac{A_1 + pB_1}{A_2 + pB_2} \tag{2.29}$$

where A_1, A_2, B_1, and B_2 are even polynomials, i.e., polynomials in p^2. Thus A_1 contains the even powers of the numerator polynomial; pB_1 con-

---

* A function is analytic at a point if it is single-valued and if its derivative exists in the neighborhood. For rational functions, the function is analytic at all points other than the locations of the poles.

tains the odd powers of the numerator polynomial. If the numerator and the denominator of $N(p)$ are multiplied by $A_2 - pB_2$, the even and odd parts of $N(p)$ are readily obtained.

$$N(p) = \frac{A_1 + pB_1}{A_2 + pB_2} \frac{A_2 - pB_2}{A_2 - pB_2} = \frac{A_1 A_2 - p^2 B_1 B_2}{A_2{}^2 - p^2 B_2{}^2} + p \frac{A_2 B_1 - A_1 B_2}{A_2{}^2 - p^2 B_2{}^2} \quad (2.30)$$
$$= \text{Ev } N(p) + \text{Od } N(p)$$

Because of the ease and accuracy with which sinusoidal steady-state measurements of a network can be made and certain steady-state properties obtained, $N(p)$ for $p = j\omega$ is of particular importance. For $p = j\omega$, (2.27) becomes

$$N(j\omega) = U(0,\omega) + jV(0,\omega) \quad (2.31)$$

$U_0(\omega) = U(0,\omega)$ and $V_0(\omega) = V(0,\omega)$ are real functions of the real variable ω only. Next, from (2.30), the even and odd parts of $N(j\omega)$ become

$$\text{Ev } N(j\omega) = \text{Re } N(j\omega) = U_0(\omega)$$
$$\text{Od } N(j\omega) = j\text{Im } N(j\omega) = jV_0(\omega) \quad (2.32)$$

Notice that the symbols Re and Im represent the real and imaginary components of a complex function. The function $\text{Im } N(j\omega) = V_0(\omega)$ is actually a real function of ω and $j\text{Im } N(j\omega)$ is the imaginary part of $N(j\omega)$. Thus for $p = j\omega$ the even part of $N(j\omega)$ is identical with the real part, and the odd part of $N(j\omega)$ is identical with the imaginary part. $U_0(\omega)$ is therefore an even function of ω (i.e., a function of ω^2) and $V_0(\omega)$ is an odd function of ω.

In polar coordinates, $N(j\omega)$ can be written

$$N(j\omega) = |N(j\omega)| e^{j\beta(\omega)} \quad (2.33)$$

where

$$|N(j\omega)| = \sqrt{U_0{}^2(\omega) + V_0{}^2(\omega)}$$
$$\beta(\omega) = \tan^{-1} \frac{V_0(\omega)}{U_0(\omega)} \quad (2.34)$$

$|N(j\omega)|$ is the magnitude function and is an even function of ω. $\beta(\omega)$ is the phase function and is an odd function of ω.* In practical problems the polar coordinates are useful because the magnitude and phase functions can be measured easily in the laboratory. It is also convenient to work with the logarithm of $N(j\omega)$.

$$\ln N(j\omega) = \alpha(\omega) + j\beta(\omega) \quad (2.35)$$

where $\alpha(\omega) = \ln |N(j\omega)|$ is referred to as the magnitude or gain function.†

As seen from (2.28), the real and imaginary parts are related to each other. Since $N(p)$ is analytic in the right half plane, it can be shown

---

* Since the $\tan^{-1}$ function is multivalued, $\beta(\omega)$ is chosen such that $-\pi \le \beta(0) \le \pi$.

† In classical filter theory the network function is defined as the ratio of excitation to response or input to output. The logarithm of the magnitude is also written $\alpha(\omega)$. It is the negative of the $\alpha(\omega)$ above and is called the loss function.

that if there are no poles on the $j\omega$ axis and if the real part of $N(j\omega)$ is known, the imaginary part is uniquely specified. The converse is also true.* If not only $N(p)$ but also $1/N(p)$ is analytic in the right half plane, $N(p)$ has no zeros in the right half plane. If there are also no poles and zeros on the $j\omega$ axis, $\ln N(p)$ is analytic in the right half plane, including the $j\omega$ axis. Therefore, $\alpha(\omega)$ and $\beta(\omega)$ are related to each other in the same manner as $U_0(\omega)$ and $V_0(\omega)$.

If $|N(j\omega)|$ is known, it is possible to determine an appropriate $N(p)$. This procedure is known as analytic continuation. Although the procedure is straightforward for rational functions, the concept may appear quite subtle the first time one encounters it. The problem here is to determine a rational function in p which has precisely the desired magnitude function for $p = j\omega$. The basis of the procedure is as follows. The square of the magnitude function is equal to

$$|N(j\omega)|^2 = N(j\omega)\overline{N(j\omega)} \tag{2.36}$$

For a rational function with real coefficients, the conjugate of a function is equal to the function of the conjugate variable.

$$\overline{N(j\omega)} = N(\overline{j\omega}) \tag{2.37}$$

Since the variable is imaginary for $p = j\omega$, the conjugate of the variable is equal to the negative of the variable. Therefore

$$\overline{N(j\omega)} = N(\overline{j\omega}) = N(-j\omega) \tag{2.38}$$

and
$$|N(j\omega)|^2 = N(j\omega)N(-j\omega) \tag{2.39}$$

In terms of the desired rational function, (2.39) can be written

$$|N(j\omega)|^2 = N(p)N(-p)|_{p=j\omega} \tag{2.40}$$

The procedure for obtaining $N(p)N(-p)$ is to generalize the variable ω in $|N(j\omega)|^2$ to the variable p. It should be remembered in case of confusion that although the notation $|N(j\omega)|^2$ is in terms of the imaginary variable $j\omega$, the variable which appears is the real variable ω^2. The desired generalization is made by substituting p/j for ω. Clearly, (2.40) is still satisfied. The remaining problem is to separate $N(p)N(-p)$ into its two constituents. This is done by a separation of poles and zeros.

If $-p$ is substituted for p in $N(p)$, it can be seen from (2.19) that $N(-p)$ has poles and zeros which are the negatives of those of $N(p)$. For example, if $N(p)$ contains the factor $(p - z_1)$, $N(-p)$ contains the factor $(-p - z_1) = -[p - (-z_1)]$. If $N(p)$ has poles and zeros as shown in Fig. 2.3a, $N(-p)$ has the set shown in Fig. 2.3b and $N(p)N(-p)$ has the combined poles and zeros shown in Fig. 2.3c. Because complex poles and zeros occur in conjugate pairs, $N(p)N(-p)$ has complex poles

---

* If the imaginary part is given, the real part is specified within an arbitrary additive constant.

and zeros in quadrangle symmetry. Poles and zeros on the $j\omega$ axis occur with even multiplicity. $N(p)N(-p)$ therefore contains the poles and zeros of $N(p)$ and their mirror images with respect to the $j\omega$ axis.

Returning to the problem at hand, one can establish an $N(p)$ from a suitable choice of one-half of the poles and one-half of the zeros of $N(p)N(-p)$. In making the choice, care must be taken not to include a pole or a zero and its negative. From Sec. 2.3, the poles chosen for

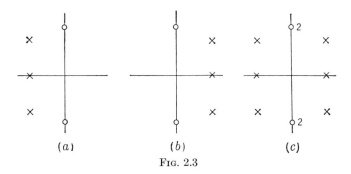

(a)   (b)   (c)

Fig. 2.3

$N(p)$ must be the left-half-plane poles, since $N(p)$ pertains to a stable network. There is no such restriction in making the choice of the zeros, unless $N(p)$ is a driving-point function. For poles or zeros of $N(p)N(-p)$ on the $j\omega$ axis, poles and zeros of one-half of the multiplicity are chosen for $N(p)$. The above procedure establishes poles and zeros of a suitable $N(p)$. The constant H [see Eq. (2.19)] is identical with the corresponding constant of $|N(j\omega)|$.

2.6 Illustrative Example. In order to illustrate the magnitude and phase functions of a network function, the transistor amplifier shown in Fig. 2.4 is analyzed. A small signal equivalent circuit is shown in Fig. 2.5.* The element values are also given in the figure. For simplicity's sake, the low-frequency coupling circuitry and the d-c bias circuitry are ignored. The network function for this circuit can be obtained by nodal analysis.

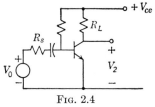

Fig. 2.4

$$N(p) = \frac{V_2}{V_0} = \frac{G'_s}{C_1} \frac{\left(p - \dfrac{g_{ee}}{C_c}\right)}{p^2 + \left(\dfrac{G_L}{C_c} + \dfrac{G'_s + G_1 + G_L + g_{ee}}{C_1}\right)p + \dfrac{G_L(G'_s + G_1)}{C_1 C_c}}$$

(2.41)

*R. L. Pritchard, Electric Network Representation of Transistors: A Survey, *Trans. IRE,* CT-3, no. 1 (March, 1956).

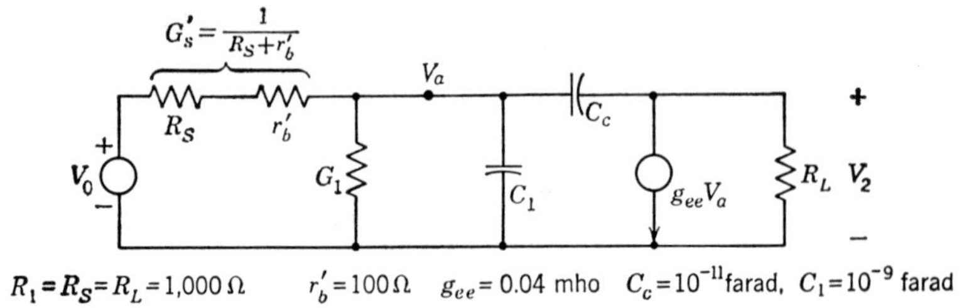

$G_s' = \frac{1}{R_S + r_b'}$
V_a
C_c
+
R_S
r_b'
+
V_0
G_1
C_1
$g_{ee}V_a$
R_L
V_2
$R_1 = R_S = R_L = 1{,}000\,\Omega$ $r_b' = 100\,\Omega$ $g_{ee} = 0.04$ mho $C_c = 10^{-11}$ farad, $C_1 = 10^{-9}$ farad

FIG. 2.5

In terms of the numerical element values

$$N(p) = 10^6 \frac{p - 4 \times 10^9}{p^2 + 1.43 \times 10^8 p + 2 \times 10^{14}} \tag{2.42}$$

$j\omega$
p plane
14.3
0.14
+400
σ

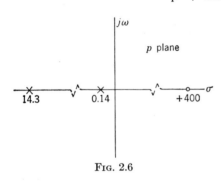

FIG. 2.6

It is convenient at this stage to normalize the variable to eliminate the large numbers. This can be accomplished, for example, by letting $p' = 10^{-7} \times p$. The process is called frequency normalization. It should be remembered that this normalization does not change the geometrical arrangement of the pole-zero locations or the nature of the gain, phase, or delay function. In essence, it amounts merely to a scale change of the axes of the plots. After normalization

$$N(10^7 p') = N'(p') = 0.1 \frac{p' - 400}{(p')^2 + 14.3p' + 2} \tag{2.43}$$

The pole-zero plot is shown in Fig. 2.6. The magnitude function for $p' = j\omega'$ is

$$\begin{aligned} |N'(j\omega')| &= 0.1 \left| \frac{-400 + j\omega'}{(2 - \omega'^2) + j14.3\omega'} \right| \\ &= 0.1 \left[\frac{1.6 \times 10^4 + \omega'^2}{4 + 200.5\omega'^2 + \omega'^4} \right]^{\frac{1}{2}} \end{aligned} \tag{2.44}$$

The phase function is

$$\beta(\omega') = \tan^{-1} \frac{\omega'}{-400} - \tan^{-1} \frac{14.3\omega'}{2 - \omega'^2} \tag{2.45}$$

Equations (2.44) and (2.45) are plotted in Fig. 2.7.

In this example it should be noted that the poles differ by two orders of magnitude. A geometric interpretation using vectors of the pole-zero plot indicates that the pole nearest the origin is dominant in determining

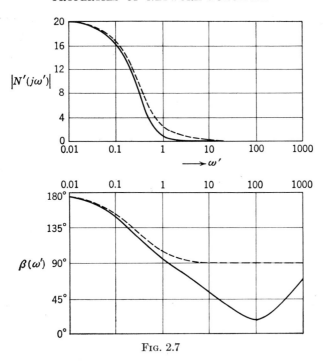

FIG. 2.7

the low-frequency gain and phase characteristics. Thus, for these low-frequency characteristics, only the dominant pole need be included in the computation. The gain and phase characteristics due only to the dominant pole are shown in the broken curves.

PROBLEMS

2.1. Determine the natural frequencies for the networks shown in Fig. P2.1.* Plot the locations of the natural frequencies on the complex-frequency plane. Sketch the loci of the natural frequencies as the shunt resistances are varied from zero to infinity.

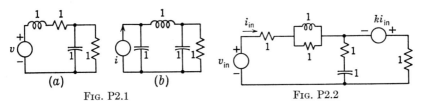

FIG. P2.1   FIG. P2.2

2.2. Given the fictitious active circuit in Fig. P2.2, determine the natural frequencies for the element values given and for $k = -3$. Is the circuit stable? Determine the range of the value of k for which the circuit is unstable.

* The element values in the figures are in ohms, henrys, or farads.

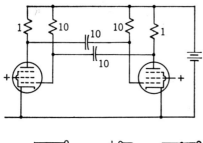

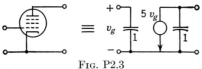

Fig. P2.3

2.3. During the fast switching action of a pentode multivibrator, the pentodes are in the active region and can be represented by the equivalent circuit in Fig. P2.3. Determine the natural frequencies of the multivibrator during the switching period.

2.4. For the equivalent circuit of the cathode-follower circuit (Fig. P2.4), sketch for $G_S = 0$ the loci of the natural frequencies with the value of the cathode-lead inductance L_K. If for a particular value of L_K the circuit is unstable, can it be made stable by increasing the source conductance G_S? Use $g_m = 0.005$ mho.

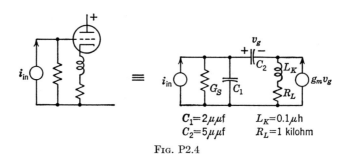

$C_1 = 2\mu\mu$f $L_K = 0.1\mu$h
$C_2 = 5\mu\mu$f $R_L = 1$ kilohm

Fig. P2.4

2.5. Is the bandpass common-emitter amplifier stable? A first-order equivalent circuit for the transistor is shown in Fig. P2.5.

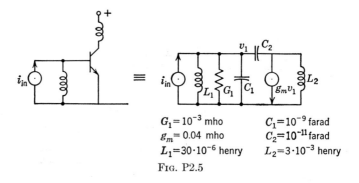

$G_1 = 10^{-3}$ mho $C_1 = 10^{-9}$ farad
$g_m = 0.04$ mho $C_2 = 10^{-11}$ farad
$L_1 = 30 \cdot 10^{-6}$ henry $L_2 = 3 \cdot 10^{-3}$ henry

Fig. P2.5

2.6. Determine the natural frequencies of the two circuits in Fig. P2.6. Relate these natural frequencies to the poles and zeros of the respective input impedances and transfer impedance V_2/I_1 of the (a) circuit and the transfer voltage ratio V_2/V_1 of the (b) circuit.

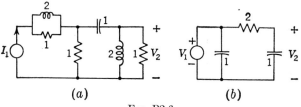

FIG. P2.6

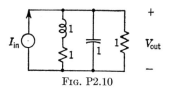

$C_1 = C_2 = R_2 = 1$

FIG. P2.7

2.7. In the circuit in Fig. P2.7, R_1 is a resistor having a v-i relation $v_{R_1} = 2i + 0.01i^2$. Is it possible to define a network function $N(p) = V_{out}/I_{in}$?

2.8. Determine the network functions V_{out}/V_{in} or V_{out}/I_{in} (depending upon the source) for the networks in Figs. P2.1 and P2.2.

2.9. For the network function for the circuit of Fig. P2.1a, $N(p) = V_{out}/V_{in}$, determine the following:

$$\text{Re } N(j\omega), \text{ Im } N(j\omega), |N(j\omega)|, \text{ Arg } N(j\omega), \text{ Ev } N(p), \text{ and Od } N(p)$$

2.10. For the "shunt-peaked" circuit (Fig. P2.10), determine $N(p) = V_{out}/I_{in}$. Plot the poles and zeros and sketch the magnitude and phase on the $j\omega$ axis.

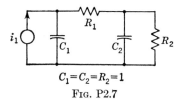

FIG. P2.10   FIG. P2.11

2.11. Determine $N(p) = V/I$ for the circuit in Fig. P2.11. If $i_{in}(t) = u(t)$ (unit step function), what is $v(t)$ for zero initial conditions?

2.12. For the vacuum-tube feedback pair, an equivalent circuit is shown (Fig. P2.12). Determine $N(p) = V_{out}/V_{in}$ and sketch $|N(j\omega)|$ and Arg $N(j\omega)$. Plot the loci of the poles and zeros as g_m is allowed to vary.

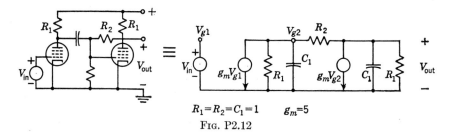

$R_1 = R_2 = C_1 = 1$ $g_m = 5$

FIG. P2.12

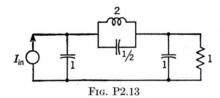

FIG. P2.13

2.13. Determine the network function V_{out}/I_{in} of the circuit in Fig. P2.13. Sketch the magnitude and phase for $p = j\omega$.

2.14. Given $N(p) = H/(p^2 + ap + 1)$ find the constraint on a that makes the magnitude of $N(j\omega)$ a monotonic decreasing function (i.e., $d|N(j\omega)|/d\omega \leq 0$ for $\omega \geq 0$).

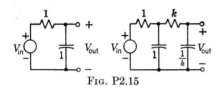

FIG. P2.15

2.15. For the two networks shown in Fig. P2.15, determine $N(p) = V_{out}/V_{in}$. Compare the poles and zeros of the two networks as k is varied.

2.16. Given $N(p) = 1/(1 + p)^2$, show that the Cauchy-Riemann conditions hold at $p = j1$.

2.17. For the following magnitude-squared functions, determine all possible $N(p)$.

(a) $\dfrac{1 + \omega^2}{1 + \omega^4}$

(b) $\dfrac{\omega^2(1 + \omega^2)}{1 - \omega^2 + \omega^4}$

(c) $\dfrac{1}{4 + 10\omega^2 + \omega^4 + \omega^6}$

(d) $\dfrac{H^2(1 - \omega^2)^2}{1 + \omega^6}$

2.18. For the following phase functions, determine $N(p)$:

(a) $-\tan^{-1}\dfrac{\omega}{1 - \omega^2}$

(b) $\tan^{-1}\dfrac{\omega}{4} - 2\tan^{-1}\omega$

2.19. For (a) $i_{in}(t) = u(t)$ and (b) $i_{in}(t) = \cos t$, determine the transient and the steady-state responses of $v(t)$.

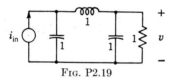

FIG. P2.19

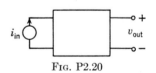

FIG. P2.20

2.20. For the situation as shown in Fig. P2.20,

$$N(p) = \frac{V_{out}}{I_{in}} = \frac{1}{(p^2 + 1)(p + 1)}$$

$$i_{in} = \cos t$$

What is $v_{out}(t)$? Can one talk about the sinusoidal steady-state component of $v_{out}(t)$?

2.21. Show that the natural frequencies of the over-all circuit as shown in Fig. P2.21 can be obtained from the zeros of $Z_1 + Z_2$.

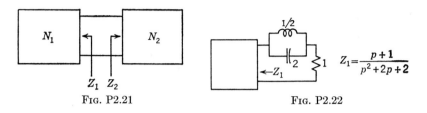

$$Z_1 = \frac{p+1}{p^2 + 2p + 2}$$

FIG. P2.21   FIG. P2.22

2.22. Using the method of Prob. 2.21, determine the natural frequencies of the circuit in Fig. P2.22.

CHAPTER 3

TRANSMISSION CRITERIA AND APPROXIMATION

3.1 Introduction. Among the most important requirements to be satisfied by a transmission network is that of minimum distortion of the input signal. From the translation theorem of the Laplace transform, one can establish the specification on the network function for ideal transmission through a network. Ideal transmission is defined as follows:

> The output signal has the exact shape of the input signal and is delayed in time t_0 with respect to the input.*

Mathematically, from the translation theorem, the relationship between the excitation $I(p)$ and the response $O(p)$ is

$$O(p) = e^{-pt_0}I(p) \tag{3.1}$$

where $I(p) = \mathcal{L}[f(t)]$
$\qquad O(p) = \mathcal{L}[f(t - t_0)]$
From (3.1) the network function for ideal transmission is

$$N(p) = e^{-pt_0} \tag{3.2}$$

The magnitude function is

$$|N(j\omega)| = 1 \tag{3.3}$$

The phase function is

$$\beta(\omega) = -t_0\omega \tag{3.4}$$

From (3.3) and (3.4) it is seen that for ideal transmission the magnitude of the Fourier spectrum of the input signal is not changed in passing through the network, while a linear phase with frequency is added to the phase of the input spectrum.

A network function of the form of (3.2) can be realized as a length of ideal transmission line terminated at both ends in its characteristic impedance. However, since $N(p)$ is not a rational function, it cannot be realized as a lumped network. For lumped networks it is necessary to make an approximation of the function in (3.2). First, it is usually true that only a portion of the infinite frequency spectrum is of interest.

---

* The trivial case of a transmission network consisting of a pair of parallel lines of zero length is, of course, the limiting case of zero delay.

That is, the major interest is in a particular frequency band (often called the passband). The problem, then, is one of approximating a flat magnitude and a linear phase in the passband. This approximation problem of obtaining a network function which has the properties described in the last chapter, and which is realizable by physical networks, is quite difficult. Simpler, although less accurate, approximations are made by concentrating on either the magnitude or the phase characteristics. Methods of obtaining the latter approximations are discussed in this chapter. The resulting network functions are all restricted to the reciprocals of polynomials, i.e., functions with poles in the finite plane and all zeros at infinity. As is shown later, the approximation restricted to the phase function provides a time response that is a better replica of the input than does the approximation restricted to the magnitude function.

3.2 The Delay Function. For a rational network function the phase function is bounded with frequency. For example, if the network function has m zeros and n poles all located in the LHP, the maximum phase is $(m - n)(\pi/2)$ radians. Therefore a network function can never approximate the ideal phase function of (3.4) over an infinite frequency band. The approximation must be over a finite band and the question arises: Does the delay concept of the ideal transmission have any meaning? The answer to this question is yes, if the phase function has a nearly linear character in the band of interest. The development follows from the principle of stationary phase.*

Assume that the input to the network is an impulse function. The output response in the time domain can be expressed with the inverse Fourier transform.

$$h(t) = \frac{1}{2\pi} \int_{-\infty}^{\infty} N(j\omega)e^{j\omega t}\, d\omega = \frac{1}{2\pi} \int_{-\infty}^{\infty} |N(j\omega)|e^{j[\omega t + \beta(\omega)]}\, d\omega \qquad (3.5)$$

The exponential function in (3.5) can be expanded into real and imaginary components. Because of the even and odd properties of the cosine and sine functions, respectively, and because of the symmetrical interval of integration, (3.5) reduces to

$$h(t) = \frac{1}{\pi} \int_{0}^{\infty} |N(j\omega)| \cos [\omega t + \beta(\omega)]\, d\omega \qquad (3.6)$$

Where the magnitude function varies slowly with frequency over the entire interval, the argument of the cosine function $\omega t + \beta(\omega)$ determines the contributions to the integral $h(t)$. If this argument varies rapidly with ω over a particular interval, the cosine oscillates rapidly between plus and minus one. Since the magnitude is assumed to change slowly,

---

* S. Goldman, "Frequency Analysis, Modulation, and Noise," pp. 111–117, McGraw-Hill Book Company, Inc., New York, 1948.

the positive and negative portions along the interval nearly cancel, and there is little contribution to $h(t)$ by this particular frequency interval, as shown in Fig. 3.1a. If over another interval the argument $\omega t + \beta(\omega)$ is almost a constant [the phase $\omega t + \beta(\omega)$ is stationary], cancellation does not occur and a significant contribution to $h(t)$ is obtained, as shown in Fig. 3.1b. The condition for stationary phase over a frequency interval is

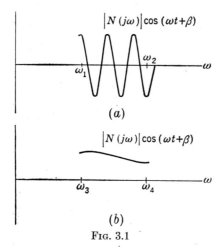

(a)

(b)

Fig. 3.1

$$\frac{d}{d\omega}[\omega t + \beta(\omega)] = 0$$

and the principal contribution from this interval occurs at (cf. Fig. 3.8)

$$t = t_0 = -\frac{d\beta}{d\omega}\Big|_{\text{in the interval}} \qquad (3.7)$$

A generalization of (3.7) is used to define the *delay function* of a network.

$$\tau(\omega) = -\frac{d\beta(\omega)}{d\omega} \qquad (3.8)$$

This definition has a physical meaning only when the following conditions are satisfied: (1) when the magnitude function varies slowly with frequency; (2) when the phase function over the frequency band of interest is nearly linear. However, it can be used as a design criterion. That is, through its use coefficients of the network function satisfying the above conditions can be obtained. A network realization of this network function provides an approximation to ideal transmission.

3.3   The Maximally Flat Delay Function. The approximation to the ideal delay function of (3.1) is made in what is known as a Taylor sense. That is, a Taylor's expansion is made of the delay function about a particular frequency for both the desired network function and the ideal delay function. As many successive coefficients of the two series are equated to each other as possible. The number of coefficients that can be equated depends upon the complexity of the network (i.e., the degrees of freedom of the network). Since the Taylor's expansion of the ideal delay function is a constant [$\tau(\omega) = t_0$], as many successive coefficients as possible of the expansion of the approximating delay function starting from the coefficient of the second term are set equal to zero.

As an example of this procedure, a network function with only two poles in the finite plane is considered. It is assumed that the low-pass frequency interval is of interest.

$$N(p) = H \frac{1}{p^2 + a_1 p + a_0} \tag{3.9}$$

The phase function is

$$\beta(\omega) = -\tan^{-1} \frac{a_1 \omega}{a_0 - \omega^2} \tag{3.10}$$

Instead of taking the derivatives immediately, it is simpler to expand the phase function in the Taylor's expansion about the origin and differentiate term by term to obtain the series expansion of the delay function. First the series expansion of $\tan^{-1}$ is used.

$$\beta(\omega) = -\frac{1}{a_0} \frac{a_1 \omega}{1 - (\omega^2/a_0)} + \frac{1}{3} \left(\frac{1}{a_0}\right)^3 \left[\frac{a_1 \omega}{1 - (\omega^2/a_0)}\right]^3 + \cdots \tag{3.11}$$

Next, the individual components are expanded by using the binomial expansion.

$$\beta(\omega) = -\frac{1}{a_0} a_1 \omega \left[1 + \frac{\omega^2}{a_0} + \left(\frac{\omega^2}{a_0}\right)^2 + \cdots\right]$$
$$+ \frac{1}{3} \left(\frac{1}{a_0}\right)^3 a_1{}^3 \omega^3 \left[1 + 3\frac{\omega^2}{a_0} + \cdots\right] + \cdots \tag{3.12}$$

The above two expansions are convergent power series in ω for small ω. Finally, collecting terms and taking derivatives with respect to ω, one obtains the delay function.

$$\tau(\omega) = -\frac{d\beta}{d\omega} = \frac{a_1}{a_0} - \left[\left(\frac{a_1}{a_0}\right)^3 - 3\frac{a_1}{a_0{}^2}\right]\omega^2 + \cdots \tag{3.13}$$

Equating coefficients with the ideal delay,

$$\frac{a_1}{a_0} = t_0$$

$$\left(\frac{a_1}{a_0}\right)^3 - 3\frac{a_1}{a_0{}^2} = 0 \quad \text{or} \quad a_1{}^2 = 3a_0$$

For convenience, the delay t_0 is normalized to unity.

$$a_1 = a_0 = 3$$

This constitutes a normalization of the frequency variable comparable to the procedure used in the example of Sec. 2.6. The necessary change in variable to provide a normalized unit delay is $(a_1/a_0)p = p'$, since

$$\cdots + a_1 p + a_0 \Big|_{p = \frac{a_0}{a_1} p'} = \cdots + a_0 p' + a_0$$

The normalized network function is

$$N(p) = H \frac{1}{p^2 + 3p + 3} \tag{3.14}$$

A similar procedure can be used to determine the network functions that have a greater number of poles. Again, all zeros are assumed at infinity. The resulting polynomials in the denominators of the network functions are simply related to a class of polynomials, the Bessel polynomials.[*] If $B_n(s)$ is used to denote a Bessel polynomial of degree n, the polynomials

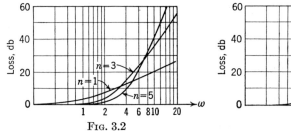

FIG. 3.2

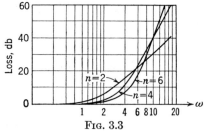

FIG. 3.3

of the network functions for maximally flat delay are $B_n(1/p) = D_n(p)$; thus $N(p) = H/D_n(p)$. Use of the recursion formulas of the Bessel polynomials makes it unnecessary to duplicate the above procedure for any number of poles. This recursion formula and the lowest orders of polynomials are listed below:

$$D_0(p) = 1$$
$$D_1(p) = p + 1$$
$$D_2(p) = p^2 + 3p + 3$$
$$D_3(p) = p^3 + 6p^2 + 15p + 15$$
$$\cdots\cdots\cdots\cdots\cdots\cdots\cdots\cdots$$
$$D_{n+1}(p) = (2n + 1) D_n(p) + p^2 D_{n-1}(p)$$

The locations of the poles of the network function are given in Table 3.1. The plots of magnitude (in terms of decibels) and delay functions for several values of n are shown in Figs. 3.2 to 3.4. In the magnitude plot the frequency where the magnitude is down 3 db from the d-c value is approximately

$$f_{3 \text{ db}} = \frac{1}{2\pi} \sqrt{(2n - 1) \ln 2} \qquad n \geq 3 \tag{3.15}$$

[*] L. Storch, Synthesis of Constant-time-delay Ladder Networks Using Bessel Polynomials, *Proc. IRE*, November, 1954, pp. 1666–1675; L. Weinberg, Network Design by Use of Modern Synthesis Techniques and Tables, *Proc. Natl. Electronics Conf.*, vol. 12, 1956; Additional Tables for Design of Optimum Ladder Networks, *J. Franklin Inst.*, July–August, 1957.

The shape of the output time response for networks having these network functions and a unit step-function input is found by taking the inverse Laplace transform.

$$f(t) = \mathcal{L}^{-1}\left[\frac{1}{p}\frac{H}{D_n(p)}\right] \tag{3.16}$$

The responses for $n = 1$, 2, and 3 are shown in Fig. 3.5. For each value of n, a value of H is used equal to the constant term of the polynomial. This provides a final value of unity for each case and permits easy comparison. Notice that the response for each curve has approximately the

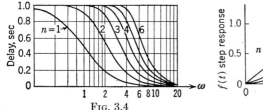

FIG. 3.4

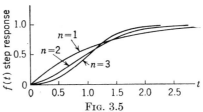

FIG. 3.5

same unit delay and that the delay is approximately the time elapsed to reach 50 per cent of the final value. However, as n increases, the response more closely approximates the ideal delay of the input step function. Another way of stating this is to say that the rise time of the response becomes smaller as n increases.

TABLE 3.1

n	Poles
1	-1
2	$-1.5 \pm j0.866$
3	-2.322, $-1.839 \pm j1.754$
4	$-2.896 \pm j0.867$, $-2.104 \pm j2.657$
5	-3.647, $-3.352 \pm j1.743$, $-2.325 \pm j3.571$

3.4   Rise Time, Bandwidth, and Overshoot.   The fundamental reason why the output pulse shapes discussed in the last section improve with n is that the bandwidth over which the phase is nearly linear increases with n. The spectrum of the input step function extends from zero to infinity, as shown in Fig. 3.6. Thus the increasing bandwidth along with the linear phase provides output spectra that are closer approximations to the input.

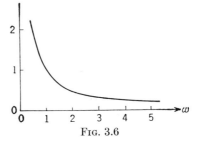

FIG. 3.6

A numerical relationship between the bandwidth of the magnitude function and the rise time of the step response can be established through the inverse Laplace transform. Actually the development is initiated in terms of an input which is an impulse function. For a unit impulse function the transform is unity. Thus the output response $h(t)$ for an input impulse is the inverse transform of the network function.

$$h(t) = \mathcal{L}^{-1}[N(p)] \qquad (3.17)$$

For network functions with no poles on the $j\omega$ axis, including infinity, the complex integration of the inverse transform reduces to a real integration along the $j\omega$ axis, i.e., the inverse Fourier transform.

$$h(t) = \frac{1}{2\pi} \int_{-\infty}^{\infty} N(j\omega)e^{j\omega t}\, d\omega = \frac{1}{2\pi} \int_{-\infty}^{\infty} |N(j\omega)|e^{j[\beta(\omega)+\omega t]}\, d\omega \qquad (3.18)$$

It is now assumed that over a frequency band

$$\beta(\omega) \approx -\omega t_0 \qquad (3.19)$$

and outside this band $|N(j\omega)|$ is small. Using these assumptions and evaluating the integral at $t = t_0$, one obtains

$$h(t_0) \approx \frac{1}{2\pi} \int_{-\infty}^{\infty} |N(j\omega)|\, d\omega \qquad (3.20)$$

The right-hand side of (3.20) is $1/2\pi$ times the area under the magnitude curve. If a rectangular passband of the same area, as shown in Fig. 3.7, is proposed, its band edge f_c constitutes a measure of the area. Conversely, the area can be interpreted as a measure of the bandwidth.

$$\int_{-\infty}^{\infty} |N(j\omega)|\, d\omega = 2\pi\, 2f_c\, N(0) \qquad (3.21)$$

The left-hand side of (3.20) is the value of the impulse response at t_0, and it is the peak value, as shown in Fig. 3.8. This last follows from the reasoning in Sec. 3.2. From the relationship of the impulse and step responses, $h(t_0)$ is also the slope of the step function evaluated at t_0, as shown in Fig. 3.9. If the slope is extrapolated to intersect the axis and the final value line,

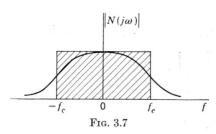

Fig. 3.7

the distance between the two intersections is a measure of the rise time t_s of the step response. From the final-value theorem

$$f(\infty) = \lim_{p \to 0} p\, \frac{N(p)}{p} = N(0) \qquad (3.22)$$

From the slope and the final value, t_s can be expressed as

$$t_s = \frac{N(0)}{h(t_0)} \tag{3.23}$$

Combining (3.20), (3.21), and (3.23), one obtains

$$t_s f_c \approx \tfrac{1}{2} \tag{3.24}$$

The exact equality holds if $\beta(\omega)$ is linear over the entire frequency interval, d-c to infinity. Thus it can be seen that the rise time of the step response and the bandwidth of the gain function of a network are inversely related.

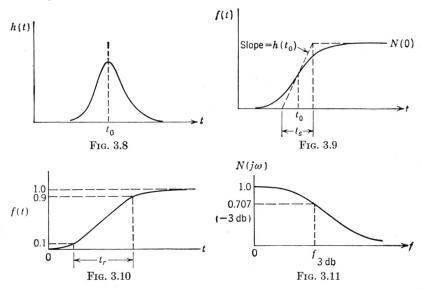

FIG. 3.8   FIG. 3.9

FIG. 3.10   FIG. 3.11

The above rise time and bandwidth definitions are not convenient to use in experimental measurements. Probably the most convenient definition of rise time, and the one most widely used in experimental work, is the 10 to 90 per cent rise time, as illustrated in Fig. 3.10. A convenient and widely used measure of bandwidth is the 3-db bandwidth, shown in Fig. 3.11. This bandwidth for the low-pass situation, as shown, is the frequency interval from zero frequency to the frequency where the gain function is 3 db down from its d-c value. For the bandpass situation, the frequency interval is taken as the difference between the lower and upper 3-db frequencies.

For an elementary network function with only one pole, the above definitions of rise time and bandwidth are simply related. If the pole lies at $-p_1$

$$N(p) = \frac{H}{p + p_1} \tag{3.25}$$

The 3-db frequency occurs at

$$f_{3\,db} = \frac{p_1}{2\pi} \tag{3.26}$$

The output time response for unit step input is

$$f(t) = \frac{H}{p_1}(1 - e^{-p_1 t}) \tag{3.27}$$

The 10 to 90 per cent rise time can be calculated from (3.27) and leads to

$$t_r = \frac{2.2}{p_1} \tag{3.28}$$

Therefore the product of rise time and bandwidth is

$$t_r f_{3\,db} = \frac{2.2}{2\pi} = 0.35 \tag{3.29}$$

It is found that for more complicated network functions (3.29) also holds, especially for those cases where there is no or negligible overshoot in the time response. Overshoot, illus-

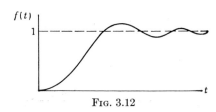

Fig. 3.12

trated in Fig. 3.12, constitutes an oscillation or ringing of the time response about the final value. Overshoot is usually expressed as a percentage of the difference between peak value and the final value to the final value. If the overshoot exceeds approximately 5 per cent, the numeric 0.35 of (3.29) must be increased and lies somewhere between 0.35 and 0.5.*

Overshoot is usually present if the network function contains complex poles. This is evident from the inverse Laplace transform of the complex-pole factor, since this factor leads to an oscillatory time contribution. However, for some network functions, e.g., the maximally flat delay functions, the observable amount of overshoot is negligible. For poles on the negative σ axis, e.g., the poles of a cascaded RC amplifier, there is no overshoot.

3.5 Elementary Design and Element Normalization. A design example is presented in this section to illustrate the use of the maximally flat delay function and two other useful techniques in design. The first is

* G. E. Valley, Jr., and H. Wallman (eds.), "Vacuum Tube Amplifiers," pp. 71–84, MIT Radiation Laboratory Series, vol. 18, McGraw-Hill Book Company, Inc., New York, 1948.

the design technique of equating coefficients which can be used to develop designs for simple networks. The second is the use of frequency and magnitude normalizations of network element values.

The problem is the design of a single-stage pentode amplifier operating between a source having a resistance of 600 ohms and load of 600 ohms, as in Fig. 3.13a. The amplifier should preserve the input pulse consistent with a three-pole maximally flat delay function and a rise time of 1 μsec. In choosing the configuration of the coupling networks, it is necessary to keep in mind two points. (1) The pentode introduces capacitances, as shown in Fig. 3.13b, where an equivalent circuit has been substituted for the pentode. These capacitances must be included in the choice and the design of the configurations. (2) Because the pentode

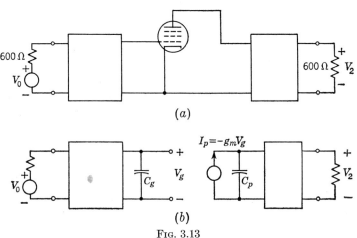

(a)

(b)

Fig. 3.13

is unilateral—there is no transmission from the output to the input of the pentode—the over-all network function is equal to the product of the network functions of the separate parts of the equivalent network.

$$N(p) = \frac{V_2}{V_0} = -g_m N_1(p) N_2(p) \qquad (3.30)$$

where
$$N_1 = \frac{V_g}{V_0} \qquad N_2 = \frac{V_2}{I_p}$$

and
$$I_p = -g_m V_g$$

Thus the poles and zeros of $N(p)$ are the combined poles and zeros of $N_1(p)$ and $N_2(p)$. In the design of the coupling networks the specified poles and zeros of $N(p)$ are separated into two groups. One group is assigned to each network. For the present problem the network function has only three finite poles. Thus one pole can be assigned to the input network and must therefore be the real negative pole. The complex pair of poles is assigned to the output network. In terms of the normalized poles of Sec. 3.3, the over-all network function for a three-pole maximally flat delay characteristic is

$$N(p) = \frac{H}{p^3 + 6p^2 + 15p + 15} = \frac{H}{(p + 2.32)(p^2 + 3.67p + 6.47)}$$

$$N_1(p) = \frac{H_1}{p + 2.32} \quad \text{and} \quad N_2(p) = \frac{H_2}{p^2 + 3.67p + 6.47} \tag{3.31}$$

Network configurations which are compatible with (3.31) and which include the pentode capacitances are chosen from experience. For example, it is probably known to the designer that simple ladder networks consisting of shunt capacitances, series inductances, and a terminating resistance, as shown in Fig. 3.14, have a network function $N(p) = V_2/I_1$

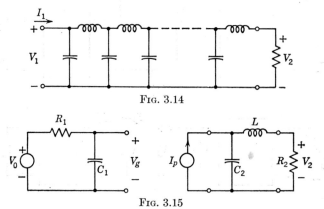

FIG. 3.14

FIG. 3.15

or V_2/V_1, which has finite poles and all zeros at infinity. Suitable configurations for the input and output networks are shown in Fig. 3.15. The network functions of these configurations are from analysis

$$N_1(p) = \frac{1/R_1 C_1}{p + 1/R_1 C_1}$$

$$N_2(p) = \frac{R_2/L C_2}{p^2 + (R_2/L)p + 1/L C_2} \tag{3.32}$$

Two procedures can be used to determine the actual element values. First, the network functions of (3.31) can be denormalized with respect to the specified rise-time and resistance levels. By equating corresponding coefficients of these denormalized functions with (3.32), the resulting equations can be solved to obtain the element values. Alternately, the corresponding coefficients of (3.31) and (3.32) can be equated to obtain normalized values of the elements. These values are then denormalized with respect to the resistance level and rise-time specifications. This second procedure is usually the simpler and is used here. Equating coefficients of (3.31) and (3.32) leads to the following equations:

$$\frac{1}{R_1 C_1} = 2.32$$

$$\frac{R_2}{L} = 3.67 \qquad R_1 = R_2 = 1 \qquad\qquad (3.33)$$

$$\frac{1}{L C_2} = 6.47$$

Rather than specify H_1 and H_2 in (3.31) as arbitrary numerics (in order to define an arbitrary d-c level for the network functions), it is possible to choose convenient values, in this case unity, for the resistances R_1 and R_2. The two choices are equivalent, since at d-c inductances and capacitances are short and open circuits, respectively, and the d-c level is a function of the resistances only. For a given choice of the resistances the values of the elements and the constant H are determined in terms of this choice. Solving (3.33), one obtains

$$\begin{aligned} C_1 &= 0.431 \\ L &= 0.272 \qquad R_1 = R_2 = 1 \qquad\qquad (3.34) \\ C_2 &= 0.568 \end{aligned}$$

The problem now is to denormalize the element values in terms of the specifications of the given amplifier. It should be remembered that the element values of (3.34) are normalized with respect to unit resistances and unit delay. The actual resistances of the amplifier should be 600 ohms. This is accomplished by multiplying each impedance element in the network by the resistance denormalization factor, 600. Since the network elements are linear, this change does not alter the character of the response and amounts to a scaling of the magnitude function by 600. Since resistances and inductances are directly proportional to impedances, they are multiplied by 600. The values of capacitances are divided by 600, because capacitances are inversely proportional to impedances.

Next, it is necessary to determine the actual delay requirement of the amplifier in order to complete the element denormalizations. The required rise time is 1 μsec. This corresponds to a 3-db bandwidth specification of 0.35 Mc or 2.2×10^6 radians/sec from (3.29). From Fig. 3.2 the three-pole response for unit delay has a 3-db radial bandwidth of 1.75 [the approximate value from (3.15) is 1.86]. Since time and frequency are inversely related, the delay denormalization can be accomplished in terms of a frequency denormalization. That is, the bandwidth of 1.75 for a unit delay is denormalized to the bandwidth of

2.2×10^6 radians/sec. To accomplish this, a linear change of frequency variable is made by the desired factor:

$$\frac{\text{Desired bandwidth}}{\text{Normalized bandwidth}} = \frac{2.2 \times 10^6}{1.75} = 1.256 \times 10^6$$

To keep the impedances of all elements invariant with this change of variable as the shift from normalized frequency to denormalized frequency occurs, all inductances and capacitances are divided by the denormalization factor. When the two denormalization factors are used, the required element values for the amplifier are

$$C_1 = \frac{0.431}{600 \times 1.256 \times 10^6} = 570 \ \mu\mu\text{f}$$

$$L = \frac{0.272 \times 600}{1.256 \times 10^6} = 1.3 \text{ mh} \qquad R_1 = R_2 = 600 \quad (3.35)$$

$$C_2 = \frac{0.568}{600 \times 1.256 \times 10^6} = 750 \ \mu\mu\text{f}$$

If the given pentode has input and output capacitances of 10 and 5 $\mu\mu$f, respectively, and a g_m of 10,000 μmho, the actual capacitances necessary at the input and the output of the pentodes are 560 and 745 $\mu\mu$f. The low-frequency gain of the amplifier is

$$\left|\frac{V_2}{V_0}\right|_{p=0} = g_m R_2 = 6 = 15.4 \text{ db} \qquad (3.36)$$

In summary, the design method of equating coefficients is very useful in the design of simple networks. It has been found especially valuable in the design of cascaded amplifiers, where simple networks can be used as the interstages and are isolated by the unilateral active devices. The limitation of the design method stems from the difficulty of solving the simultaneous nonlinear algebraic equations. For any network functions containing more than three finite poles and zeros, the solution of the equations is difficult and may not be possible at all.

As a convenience, the following formulas are listed for element denormalization by a resistance denormalization factor r_n and a frequency denormalization factor Ω_n:[8]*

$$L_{act} = \frac{r_n}{\Omega_n} L_n$$

$$C_{act} = \frac{1}{r_n \Omega_n} C_n \qquad (3.37)$$

$$R_{act} = r_n R_n$$

* Superior numbers refer to the publications listed in the Selected Bibliography at the back of the book.

These formulas can also, of course, be used in analysis to normalize a set of actual element values. The choices of r_n and Ω_n are usually indicated by the given problem.

3.6 Maximally Flat Magnitude Function. In many types of communication systems it is not necessary to preserve exactly the input signal shape or, alternately, to preserve both the magnitude and the phase of the input spectrum. An example is a frequency multiplex system where the carriers are modulated with audio signals. As mentioned in Chap. 1, since the human ear is insensitive to phase, one can ignore the phase characteristics and concentrate on the shape of the magnitude function. The problem then is one of filtering so as to reject signals in adjacent channels and also outband noise. The ideal filter has the magnitude function shown in Fig. 3.16 for the low-pass case. For convenience, a normalized d-c magnitude and cutoff frequency are used. Two approximations to the ideal-filter characteristic are presented in

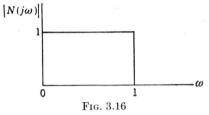

Fig. 3.16

this and the next sections. Again, the approximating network functions are restricted to have finite poles only. It is shown in a later chapter how to transform this low-pass design criterion into bandpass criteria.

Clearly, the ideal-filter characteristic of Fig. 3.16 cannot be realized, because of the sharp corners and because of the total rejection over a semi-infinite frequency band.* Since the network functions are rational, the magnitude functions are smooth, continuous functions of ω. As a first method of approximation to this ideal-filter function, the flatness at both low and high frequencies is striven for. For network functions that are reciprocals of polynomials

$$N(p) = \frac{H}{p^n + a_{n-1}p^{n-1} + \cdots + a_0} \tag{3.38}$$

The high-frequency behavior is

$$N(p) \sim \frac{H}{p^n}\bigg|_{p=j\omega \to \infty} \tag{3.39}$$

From (3.39) it is seen that the flatness of the magnitude function near infinity is directly related to n. If a greater flatness is desired at high frequencies—i.e., if rejection is desired over a larger frequency interval— n must be increased.

The flatness at low frequencies is obtained by adjusting the coefficients of the denominator polynomial so that as many derivatives as possible

* Valley and Wallman, *op. cit.*, pp. 721–726.

of the magnitude function at d-c are equal to zero. As with the delay function of Sec. 3.3, this zero-derivative criterion is termed a maximally flat criterion. As an example of this procedure, a network function with only three poles in the finite plane is used. In general, the network function has the form

$$N(p) = \frac{H}{p^3 + a_2 p^2 + a_1 p + a_0} \tag{3.40}$$

It is convenient to normalize this function with respect to the d-c value H/a_0.

$$\frac{N(p)}{N(0)} = \frac{1}{(1/a_0)p^3 + (a_2/a_0)p^2 + (a_1/a_0)p + 1} \tag{3.41}$$

A frequency normalization (a linear change of the variable) of $p' = (1/a_0)^{1/3} p$ leads to

$$N(p) = \frac{1}{p^3 + b_2 p^2 + b_1 p + 1} \tag{3.42}$$

For convenience, in (3.42) the notations $N(0)$ and p' are not used. It is understood that $N(p)$ is normalized in both frequency and magnitude. It should be noted that (3.42) has only two arbitrary coefficients in comparison with the four coefficients in (3.40). Since no loss of generality with respect to the nature of the function has occurred, one can conclude that there are two degrees of freedom in adjusting the flatness of the magnitude function.

To obtain a maximally flat magnitude about d-c, the coefficients b_1 and b_2 of (3.42) are calculated by setting equal to zero successive derivatives of the magnitude function evaluated at d-c.

$$\frac{d^k}{d\omega^k} |N(j\omega)|_{\omega=0} = 0 \tag{3.43}$$

Since the magnitude function $|N(j\omega)|$ is an even function, the odd derivatives at $\omega = 0$ are automatically equal to zero. The magnitude function for this example has the form

$$|N(j\omega)| = [N(p)N(-p)]^{1/2}_{p=j\omega} = \frac{1}{(\omega^6 + c_2\omega^4 + c_1\omega^2 + 1)^{1/2}} \tag{3.44}$$

The coefficients c_1 and c_2 are used for convenience. The derivatives of this function, evaluated at the origin, are most easily found from the Maclaurin series expansion

$$f(\omega) = f(0) + f'(0)\omega + \frac{f''(0)}{2!} \omega^2 + \cdots \tag{3.45}$$

The coefficients of this series are directly related to the values of the derivatives at $\omega = 0$. Since a power series is unique within a region of convergence (the region about $\omega = 0$ for the present case), the series can be found immediately from the binomial expansion. Equation (3.44) can then be expressed in series form as

$$|N(j\omega)| = 1 - \frac{c_1}{2}\omega^2 + \left(-\frac{c_2}{2} + \frac{3}{8}c_1^2\right)\omega^4 + \cdots \tag{3.46}$$

It is evident from (3.46) that the odd derivatives are equal to zero. Since there are only two degrees of freedom, it is expected that only the first two successive even derivatives can be set equal to zero. This leads to

$$c_1 = c_2 = 0$$

Consequently,

$$|N(j\omega)| = \frac{1}{(1 + \omega^6)^{\frac{1}{2}}} \tag{3.47}$$

Using the principle of analytic continuation as in the last chapter, one obtains

$$N(p)N(-p) = \frac{1}{(1 - p^6)} \tag{3.48}$$

The poles of $N(p)$ and their negatives are thus the sixth roots of unity. Instead of determining the roots for this specific case, it is possible to treat the general case of n poles. If a similar procedure is used for the general case, the result is

$$|N(j\omega)| = \frac{1}{(1 + \omega^{2n})^{\frac{1}{2}}}$$
$$N(p)N(-p) = \frac{1}{1 + (-1)^n p^{2n}} \tag{3.49}$$

The poles of $N(p)$ and their negatives are found from

$$p^{2n} = (-1)^{n+1} \tag{3.50}$$

and are the $2n$th roots of one for n odd or the $2n$th roots of minus one for n even.

$$p_k = e^{j[(2k-1)/2n]\pi} \quad n \text{ even}$$
$$p_k = e^{j(k/n)\pi} \quad n \text{ odd} \qquad k = 1, 2, \ldots, 2n \tag{3.51}$$

In terms of the real and imaginary coordinates of the poles, the following formulas are valid for both n even and odd:

$$p_k = \sigma_k + j\omega_k$$
$$\sigma_k = \sin \frac{2k-1}{2n}\pi$$
$$\omega_k = \cos \frac{2k-1}{2n}\pi \tag{3.52}$$

All the poles of $N(p)N(-p)$ lie on the unit circle, and the poles of $N(p)$ are those lying in the left half plane. The pole locations of $N(p)$ for $n = 2$ and $n = 3$ are shown in Fig. 3.17. Plots of the magnitude functions are shown in Fig. 3.18. As indicated on the curves and as can be calculated from (3.49), the 3-db bandwidth for this normalized maximally

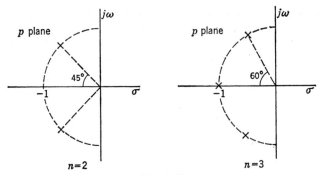

Fig. 3.17

flat magnitude function is unity for all n. It is clear from the curves that, as expected, both the flatness and the sharpness of cutoff are improved as n increases.

For reference, the responses obtained from a step-function input for $n = 2$ and $n = 3$ are shown in Fig. 3.19. Appreciable overshoots, which increase with increasing n, are obtained as a result of the close proximity of complex poles to the $j\omega$ axis. If these step responses are compared

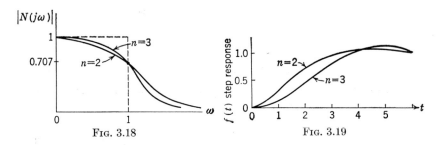

Fig. 3.18   Fig. 3.19

with those of the corresponding maximally flat delay functions for the same frequency normalization, it is found that the 10 to 90 per cent rise times for the present case are smaller.

3.7 The Equal-ripple Magnitude Function. As an introduction to another approximation of the ideal-filter curve, the desired magnitude function is written in the form

$$|N(j\omega)| = \frac{1}{[1 + \epsilon^2 f^2(\omega)]^{\frac{1}{2}}} \tag{3.53}$$

The approximation problem is converted directly from one in terms of $|N(j\omega)|$ to one involving a choice of $f^2(\omega)$, so that the desired approximation can be obtained. For example, in the maximally flat magnitude approximation, a function must be chosen which has the proper number of derivatives equal to zero at $\omega = 0$. $f^2(\omega)$ can be chosen equal to ω^{2n} from a knowledge of Maclaurin's series, since, if $|N(j\omega)|$ is maximally flat, its reciprocal must be maximally flat, as must $f^2(\omega)$.

In this section an approximation is developed which deviates from the ideal-filter curve in an equal-ripple manner in the passband, as shown in Fig. 3.20.* As indicated in the figure, the parameter ϵ determines the magnitude of the ripple. The band edge is normalized with respect to the frequency where the magnitude function breaks away from the equal-ripple deviation. This type of bandwidth specification is usually called the tolerance bandwidth.

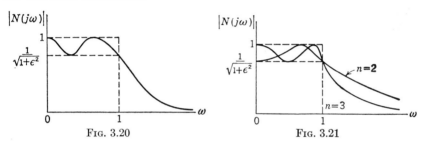

FIG. 3.20   FIG. 3.21

For an all-pole approximation, $f(\omega)$ must be a polynomial which must have an equal-ripple variation over the interval zero to one. Such a polynomial is the Chebyshev polynomial $C_n(\omega)$.[8] In trigonometric form,

$$C_n(\omega) = \cos{(n \cos^{-1}\omega)} \quad 0 \le \omega \le 1$$
$$= \cosh{(n \cosh^{-1}\omega)} \quad \omega \ge 1 \tag{3.54}$$

Clearly, this polynomial varies between plus and minus one in the passband. The lowest-order polynomials and the recursion formula are

$$C_0(\omega) = 1$$
$$C_1(\omega) = \omega$$
$$C_2(\omega) = 2\omega^2 - 1 \tag{3.55}$$
$$C_3(\omega) = 4\omega^3 - 3\omega$$
$$C_{n+1}(\omega) = 2\omega C_n(\omega) - C_{n-1}(\omega)$$

The magnitude functions $|N(j\omega)|$ for $n = 2$ and $n = 3$ for a given ϵ are shown in Fig. 3.21. The different values at d-c for n even and n odd should be noted. With a knowledge of such a polynomial, the next prob-

* It can be proved mathematically that this equal-ripple approximation provides the minimum absolute deviation from the ideal-filter curve in the passband. See Ref. 8.

lem is to determine the pole locations for $N(p)$. If (3.53) is analytically continued, using (3.54),

$$N(p)N(-p) = \frac{1}{1 + \epsilon^2 C_n^2(p/j)} \tag{3.56}$$

The poles p_k are the zeros of

$$1 + \epsilon^2 C_n^2 \left(\frac{p_k}{j}\right) = 0 \tag{3.57}$$

From (3.54) and (3.57)

$$C_n \left(\frac{p_k}{j}\right) = \cos n \left(\cos^{-1} \frac{p_k}{j}\right) = \pm j \frac{1}{\epsilon} \tag{3.58}$$

To solve (3.58), trigonometric identities are used together with a transformation of the complex variable p. The new complex variable is defined by

$$w = u + jv = \cos^{-1} \frac{p}{j} \tag{3.59}$$

In terms of this new variable, the trigonometric part of (3.58) is the cosine of a complex number.

$$\begin{aligned}
\cos nw_k &= \cos (nu_k + jnv_k) \\
&= \cos nu_k \cos jnv_k - \sin nu_k \sin jnv_k \\
&= \cos nu_k \cosh nv_k - j \sin nu_k \sinh nv_k = \pm j \frac{1}{\epsilon}
\end{aligned} \tag{3.60}$$

Equating real and imaginary parts in (3.60) leads to

$$\begin{aligned}
\cos nu_k \cosh nv_k &= 0 \\
\sin nu_k \sinh nv_k &= \pm \frac{1}{\epsilon}
\end{aligned} \tag{3.61}$$

Cosh nv_k cannot be equal to zero for real v_k; therefore

$$\cos nu_k = 0$$
$$u_k = \frac{\pi}{2n} (2k - 1) \qquad k = 1, 2, \ldots, 2n \tag{3.62}$$

From (3.62) and the remaining equation of (3.61)

$$v_k = v = \frac{1}{n} \sinh^{-1} \frac{1}{\epsilon} \tag{3.63}$$

Notice that there is not a set of v_k as in the case of u_k. The imaginary parts of the w_k are all equal and depend only on given values of n and ϵ.

From these fixed values of w_k the corresponding locations p_k can be determined from (3.59).

$$p_k = \sigma_k + j\omega_k = j \cos w_k = j \cos (u_k + jv)$$
$$\sigma_k = \sin u_k \sinh v \tag{3.64}$$
$$\omega_k = \cos u_k \cosh v$$

Similarly to the maximally flat magnitude function, the poles lie on a simple locus in the complex plane. From a manipulation of (3.64)

$$\frac{\sigma_k{}^2}{\sinh^2 v} + \frac{\omega_k{}^2}{\cosh^2 v} = 1 \tag{3.65}$$

Thus the poles lie on an ellipse which has the semi-major axis $\cosh v$ and the semi-minor axis $\sinh v$.

Since both the shape and the size of the ellipse vary with the parameter ϵ, it is often convenient to introduce another frequency normalization to give the semi-major axis a value of unity. This is accomplished by dividing (3.64) by $\cosh v$. With this normalization the pole locations are

$$\sigma_k = \sin u_k \tanh v$$
$$\omega_k = \cos u_k \tag{3.66}$$
$$u_k = \frac{2k - 1}{2n} \pi \qquad k = 1, 2, \ldots, 2n$$

The tolerance bandwidth is now $1/\cosh v$. Coincidentally, it is easily shown that the 3-db bandwidth for $n \geq 2$ is approximately unity. Equations (3.66) and (3.52) should now be compared. The imaginary parts of the equal-ripple pole locations are identical with those of the maximally flat magnitude case. The values of the real parts are equal to the values of the real parts of the maximally flat magnitude case reduced by $\tanh v$. The pole locations for $n = 3$ are shown in Fig. 3.22 with this frequency normalization. In the limit, as $\epsilon \to 0$, $v \to \infty$, $\tanh v \to 1$. Hence in the limit the equal-ripple case becomes the maximally flat magnitude case. That is, the maximally flat magnitude function is the limiting case of the equal-ripple magnitude function.

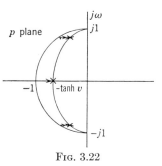

FIG. 3.22

3.8 Filter-design Examples. As an illustration of the use of the maximally flat magnitude and equal-ripple filter approximations, assume that a low-pass filter has the following specifications:

(a) The allowable deviation from ideal in the passband must be equal to or less than $\frac{1}{2}$ db. The passband extends from 0 to 1 radian/sec.

(*b*) The attenuation must be at least 18 db at frequencies higher than 2 radians/sec.

(*c*) The filter is to operate between two equal resistances of 1 ohm.

The equal-ripple filter is designed first. From (3.53) and (3.56) the magnitude function is

$$|N(j\omega)| = \frac{1}{[1 + \epsilon^2 C_n{}^2(\omega)]^{\frac{1}{2}}} \qquad (3.67)$$

The tolerance band edge, as illustrated in Fig. 3.21, is unity. Therefore

$$|N(j1)| = \frac{1}{(1 + \epsilon^2)^{\frac{1}{2}}} \qquad (3.68)$$

For the allowable tolerance of $\frac{1}{2}$ db

$$|N(j1)| = 0.945$$

The required ϵ is

$$\epsilon = 0.347$$

The parameter n, the number of poles, is determined through use of the lower form of (3.54) together with (3.53). At $\omega = 2$, the 18-db rejection requirement leads to

$$|N(j2)| = \frac{1}{[1 + \epsilon^2 \cosh^2 (n \cosh^{-1} 2)]^{\frac{1}{2}}} = 0.125$$

The equality is satisfied for $n = 2.94$. Since n must be an integer, $n = 3$ is used.

These values of n and ϵ complete the pole locations, from which $N(p)$ can be determined. From (3.62) and (3.63)

$$v = \tfrac{1}{3} \sinh^{-1} 1/\epsilon = 0.593$$

$$u_1 = \frac{\pi}{6}, \; u_2 = \frac{\pi}{2}, \; \cdots, \; u_6 = \frac{11\pi}{6}$$

From (3.64) the poles in the left half plane are

$$p_1 = -0.628 \qquad p_2 = -0.314 + j1.022 \qquad p_3 = -0.314 - j1.022$$

$$N(p) = \frac{H}{p^3 + 1.256p^2 + 1.549p + 0.72} \qquad (3.69)$$

In Sec. 3.5 it is indicated that a simple ladder network, as shown in Fig. 3.23, provides a transfer function with no finite transmission zeros. The network shown has the following transfer function, which is compatible with (3.69):

$$N(p) = \frac{V_2}{V_0} = \frac{1/LC_1C_2}{p^3 + \dfrac{C_1 + C_2}{C_1C_2} p^2 + \left(\dfrac{1}{C_1C_2} + \dfrac{C_1 + C_2}{LC_1C_2}\right) p + \dfrac{2}{LC_1C_2}} \qquad (3.70)$$

Equating corresponding coefficients of (3.69) and (3.70), one obtains

$$L = 1.08$$
$$C_1 = 1.42$$
$$C_2 = 1.82$$

If a maximally flat magnitude approximation is used, the magnitude function is of the form

$$|N(j\omega)| = \frac{1}{(1 + \epsilon^2\omega^{2n})^{\frac{1}{2}}} \qquad (3.71)$$

Note that in the above form, where ϵ^2 is included, the tolerance bandwidth rather than the 3-db bandwidth is unity. Since ϵ is already known from the previous example, only n is unknown. If (3.71) is solved for a minimum of 18-db attenuation at $\omega = 2$, $n = 5$ and the efficiency of the equal-ripple filter is evident. The design of this maximally flat magnitude filter is not attempted

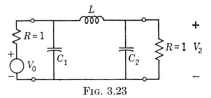

Fig. 3.23

with the method of equating coefficients, since the required number of poles is greater than three.

3.9 A Simple Method of Arbitrary Magnitude Approximation. Many equalization problems in both communication and control systems include the approximation of an arbitrary magnitude function by a realizable network function. Of the many methods available, there is one that is not only simple but useful, especially in the design of networks having only resistances and capacitances. The method to be discussed is restricted to network functions with poles and zeros all on the negative real axis. This type of network function has the form

$$N(p) = \frac{(p + a_1)(p + a_2) \cdots (p + a_m)}{(p + b_1)(p + b_2) \cdots (p + b_n)} \qquad (3.72)$$

where a_i and b_i are positive real numbers. The starting point is not an arbitrary magnitude function; instead, the details of the method are brought out first by a manipulation of (3.72). If the logarithm of (3.72) is taken for $p = j\omega$, one obtains

$$\ln N(j\omega) = \sum_{i=1}^{m} \ln (a_i + j\omega) - \sum_{i=1}^{n} \ln (b_i + j\omega) \qquad (3.73)$$

$$\alpha(\omega) = \ln |N(j\omega)| = \frac{1}{2} \sum_{i=1}^{m} \ln (a_i^2 + \omega^2) - \frac{1}{2} \sum_{i=1}^{n} \ln (b_i^2 + \omega^2) \qquad (3.74)$$

The use of the logarithm permits attention to be centered on the contributions of the individual poles and zeros. A typical term of (3.74) for a zero is

$$\alpha(\omega) = \tfrac{1}{2} \ln (a^2 + \omega^2) \quad (3.75)$$

At low frequencies, (3.75) has an asymptotic behavior of

$$\alpha(\omega) \sim \ln a \quad (3.76)$$

At high frequencies, the asymptote is

$$\alpha(\omega) \sim \ln \omega \quad (3.77)$$

These asymptotes are plotted in Fig. 3.24, with the axis of the abscissa scaled in terms of ln frequency rather than frequency to obtain a linear high-frequency asymptote with a slope of 1 neper/ln radian or 6 db/octave. The intersection of the two asymptotes occurs at $\omega = a$ and is

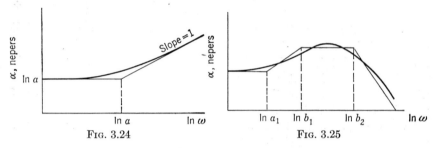

FIG. 3.24   FIG. 3.25

called the corner or break frequency. The value of the actual magnitude at the corner frequency is

$$\alpha(a) = \ln a + \tfrac{1}{2} \ln 2 \quad (3.78)$$

Thus the actual curve is $\tfrac{1}{2} \ln 2$ or 3 db higher than the value at the intersection. The contribution due to the poles of (3.74) is the same as above, except for the negative sign.

With the above in mind, assume that the magnitude curve to be approximated is as shown in Fig. 3.25, where the plot is made in terms of ln ω. Such a specification often arises in the design of feedback networks for simple control systems or feedback amplifiers. This curve is approximated by straight line segments having slopes that are multiples of unity, including zero, as shown in the figure. The intersections of the different line segments correspond to the corner frequencies, i.e., the desired poles or zeros. Because the actual curve and the asymptotes, as shown in Fig. 3.24, are different, the approximating network function has a smooth characteristic, i.e., no sharp discontinuities. For the example shown in the figure, three corner frequencies are used. The network function has the form

$$N(p) = H \frac{p + a_1}{(p + b_1)(p + b_2)} \quad (3.79)$$

If networks containing only resistances and capacitances are to be used, as is often the case in control systems, the poles of $N(p)$ must be simple. This is proved in Chap. 10. In this case the slopes between adjacent segments can be diminished by only unity. It should be clear that if a better approximation is desired, a greater number of line segments are needed; consequently the network function must have a greater number of poles and zeros.

PROBLEMS

3.1. Determine and sketch the delay functions $\tau(\omega)$ of the following $N(p)$:

$$(a) \; \frac{1}{p^2 + p + 1} \qquad (b) \; \frac{p^2 - p + 1}{p^2 + p + 1} \qquad (c) \; \frac{1}{p^3 + 2p^2 + 2p + 1}$$

3.2. Using the principle of stationary phase, show that if

$$N(j\omega) = N_0(j\omega)(1 + a_1 \cos \omega t_1)$$

then

$$h(t) = h_0(t) + \frac{a_1}{2} h_0(t - t_1) + \frac{a_1}{2} h_0(t + t_1)$$

where

$$h_0(t) = \frac{1}{2\pi} \int_{-\infty}^{\infty} |N_0(j\omega)| e^{j\beta(\omega)} e^{j\omega t} \, d\omega$$

$$N_0(j\omega) = |N_0(j\omega)| e^{j\beta(\omega)}$$

If $h_0(t)$ is as shown in Fig. P3.2, plot $h(t)$ for values of $a_1 = \frac{1}{2}$ and $t_1 = 1$. This problem illustrates the paired-echo type of distortion.

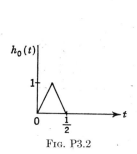

Fig. P3.2

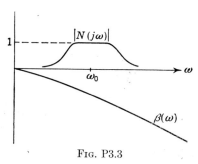

Fig. P3.3

3.3. A bandpass filter has the magnitude and phase functions shown in Fig. P3.3. The input is an amplitude-modulated sinusoid

$$(1 + m \cos \omega_a t) \cos \omega_0 t$$

Show that it can also be written as

$$\text{Re}\left(e^{j\omega_0 t} + \frac{m}{2} e^{j(\omega_0 + \omega_a)t} + \frac{m}{2} e^{j(\omega_0 - \omega_a)t} \right)$$

and that the steady-state output response can therefore be written

$$\text{Re}\left[N(j\omega) \left(e^{j\omega_0 t} + \frac{m}{2} e^{j(\omega_0 + \omega_a)t} + \frac{m}{2} e^{j(\omega_0 - \omega_a)t} \right) \right]$$

Determine the delay time of the modulated signal through the network.

3.4. Determine the conditions for maximally flat delay for the network functions below having one zero and two poles and two zeros and three poles.

(a) $\dfrac{p + b_0}{p^2 + a_1 p + a_0}$ $\qquad\qquad$ (b) $\dfrac{p^2 + b_1 p + b_0}{p^3 + a_2 p^2 + a_1 p + a_0}$

3.5. For the shunt-peaked network shown in Fig. P3.5, determine the values of L and C that will give $N(p)$ a maximally flat delay characteristic.

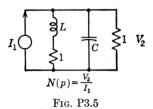

$$N(p) = \frac{V_2}{I_1}$$

Fig. P3.5

3.6. For network functions considered in Sec. 3.3, plot for $n = 2$ and $n = 3$ the impulse and step responses. Compute the 3-db bandwidth and 10 to 90 per cent rise-time products.

3.7. A network is desired which is to have a 10 to 90 per cent rise time of 1 μsec and a delay of at least 1 μsec. For an all-pole maximally flat delay function, determine $N(p)$.

3.8. Design the input and output coupling networks for the pentode amplifier in Fig. P3.8. The over-all transfer function is to have a maximally flat delay character-istic ($n = 4$). The required 3-db bandwidth is 1 Mc. Calculate the rise time, delay, and d-c gain $(V_2/V_0)(0)$ of the amplifier. Note that R_1 and R_2 are free to be chosen.

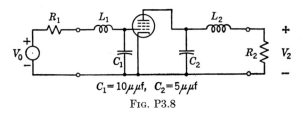

$C_1 = 10\mu\mu f, \quad C_2 = 5\mu\mu f$

Fig. P3.8

3.9. For a "one-pole" bandpass network having a network function

$$N(p) = H \frac{p}{p^2 + a p + \omega_0^2}$$

determine the product of the 3-db bandwidth and the 10 to 90 per cent envelope rise time. The 3-db bandwidth for the bandpass case is defined as the frequency interval for $\omega > 0$ between the lower and the upper -3-db frequencies. To determine the envelope rise time, let the input be $u(t) \sin \omega_0 t$.

3.10. For the following network function

$$N(p) = \frac{1}{p^2 + 2 \cos \theta p + 1}$$

determine the impulse and step responses for $\theta = 60°$. Calculate the overshoot of the step response as a function of the angle θ.

3.11. Determine the network function $Z_{21} = V_2/I_1$ of the ladder network in Fig. P3.11. If $R = 1,000$, design the remaining elements for a filter with maximally flat magnitude characteristic and 3-db cutoff frequency at 4 kc.

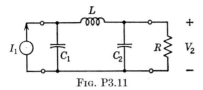

FIG. P3.11

3.12. Determine the transfer function for a low-pass filter having a magnitude characteristic that is (a) maximally flat and (b) equal ripple in the passband. The passband, which is to extend from d-c to $\omega = 2$, is defined for a 1-db tolerance. The loss for $\omega \geq 10$ must be at least 30 db.

3.13. Derive an expression for the 3-db frequency of an equal-ripple magnitude low-pass transfer function in terms of n and ϵ. Show that for $n \geq 2$ the 3-db bandwidth is approximately equal to unity for the normalization of (3.66).

3.14. Given

$$|N(j\omega)|^2 = \frac{1 + b_1\omega^2 + b_2\omega^4 + \cdots + b_m\omega^{2m}}{1 + a_1\omega^2 + \cdots + a_n\omega^{2n}}$$

Show that for maximally flat magnitude and for $m < n$

$$a_i = b_i \qquad i = 1, \ldots, m$$
$$a_i = 0 \qquad i = m + 1, \ldots, n - 1$$

3.15. For the shunt-peaked network shown in Fig. P3.5, determine the values of L and C that will give $N(p)$ a maximally flat magnitude characteristic.

3.16. For the generalized shunt-peaked network in Fig. P3.16, show that for any resistance ratio the network can be designed to have a maximally flat magnitude characteristic. Remember that the network can always be resistance-normalized so that one resistance is unity.

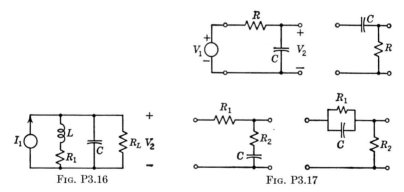

FIG. P3.16   FIG. P3.17

3.17. For the four networks shown in Fig. P3.17, determine and plot the pole-zero locations of the transfer voltage ratio V_2/V_1. From the pole-zero plot, construct the actual and the asymptotic $20 \log_{10} |(V_2/V_1)(j\omega)|$ vs. $\log_{10} \omega$ and Arg $(V_2/V_1)(j\omega)$ vs. $\log_{10} \omega$ plots.

3.18. Determine the transfer voltage ratio V_2/V_1 for the RC ladder shown in **Fig. P3.18.** Using the method of Sec. 3.9, approximate the magnitude function and determine values for C_1, C_2, and R_2.

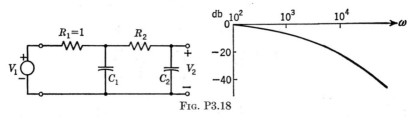

Fig. P3.18

3.19. Using the basic networks of Fig. P3.17 coupled with the ideal active circuit in Fig. P3.19, achieve an approximate realization of the magnitude function as shown. The ideal active circuit has an infinite input impedance and zero output impedance.

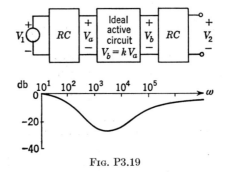

Fig. P3.19

CHAPTER 4

2-PORT NETWORKS

4.1 The Realization Problem. Illustrated in the last chapter, for certain general specifications, is one part of the synthesis problem, that of approximation. This part results in a network function which satisfies certain broad necessary conditions, imposed primarily from stability considerations, and which in one sense approximates the given specification. It is seen in Chap. 3 that an actual network design can be realized from the developed network function if it is sufficiently simple. From experience, a network configuration can be chosen and the element values obtained by the method of equating coefficients, but, as was pointed out, this method is severely limited. The remaining chapters in this book are an introduction to the network realization problem.

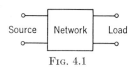

Fig. 4.1

Usually the communication or control network has a pair of terminals connected to the load and a pair of terminals connected to the source, as illustrated in Fig. 4.1. The terminal pairs of the network available to the outside environment are called *ports*. To be precise, a port is a pair of terminals in which the current flowing into one terminal is equal to the current flowing out of the other terminal. The network of Fig. 4.1 is called a 2-port network. One port is the input port and the other is the output port. Because of the prevalence and practicality of 2-port networks, attention is centered in this book on networks of this type. The special case of a 1-port network, in which the input pair of terminals and the output pair of terminals are the same, is also included.

Only with the 1-port can the realization procedure start directly from the given network function. Here the network function is either the input impedance or its reciprocal, the input admittance. The input impedance or admittance is often called the driving-point impedance or admittance. In the 2-port the network function is the ratio of a voltage or a current function at the output port to the voltage or current function at the input port. That is, it is one of the following: a transfer voltage ratio, a transfer current ratio, a transfer impedance, or a transfer admittance. It is necessary to derive from the network function of the

49

2-port a set of parameters that characterize the 2-port. Two of the parameters are always special driving-point functions. Every realization procedure presently used stems from the development of these driving-point functions.

In the following sections 1-port VI descriptions are taken up first. The discussion constitutes a review of analysis procedures and indicates how a given source and a load can be described. It also indicates a method which can be used to obtain certain sets of 2-port parameters.

4.2   1-port VI Descriptions. Consider a network with n meshes. For generality, any number of sources and elements

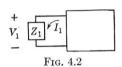

FIG. 4.2

may be included. With respect to one branch Z_1 in any mesh, the question is how to obtain the VI description of the port looking back into the network, as shown in Fig. 4.2. If a mesh analysis of the entire network is used, equilibrium equations in the transform domain of the following form are obtained:

$$\begin{aligned}
b_{11}I_1 + b_{12}I_2 + \cdots + b_{1n}I_n &= V_1{}^e \\
b_{21}I_1 + b_{22}I_2 + \cdots + b_{2n}I_n &= V_2{}^e \\
\cdots\cdots\cdots\cdots\cdots\cdots\cdots\cdots\cdots\cdots \\
b_{n1}I_1 + b_{n2}I_2 + \cdots + b_{nn}I_n &= V_n{}^e
\end{aligned} \tag{4.1}$$

where b_{ij} are the self- or mutual impedances of the meshes. The I_1, $I_2, \ldots, I_n$ are the mesh currents. The $V_1{}^e, V_2{}^e, \ldots, V_n{}^e$ are the effective voltage sources of the meshes. The individual terms may include contribution from current sources if there are current sources in the network. As indicated in Fig. 4.2, the current I_1 is the mesh current of interest. Equation (4.1) can be solved to obtain

$$I_1 = \sum_{k=1}^{n} \frac{\Delta_{k1}}{\Delta} V_k{}^e \tag{4.2}$$

The procedure now is to bring out from the determinant and its cofactors the contributions due to Z_1. Since Z_1 occurs only in the self-impedance b_{11}, the cofactors Δ_{k1} do not include Z_1. The determinant can be expanded by the Laplace expansion to obtain the following:

$$\Delta = Z_1\Delta_{11} + \Delta_0 \tag{4.3}$$

where Δ_0 is the determinant Δ in which Z_1 is set equal to zero. Inserting (4.3) into (4.2) and rearranging, one obtains

$$I_1\left(Z_1 + \frac{\Delta_0}{\Delta_{11}}\right) = \sum_{k=1}^{n} \frac{\Delta_{k1}}{\Delta_{11}} V_k{}^e \tag{4.4}$$

This equation has the form

$$I_1(Z_1 + Z_{eq}) = V_{eq} \tag{4.5}$$

where $\qquad Z_{eq} = \dfrac{\Delta_0}{\Delta_{11}} \qquad$ and $\qquad V_{eq} = \sum_{k=1}^{n} \dfrac{\Delta_{k1}}{\Delta_{11}} V_k^{e} \tag{4.6}$

Since $I_1 Z_1 = V_1$, the VI description of the 1-port is

$$V_1 = (-I_1)Z_{eq} + V_{eq} \tag{4.7}$$

It is conventional in setting up the VI description of a port to designate the current into the upper node of the port as positive. This is illustrated in Fig. 4.3. Thus I_1 above is taken as $-I_1'$, and (4.7) becomes

$$V_1 = I_1' Z_{eq} + V_{eq} \tag{4.8}$$

From (4.8) it is seen that if all sources within the network are reduced to zero, Z_{eq} is the input impedance of the 1-port. If the port is open-circuited externally, i.e., $I_1' = 0$, V_{eq} is the voltage that appears at the

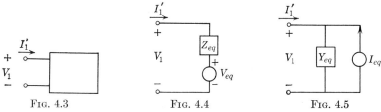

FIG. 4.3   FIG. 4.4   FIG. 4.5

port and is the open-circuit voltage. It is easily shown that the individual components in (4.6) are the open-circuit voltages due to each source within the network. V_{eq} is the superposition of all the contributions. In essence, (4.8) is Thévenin's theorem and can be represented as the equivalent circuit shown in Fig. 4.4. The circuits of Figs. 4.3 and 4.4 are equivalent in that both have the same VI description with respect to the available port.

If a nodal analysis is used rather than a mesh analysis, the following equation, comparable to (4.8), is obtained:

$$I_1' = V_1 Y_{eq} - I_{eq} \tag{4.9}$$

The VI description of the port in this form is known as Norton's theorem. Y_{eq} is the input admittance of the port when the sources are reduced to zero. I_{eq} is the current which flows through the port if short-circuited. The equivalent circuit corresponding to (4.9) is shown in Fig. 4.5. From a comparison of (4.8) and (4.9) it can be seen that

$$Z_{eq} = \frac{1}{Y_{eq}} = \frac{V_{eq}}{I_{eq}} \tag{4.10}$$

4.3 Open-circuit 2-port Impedances. A procedure similar to that used for the 1-port can be used to obtain the VI description of a 2-port. Assume that the situation is as shown in Fig. 4.6a. The VI description of the 2-port independent of the source and the load is desired.

For a nodal analysis of an arbitrary 2-port together with the source and the load, the equation has the form

$$a_{11}V_1 + a_{12}V_2 + \cdots + a_{1n}V_n = I_0$$
$$a_{21}V_1 + a_{22}V_2 + \cdots + a_{2n}V_n = 0$$
$$\cdots \cdots \cdots \cdots \cdots \cdots \cdots \cdots \cdots \qquad (4.11)$$
$$a_{n1}V_1 + a_{n2}V_2 + \cdots + a_{nn}V_n = 0$$

For convenience, all independent sources in the 2-port are ignored. The contribution of independent sources can always be added by using superposition. In the remainder of the book it is always assumed that there are no independent sources within a 2-port. In (4.11), V_1 and V_2 are

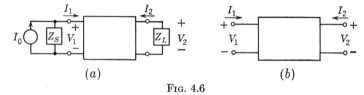

$$(a) \qquad\qquad\qquad\qquad (b)$$

$$\text{FIG. 4.6}$$

the port voltages. The equations can be simply modified also to include the port currents I_1 and I_2. From the method of setting up the nodal equations, the source admittance Y_s and the load admittance Y_L appear only in the self-admittance a_{11} and a_{22}, respectively.

$$a_{11} = Y_s + a'_{11}$$
$$a_{22} = Y_L + a'_{22} \qquad (4.12)$$

The contribution due to Y_s and Y_L can be moved to the right-hand side of the equations. The right side of the first equation becomes

$$I_0 - Y_s V_1 = I_1 \qquad (4.13)$$

Similarly, in the second equation the right-hand side becomes

$$- Y_L V_2 = I_2 \qquad (4.14)$$

The complete set of equations is then

$$a'_{11}V_1 + a_{12}V_2 + \cdots + a_{1n}V_n = I_1$$
$$a_{21}V_1 + a'_{22}V_2 + \cdots + a_{2n}V_n = I_2$$
$$\cdots \cdots \cdots \cdots \cdots \cdots \cdots \cdots \cdots \qquad (4.15)$$
$$a_{n1}V_1 + a_{n2}V_2 + \cdots + a_{nn}V_n = 0$$

It should be noted that (4.15) describes the 2-port alone, independent of the source and the load, as shown in Fig. 4.6b.

These equations are next solved for V_1 and V_2.

$$V_1 = \frac{\Delta_{11}}{\Delta} I_1 + \frac{\Delta_{21}}{\Delta} I_2$$
$$V_2 = \frac{\Delta_{12}}{\Delta} I_1 + \frac{\Delta_{22}}{\Delta} I_2$$

(4.16)

The coefficients clearly have the dimensions of the impedance, and the equations are more simply written as follows:

$$V_1 = z_{11}I_1 + z_{12}I_2$$
$$V_2 = z_{21}I_1 + z_{22}I_2$$

(4.17)

The two equations in (4.17) constitute one VI description of the 2-port. Each equation expresses the voltage at a port in terms of linear combination of the two currents. The impedances z_{ij} are called the *open-circuit impedance* parameters of the 2-port. The term *open circuit* is used because the individual parameters are the relationships between external voltages and currents when one of the 2-ports is an open circuit. For example, if the output is an open circuit, i.e., $I_2 = 0$, and the excitation is the current I_1,

$$z_{11} = \frac{V_1}{I_1}\bigg|_{I_2=0}$$

z_{11} is clearly the open-circuit input impedance. Similarly

$$z_{21} = \frac{V_2}{I_1}\bigg|_{I_2=0}$$

Thus z_{21} is the open-circuit forward-transfer impedance. If the input is an open circuit, i.e., $I_1 = 0$, and if the excitation is the current I_2,

$$z_{22} = \frac{V_2}{I_2}\bigg|_{I_1=0}$$
$$z_{12} = \frac{V_1}{I_2}\bigg|_{I_1=0}$$

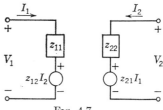

FIG. 4.7

z_{22} and z_{12} are the open-circuit output impedance and reverse-transfer impedance, respectively.

An equivalent circuit for the 2-port can be obtained from (4.17) by identifying these equations as mesh equations of a two-mesh network. This is shown in Fig. 4.7 and is known as a two-generator equivalent. A one-generator equivalent circuit can be obtained through a manipulation of (4.17). If $z_{12}I_1$ is added to and subtracted from the second equation, the equations become

$$V_1 = z_{11}I_1 + z_{12}I_2$$
$$V_2 = z_{12}I_1 + z_{22}I_2 + (z_{21} - z_{12})I_1$$

(4.18)

The equivalent circuit shown in Fig. 4.8 can be identified from these equations. This circuit is called a T circuit. Notice that if

$$z_{12} = z_{21} \tag{4.19}$$

the dependent-voltage generator in Fig. 4.8 vanishes, and the equivalent

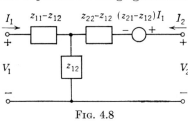

FIG. 4.8

circuit becomes a simple T. The 2-port then must consist of bilateral elements, for with bilateral elements the nodal equations can always be written in such a way that the nodal determinant is symmetrical; hence the cofactors Δ_{12} and Δ_{21} are equal. This property is commonly referred to as the reciprocity property or the *Reciprocity Theorem*. Such a 2-port is called a *reciprocal 2-port*.

For an example of the development of an equivalent circuit for a 2-port, assume that the following open-circuit impedance measurements of a junction transistor are obtained:

$$z_{11} = r_{11} = 625 \text{ ohms}$$
$$z_{12} = r_{12} = 600 \text{ ohms}$$
$$z_{21} = r_{21} = 0.98 \text{ megohm}$$
$$z_{22} = r_{22} = 1 \text{ megohm}$$

As indicated above, the open-circuit impedances are purely resistive. Using Fig. 4.8, one obtains the equivalent circuit of the transistor shown

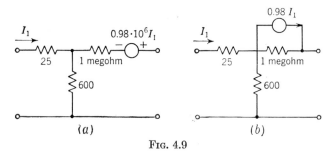

FIG. 4.9

in Fig. 4.9a. A more widely used equivalent circuit is obtained if the series resistor and the voltage generator are replaced by their Norton equivalent. This is illustrated in Fig. 4.9b.

4.4   Short-circuit 2-port Admittances. Another description of the terminal VI relations of a 2-port is obtained through the use of a mesh analysis rather than the node analysis. In a development similar to that used in the last section, a set of parameters identified as the set of short-

circuit admittance parameters is defined.   The solution of a set of general
mesh equations is of the form

$$I_1 = \frac{\Delta'_{11}}{\Delta'} V_1 + \frac{\Delta'_{21}}{\Delta'} V_2$$

$$I_2 = \frac{\Delta'_{12}}{\Delta'} V_1 + \frac{\Delta'_{22}}{\Delta'} V_2$$

(4.20)

In these equations the terminal voltages V_1 and V_2 are taken as independent variables and the currents I_1 and I_2 are taken as dependent
variables.   The prime notation signifies that these determinants and
cofactors stem from a mesh analysis rather than the nodal analysis used
in the last section.

The coefficients in (4.20) have the dimension of admittance, and the
equations are more simply written as follows:

$$I_1 = y_{11}V_1 + y_{12}V_2$$
$$I_2 = y_{21}V_1 + y_{22}V_2$$

(4.21)

The admittances y_{ij} are called the *short-circuit admittance* parameters.
The term *short circuit* is used because the parameters relate the terminal
voltage and current when one of the ports is short-circuited.   For example, if the output is a short circuit, i.e., $V_2 = 0$, and the excitation is the
voltage V_1,

$$y_{11} = \frac{I_1}{V_1}\bigg|_{V_2=0}$$

$$y_{21} = \frac{I_2}{V_1}\bigg|_{V_2=0}$$

y_{11} and y_{21} are the short-circuit input and forward-transfer admittances,
respectively.   If the input is a short circuit, i.e., $V_1 = 0$, and the excitation is the voltage V_2,

$$y_{22} = \frac{I_2}{V_2}\bigg|_{V_1=0}$$

$$y_{12} = \frac{I_1}{V_2}\bigg|_{V_1=0}$$

y_{22} and y_{12} are the output and reverse-transfer admittances.

Equation (4.21) can be identified simply as the two-node-pair two-
generator equivalent circuit shown in Fig. 4.10a.   With a manipulation
similar to that used in developing (4.18), one can obtain the one-generator
equivalent circuit, shown in Fig. 4.10b.   The negative sign associated
with y_{12} is explained by the fact that both I_1 and I_2 are defined as positive
into the 2-port.   This type of circuit is referred to as a π circuit.

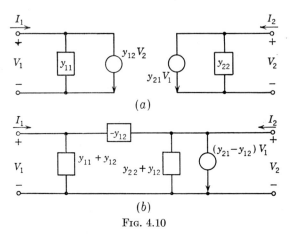

(a)

(b)

FIG. 4.10

The reader is probably familiar with the equivalent circuit of a pentode in the common cathode connection. This circuit, shown in Fig. 4.11, has a configuration identical with that of Fig. 4.10b. Hence, for the pentode,

$$y_{11} = p(C_{gk} + C_{gp})$$
$$y_{12} = -pC_{gp}$$
$$y_{22} = p(C_{pk} + C_{gp}) + \frac{1}{r_p}$$
$$y_{21} = g_m - pC_{gp}$$

Since a 2-port may be equally well described by short-circuit and open-circuit parameters, there must be an interrelationship between them. It is taken up in the next chapter.

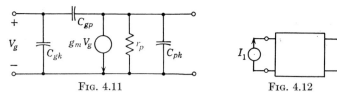

FIG. 4.11   FIG. 4.12

4.5 The Relations of Network Functions to Open- and Short-circuit Parameters. It is possible now to relate the open- and short-circuit parameters to various network functions. The simplest relationship is that pertaining to the 2-port shown in Fig. 4.12. Here the load is an open circuit and the source is an ideal current source with a zero internal admittance. The network function is simply the open-circuit forward-transfer impedance z_{21}. For the dual situation, i.e., where the source is an ideal voltage source with a zero internal impedance and a short-circuit load, the network function of the 2-port is the short-circuit forward-transfer admittance y_{21}.

The thought of an open- or short-circuit load may at first be unsettling. However, these load conditions arise in many practical problems. As an example, consider the open-circuit load. This may be approximated very accurately at low frequencies if the load is the input of a pentode. At low frequencies the input capacitance of the pentode can be neglected. At higher frequencies, where the input capacitance cannot be neglected, this capacitance may be absorbed into the 2-port proper. That is, the synthesis of the 2-port is designed for an open-circuit load but is constrained to have a final shunt capacitance, all or part of which is supplied by the actual load. In a similar fashion, a short-circuit load is approximately provided by the input impedance of some feedback amplifiers or by the input impedance of transistors in some configurations. Sources with zero admittance or impedance are approximately obtained

FIG. 4.13   FIG. 4.14

for sources such as pentode and cathode or emitter followers, respectively.

Another source and load situation which often arises is that shown in Fig. 4.13. Here the source is a voltage source, the load is an open circuit, and the network function is the transfer voltage ratio. Using (4.17) or (4.21) under the condition that $I_2 = 0$, one obtains

$$t_V = \frac{V_2}{V_1} = \frac{z_{21}}{z_{11}} = \frac{-y_{21}}{y_{22}} \tag{4.22}$$

If the load is a resistance R and the source is a current source, as illustrated in Fig. 4.14, the network function is the loaded forward-transfer impedance Z_{21}.

$$Z_{21} = \frac{V_2}{I_1} \tag{4.23}$$

Notice that for this loaded situation a capital-letter notation is used. Equation (4.23) can be related to the open-circuit impedance parameters by a manipulation of the second equation of (4.17).

$$V_2 = z_{21}I_1 + z_{22}I_2$$

With a resistive load,

$$V_2 = -I_2R \tag{4.24}$$

Combining the last two equations, one obtains

$$Z_{21} = \frac{V_2}{I_1} = \frac{z_{21}R}{z_{22} + R} \tag{4.25}$$

If the 2-port is normalized with regard to the value of the load resistance, i.e., if $R = 1$, (4.25) becomes

$$Z_{21} = \frac{z_{21}}{z_{22} + 1} \tag{4.26}$$

If the source is a voltage source, as in Fig. (4.15), a similar procedure can be used to obtain the loaded forward-transfer admittance,

$$Y_{21} = \frac{I_2}{V_1} = \frac{y_{21}G}{y_{22} + G} \tag{4.27}$$

where $G = 1/R$. From (4.24) the loaded voltage-transfer ratio is

$$\frac{V_2}{V_1} = -RY_{21} = \frac{-y_{21}}{y_{22} + G} \tag{4.28}$$

For a reciprocal 2-port ($z_{12} = z_{21}$), the situations of Figs. 4.14 and 4.15 can be manipulated to obtain further results. For example, if the source

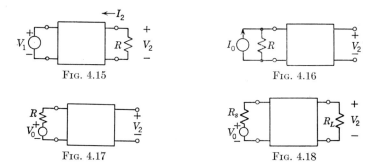

FIG. 4.15   FIG. 4.16

FIG. 4.17   FIG. 4.18

is the parallel combination of a current source and a conductance, while the load is an open circuit as shown in Fig. 4.16, the input-loaded forward-transfer impedance is

$$\frac{V_2}{I_0} = \frac{z_{21}}{z_{11}/R + 1} \tag{4.29}$$

This is obtained by setting $I_2 = 0$ in the equations of (4.17) and determining I_1 in terms of I_0. If the Thévenin equivalent of the source of Fig. 4.16 is used to obtain the situation shown in Fig. 4.17, the network function is

$$\frac{V_2}{V_0} = \frac{z_{21}}{z_{11} + R} \tag{4.30}$$

A more general situation than those above is that illustrated in Fig. 4.18. Here the source has an internal resistance R_s, and the load is a resistance R_L. The network function can be defined as the transfer voltage ratio V_2/V_0. It can be related to the open-circuit impedance parameters of the 2-port through a manipulation of the following equations:

$$V_1 = V_0 - I_1 R_s$$
$$V_2 = -I_2 R_L$$
$$V_0 = (z_{11} + R_s) I_1 + z_{12} I_2$$
$$0 = z_{21} I_1 + (z_{22} + R_L) I_2$$

The result is

$$\frac{V_2}{V_0} = \frac{z_{21} R_L}{(z_{11} + R_s)(z_{22} + R_L) - z_{12} z_{21}} \qquad (4.31)$$

A summary of the relationship between pertinent network functions and either the open- or short-circuit parameters is presented in Table 4.1.

TABLE 4.1

Source	Load	Specifications
∞	∞	$\dfrac{V_2}{I_1} = z_{21}$
0	0	$\dfrac{I_2}{V_1} = y_{21}$
0	∞	$t_V = \dfrac{V_2}{V_1} = \dfrac{z_{21}}{z_{11}} = \dfrac{-y_{21}}{y_{22}}$
∞	0	$t_I = \dfrac{I_2}{I_1} = \dfrac{y_{21}}{y_{11}} = \dfrac{-z_{21}}{z_{22}}$
∞	R	$Z_{21} = \dfrac{V_2}{I_1} = \dfrac{z_{21} R}{z_{22} + R}$
0	R	$Y_{21} = \dfrac{I_2}{V_1} = \dfrac{y_{21}/R}{y_{22} + 1/R}$
R	∞	$t_V = \dfrac{V_2}{V_0} = \dfrac{z_{21}}{z_{11} + R}$
R	0	$t_I = \dfrac{I_2}{I_0} = \dfrac{y_{21}}{y_{11} + G}$
R_1	R_2	$t_V = \dfrac{V_2}{V_0} = \dfrac{z_{21} R_2}{(z_{11} + R_1)(z_{22} + R_2) - z_{12} z_{21}}$

4.6 Insertion Voltage Ratio. The transfer voltage ratios and the transfer impedances and admittances presented in the last section are important; however, there are alternate methods of defining network functions. The network function to be introduced in this section is the insertion voltage ratio. In essence, it is a measure of the effect due to

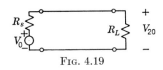

FIG. 4.19

inserting a 2-port between a given load and a given source. The reference function is not the source or input function directly, but is the output voltage V_{20}, which appears across the load if the source is connected directly to the load. This is illustrated in Fig. 4.19. The insertion voltage ratio is the ratio of the output voltage V_2, with the 2-port present, to V_{20}.

$$\text{IVR} = \frac{V_2}{V_{20}} \tag{4.32}$$

Since

$$V_{20} = \frac{R_L}{R_s + R_L} V_0 \tag{4.33}$$

the insertion voltage ratio and the transfer voltage ratio V_2/V_0 are related by a constant multiplier.

$$\text{IVR} = \frac{R_s + R_L}{R_L} \frac{V_2}{V_0} \tag{4.34}$$

The insertion voltage ratio is also useful for those situations where the source is a pure current source. In this case the ratio is clearly Z_{21}/R_L. In an analogous manner, the insertion current ratio can also be defined as I_2/I_{20}.

PROBLEMS

4.1. Find the Thévenin's and Norton's equivalents for the networks in Fig. P4.1.

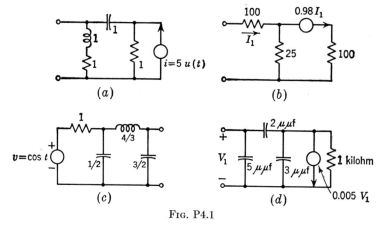

(a)   (b)

(c)   (d)

FIG. P4.1

4.2. Discuss by physical reasoning why the equivalent voltage term in Eq. (4.6) can be identified as the sum of the open-circuit voltages from each source.

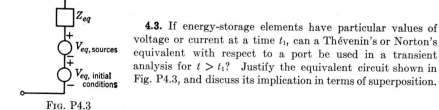

FIG. P4.3

4.3. If energy-storage elements have particular values of voltage or current at a time t_1, can a Thévenin's or Norton's equivalent with respect to a port be used in a transient analysis for $t > t_1$? Justify the equivalent circuit shown in Fig. P4.3, and discuss its implication in terms of superposition.

4.4. Find the open- and short-circuit parameters (the z and y parameters) for the circuits in Fig. P4.4.

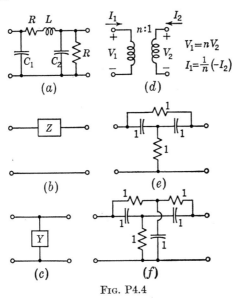

FIG. P4.4

4.5. Determine the z or y parameters of the circuits in Fig. P4.5.

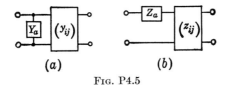

FIG. P4.5

4.6. Determine the z and y parameters of the circuit in Fig. P4.6.

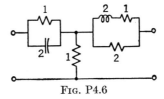

FIG. P4.6

4.7. Find the z or y parameters of the over-all 2-port shown in Fig. P4.7.

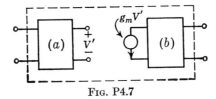

FIG. P4.7

4.8. Find the over-all z parameters of a cascade of two 2-ports in terms of the z parameters of the individual 2-ports.

4.9. Find the T- and π-equivalent circuits for the circuits in Fig. P4.4e and f.

4.10. Develop a conventional π-equivalent circuit for a grounded grid triode (Fig. P4.10).

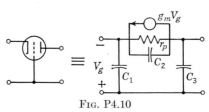

FIG. P4.10

4.11. Develop a π-equivalent circuit for a common emitter transistor circuit, as shown in Fig. P4.11.

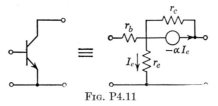

FIG. P4.11

4.12. Reduce the network shown in Fig. P4.12 by T- to π-network transformation and by series or parallel combinations. Would it be easier to achieve a simplification by immediately finding a T or π equivalent for the 2-port?

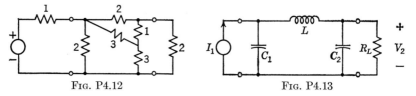

FIG. P4.12   FIG. P4.13

4.13. For the network in Fig. P4.13, determine the z parameters. Explain by physical reasoning the following asymptotic relations:

$$z_{11}\Big|_{p\to\infty} = \frac{1}{pC_1} \qquad z_{22}\Big|_{p\to\infty} = \frac{1}{pC_2} \qquad z_{21}\Big|_{p\to\infty} = \frac{1}{p^3LC_1C_2}$$

Determine the loaded transfer impedance $Z_{21} = V_2/I_1$ from the z parameters.

4.14. For the network of Fig. P4.10, determine from the 2-port parameters the transfer voltage ratio V_2/V_1, if a voltage source is applied at the input and a resistance R_L is applied at the output.

4.15. For the network of Fig. P4.11, determine from the 2-port parameters the transfer current ratio I_2/I_1 if a current source is applied at the input and a resistance R_L is applied at the output.

4.16. What is the insertion voltage ratio of the circuit in Fig. P4.16? How is it related to the transfer impedance V_2/I_1? If a Norton's equivalent is used for the source, how is the insertion voltage ratio related to the transfer impedance V_2/I_0?

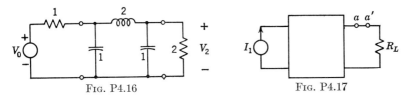

FIG. P4.16   FIG. P4.17

4.17. Show that the natural frequencies of the system of Fig. P4.17 are the zeros of the impedance seen by looking into the system from $a - a'$. What are the natural frequencies if the current source I_1 is replaced by a voltage source V_1?

4.18. For each circuit in Fig. P4.18, what are the natural frequencies of the entire circuit and how are they related to the poles and zeros of z_{11} and y_{11} of the 2-port?

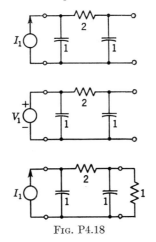

FIG. P4.18

CHAPTER 5

OTHER 2-PORT DESCRIPTIONS

5.1 Open-circuit Impedance and Short-circuit Admittance Matrices.
The open-circuit and short-circuit parameters are only two of a variety
of parameter sets that can be used to describe a 2-port. In introducing
the other descriptions, use is made of matrix algebra. The elements of
matrix algebra are presented in the second section of this chapter. Its
application to 2-port descriptions is explained in this section in conjunction with the open- and short-circuit parameters.

The open-circuit equations (4.17) can be written as a matrix equation
as follows:

$$\left.\begin{matrix} V_1 \\ V_2 \end{matrix}\right] = \begin{bmatrix} z_{11} & z_{12} \\ z_{21} & z_{22} \end{bmatrix} \left.\begin{matrix} I_1 \\ I_2 \end{matrix}\right] \tag{5.1}$$

or
$$\mathbf{V}] = [\mathbf{Z}]\,\mathbf{I}] \tag{5.2}$$

$\mathbf{V}]$ and $\mathbf{I}]$ are column matrices and $[\mathbf{Z}]$ is a square matrix which is called
the open-circuit impedance matrix. A column matrix is a matrix of n
rows but only one column, while a square matrix has an equal number of
rows and columns. It is important to recognize that a matrix is a notation. For example, a square matrix of n rows and n columns is a table of
n^2 entities, or elements. Although a square matrix is similar to a determinant in form, a determinant is a specific function or has a specific value
which depends upon the n^2 elements.

The right-hand side of (5.1) or (5.2) involves matrix multiplication.
It is expected that the product matrix is a column matrix because of the
equality with the left-hand side, which is a column matrix. By definition,
two matrices are equal if the corresponding elements of the two matrices
are equal. Keeping this in mind together with the form of (4.17), one can
establish the rule of matrix multiplication. The product must be of the
following form:

$$\left.\begin{matrix} V_1 \\ V_2 \end{matrix}\right] = \left.\begin{matrix} z_{11}I_1 + z_{12}I_2 \\ z_{21}I_1 + z_{22}I_2 \end{matrix}\right]$$

The first element of the product matrix is the sum of the two quantities.
The first quantity is the product of the element in the first row and the
first column of the first matrix and the corresponding element of the

second matrix.   The second quantity of the sum is the product of the element in the first row and the second column of the first matrix and the element in the second row and the first column of the second matrix. The other element of the product column matrix is another sum obtained in a similar fashion by multiplying successive elements in the second row of the first matrix by successive elements in the first column of the second matrix.   Multiplication of more general matrices is discussed in the next section.   Notice that with multiplication defined as above, it is not commutative, i.e., $[\mathbf{A}][\mathbf{B}] \neq [\mathbf{B}][\mathbf{A}]$.

Similarly, the short-circuit admittance Eqs. (4.21) can be written in matrix form:

$$\begin{bmatrix} I_1 \\ I_2 \end{bmatrix} = \begin{bmatrix} y_{11} & y_{12} \\ y_{21} & y_{22} \end{bmatrix} \begin{bmatrix} V_1 \\ V_2 \end{bmatrix} \qquad (5.3)$$

or
$$\mathbf{I}] = [\mathbf{Y}]\ \mathbf{V}] \qquad (5.4)$$

The matrix $[\mathbf{Y}]$ is called the short-circuit admittance matrix.   If (5.4) is substituted into (5.2), one obtains

$$\mathbf{V}] = [\mathbf{Z}][\mathbf{Y}]\ \mathbf{V}] \qquad (5.5)$$

The only way the above equality can be satisfied for any value of $\mathbf{V}]$ is for the product $[\mathbf{Z}][\mathbf{Y}]$ to have the following form:

$$[\mathbf{Z}][\mathbf{Y}] = [\mathbf{1}] = \begin{bmatrix} 1 & 0 \\ 0 & 1 \end{bmatrix} \qquad (5.6)$$

The matrix $[\mathbf{1}]$ is called the unit matrix, which has the property that

$$[\mathbf{1}][\mathbf{A}] = [\mathbf{A}][\mathbf{1}] = [\mathbf{A}] \qquad (5.7)$$

If the product of two square matrices, such as $[\mathbf{Z}][\mathbf{Y}]$, is equal to the unit matrix, one is the inverse matrix of the other.   Thus

$$[\mathbf{Z}] = [\mathbf{Y}]^{-1} \qquad \text{and} \qquad [\mathbf{Y}] = [\mathbf{Z}]^{-1} \qquad (5.8)$$

The superscript -1 denotes the inverse of that matrix.   The method of finding the elements of the inverse matrix can be illustrated by solving (4.17) for I_1 and I_2 by Cramer's rule:

$$\begin{aligned} I_1 &= \frac{z_{22}}{|z|}\ V_1 - \frac{z_{12}}{|z|}\ V_2 \\ I_2 &= \frac{-z_{21}}{|z|}\ V_1 + \frac{z_{11}}{|z|}\ V_2 \end{aligned} \qquad (5.9)$$

where $|z| = z_{11}z_{22} - z_{12}z_{21}$ is the determinant of (4.17).   Equations (5.9) and (4.21) are identical for a given 2-port.   Thus the coefficients of (5.9) are equal to the corresponding short-circuit parameters of (4.21).

$$y_{11} = \frac{z_{22}}{|z|} \qquad y_{12} = \frac{-z_{12}}{|z|} \qquad y_{21} = \frac{-z_{21}}{|z|} \qquad y_{22} = \frac{z_{11}}{|z|} \qquad (5.10)$$

In addition, the matrix of the coefficients of (5.9) is $[\mathbf{Y}]$, i.e., the inverse matrix of $[\mathbf{Z}]$, $[\mathbf{Z}]^{-1}$. In a similar manner, the elements of $[\mathbf{Y}]^{-1}$ can be found; the result is the relationships below:

$$z_{11} = \frac{y_{22}}{|y|} \qquad z_{12} = \frac{-y_{12}}{|y|} \qquad z_{21} = \frac{-y_{21}}{|y|} \qquad z_{22} = \frac{y_{11}}{|y|} \qquad (5.11)$$

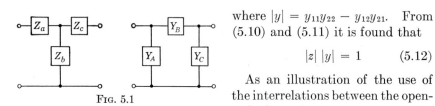

FIG. 5.1

where $|y| = y_{11}y_{22} - y_{12}y_{21}$. From (5.10) and (5.11) it is found that

$$|z|\,|y| = 1 \qquad (5.12)$$

As an illustration of the use of the interrelations between the open- and short-circuit parameters, the familiar T- to π-network transformation is developed. For the T network of Fig. 5.1

$$z_{11} = Z_a + Z_b$$
$$z_{12} = Z_b = z_{21}$$
$$z_{22} = Z_b + Z_c$$
$$|z| = Z_aZ_b + Z_bZ_c + Z_cZ_a$$

For the π network of Fig. 5.1

$$y_{11} = Y_A + Y_B$$
$$y_{12} = -Y_B = y_{21}$$
$$y_{22} = Y_B + Y_C$$
$$|y| = Y_AY_B + Y_BY_C + Y_CY_A$$

From (5.10) and (5.11)

$$Y_A = \frac{Z_c}{|z|} \qquad Y_B = \frac{Z_b}{|z|} \qquad Y_C = \frac{Z_a}{|z|}$$
$$Z_a = \frac{Y_C}{|y|} \qquad Z_b = \frac{Y_B}{|y|} \qquad Y_c = \frac{Y_A}{|y|} \qquad (5.13)$$

5.2   Elements of Matrix Algebra.   The introduction to matrix algebra is continued in this section, with major emphasis on several basic operational rules and definitions.   A general matrix may have any number of rows and columns.

$$[\mathbf{A}] = [a_{ij}] = \begin{bmatrix} a_{11} & a_{12} & \cdots & a_{1m} \\ a_{21} & a_{22} & \cdots & a_{2m} \\ \cdots & \cdots & \cdots & \cdots \\ a_{n1} & a_{n2} & \cdots & a_{nm} \end{bmatrix} \qquad (5.14)$$

The first subscript of any element pertains to its row location. The second subscript pertains to its column location. This notation is similar to that used in determinants. If the number of rows n is not equal to the number of columns m, a matrix is said to be rectangular. If $n = 1$ the matrix is called a row matrix, while if $m = 1$ the matrix is called a column matrix. If m is equal to n, the matrix is said to be square and of order n. The main diagonal of a square matrix is that from the upper left to the lower right. A matrix, as shown below, whose elements are all zero except for those on the main diagonal is called a diagonal matrix.

$$\begin{bmatrix} a_{11} & 0 & 0 & 0 \\ 0 & a_{22} & \cdot\cdot & \cdot\cdot\cdot \\ 0 & \cdot\cdot & \cdot\cdot & \cdot\cdot\cdot \\ 0 & 0 & \cdot\cdot\cdot & a_{nn} \end{bmatrix} \tag{5.15}$$

If all the a_{ii} are equal to unity, the matrix is the unit matrix.

$$[\mathbf{1}] = \begin{bmatrix} 1 & 0 & 0 & \cdot\cdot\cdot & 0 \\ 0 & 1 & 0 & \cdot\cdot\cdot & 0 \\ & & \cdot\cdot\cdot\cdot\cdot\cdot & & \\ 0 & 0 & 0 & \cdot\cdot\cdot & 1 \end{bmatrix} \tag{5.16}$$

The transpose of a matrix is obtained by interchanging the rows and columns of the original matrix. It is denoted by $[\mathbf{A}]_t$.

$$[\mathbf{A}] = [a_{ij}]$$
$$[\mathbf{A}]_t = [a_{ji}] \tag{5.17}$$

A square matrix is said to be symmetric if it is equal to its transpose. Thus a symmetric matrix is symmetrical about its main diagonal, and $a_{ij} = a_{ji}$. The diagonal matrix is clearly symmetric.

The sum of two matrices is denoted as follows:

$$[\mathbf{A}] + [\mathbf{B}] = [\mathbf{C}] \tag{5.18}$$

and individual elements of the sum matrix c_{ij} are equal to the sum of the elements of the original matrices having the same subscripts; that is,

$$c_{ij} = a_{ij} + b_{ij} \qquad i = 1, 2, \ldots, n; j = 1, 2, \ldots, m \tag{5.19}$$

If the matrices $[\mathbf{A}]$ and $[\mathbf{B}]$ do not have the same number of rows or the same number of columns, one must augment either or both matrices with additional rows and columns of zeros so that both have the same number of rows and columns. From (5.19) it is clear that the commutative law as well as the associative law hold for addition. For example,

$$[\mathbf{A}] + [\mathbf{B}] = [\mathbf{B}] + [\mathbf{A}] \tag{5.20}$$

If a matrix is multiplied by a constant, by definition every element in the matrix is multiplied by the constant.

$$k[\mathbf{A}] = [ka_{ij}] \tag{5.21}$$

This definition is often useful in the normalization of a network with regard to resistance level.

The product of two matrices is denoted by

$$[\mathbf{A}][\mathbf{B}] = [\mathbf{C}] \tag{5.22}$$

$$c_{ij} = \sum_{k=1}^{m_a} a_{ik}b_{kj} \qquad i = 1, 2, \ldots, n_a; j = 1, 2, \ldots, m_b \tag{5.23}$$

Since the index of summation k is the second subscript of the elements of [**A**] and the first subscript of the elements of [**B**], the number of columns of [**A**], m_a, must be equal to the number of rows of [**B**], n_b, in order to obtain a meaningful product, i.e., $m_a = n_b$. The product matrix thus has the same number of rows as [**A**] and the same number of columns as [**B**]. Because of this special rule of multiplication, the commutative law does not hold, in general, for matrix multiplication.

$$[\mathbf{A}][\mathbf{B}] \neq [\mathbf{B}][\mathbf{A}] \tag{5.24}$$

Since the commutative law does not hold, care must be taken to note whether a matrix is premultiplied or postmultiplied by another matrix. In the product [**A**] times [**B**], [**B**] is premultiplied by [**A**], or [**A**] is postmultiplied by [**B**]. Exceptions to (5.24) occur if either [**A**] or [**B**] is a unit matrix, and if [**A**] is the inverse of [**B**].

The inverse matrix, as illustrated in the last section, is defined by the equation

$$[\mathbf{A}][\mathbf{A}]^{-1} = [\mathbf{A}]^{-1}[\mathbf{A}] = [\mathbf{1}] \tag{5.25}$$

where [**A**] must be a square matrix. Using for the moment the notation [**B**] = [**A**]$^{-1}$, one can define the elements of [**B**] as follows:

$$b_{ij} = \frac{|A_{ji}|}{|A|} \tag{5.26}$$

where $|A|$, known as the determinant of the matrix, has the same elements as [**A**]. $|A_{ji}|$ is the cofactor of a_{ji}. Clearly, the value of $|A|$ must be non-zero if the inverse matrix is to exist.

Two other rules are also important. First, the associative and the distributive laws hold for matrix multiplication. That is,

$$([\mathbf{A}][\mathbf{B}])[\mathbf{C}] = [\mathbf{A}]([\mathbf{B}][\mathbf{C}])$$
$$[\mathbf{A}]([\mathbf{B}] + [\mathbf{C}]) = [\mathbf{A}][\mathbf{B}] + [\mathbf{A}][\mathbf{C}] \tag{5.27}$$

These follow directly from the definition of multiplication. Second, the inverse of a product matrix is equal to the product of the inverse of the second matrix and the inverse of the first matrix.

$$([\mathbf{A}][\mathbf{B}])^{-1} = [\mathbf{B}]^{-1}[\mathbf{A}]^{-1} \tag{5.28}$$

The proof is the result of

$$([\mathbf{A}][\mathbf{B}])^{-1}([\mathbf{A}][\mathbf{B}]) = [\mathbf{B}]^{-1}[\mathbf{A}]^{-1}[\mathbf{A}][\mathbf{B}] = [\mathbf{1}]$$

5.3 The Transmission Matrix. The open- and short-circuit parameters are developed by choosing either the two currents or the two voltages at the ports as the dependent variables. Other possibilities may be obtained by choosing as dependent variables any two of the four voltages and currents of the ports. For four quantities taken two at a time, there are $4!/2!2! = 6$ possible sets of parameters. If the voltage and current at the input port are chosen as the dependent variables, the following matrix equation is defined:

$$\begin{bmatrix} V_1 \\ I_1 \end{bmatrix} = \begin{bmatrix} A & B \\ C & D \end{bmatrix} \begin{bmatrix} V_2 \\ -I_2 \end{bmatrix} \qquad (5.29)$$

The matrix $[ABCD]$ is called the transmission matrix. The elements of the matrix are called the transmission parameters. The minus sign is used with I_2 for historical reasons. The matrix was originally defined in conjunction with transmission-line description, in which the output current was designated as positive out of the output port. From an inspection of (5.29) it can be seen that A is the reciprocal of the open-circuit transfer voltage ratio. B is the negative reciprocal of the short-circuit transfer admittance. C is the reciprocal of the open-circuit transfer impedance. D is the negative reciprocal of the short-circuit transfer current ratio. In terms of the open- and short-circuit parameters, the transmission parameters are

$$A = \frac{z_{11}}{z_{21}}$$

$$B = -\frac{1}{y_{21}}$$

$$C = \frac{1}{z_{21}} \qquad (5.30)$$

$$D = -\frac{y_{11}}{y_{21}}$$

If reciprocity holds for the 2-port

$$AD - BC = 1 \qquad (5.31)$$

For this case, as expected, only three of the parameters are independent.

In a similar manner, the output voltage and current can be used as the dependent variables, and another transmission matrix can be defined.

$$\begin{bmatrix} V_2 \\ I_2 \end{bmatrix} = \begin{bmatrix} \mathcal{A} & \mathcal{B} \\ \mathcal{C} & \mathcal{D} \end{bmatrix} \begin{bmatrix} V_1 \\ -I_1 \end{bmatrix} \qquad (5.32)$$

If reciprocity holds for the 2-port, there is a simple relationship between the two transmission matrices.

$$\begin{bmatrix} A & B \\ C & D \end{bmatrix} = \begin{bmatrix} \mathcal{D} & \mathcal{B} \\ \mathcal{C} & \mathcal{A} \end{bmatrix} \qquad (5.33)$$

5.4   The Hybrid Matrices.   The hybrid matrices describe the 2-port if the voltage of one port and the current of the other port are taken as the dependent variables.   Two hybrid matrices are possible, completing the set of six matrices discussed earlier.   The hybrid matrix that has proved useful in describing transistors is defined by taking the input current and the output voltage as the independent variables.

$$\begin{bmatrix} V_1 \\ I_2 \end{bmatrix} = \begin{bmatrix} h_{11} & h_{12} \\ h_{21} & h_{22} \end{bmatrix} \begin{bmatrix} I_1 \\ V_2 \end{bmatrix} \tag{5.34}$$

From an inspection of (5.34)

$$h_{11} = \frac{1}{y_{11}}$$

$$h_{12} = \frac{z_{12}}{z_{22}}$$

$$h_{21} = \frac{y_{21}}{y_{11}} \tag{5.35}$$

$$h_{22} = \frac{1}{z_{22}}$$

The advantage of using these parameters in characterizing a transistor lies in the relative ease with which they can be measured.   The transistor in the common-base configuration, such as the one shown in Fig. 4.9, has a high input admittance and a high output impedance in normal operation.

For a 2-port with high input admittance, it is easier to provide a known input current rather than a known input voltage.   The inverse is true when the port has a high input impedance.   Correspondingly, it is easier to provide an a-c short circuit if the output impedance is high or an open circuit if the input impedance is low.

The second hybrid matrix is defined by taking the input voltage and the output current as the independent variables.

$$\begin{bmatrix} I_1 \\ V_2 \end{bmatrix} = \begin{bmatrix} g_{11} & g_{12} \\ g_{21} & g_{22} \end{bmatrix} \begin{bmatrix} V_1 \\ I_2 \end{bmatrix} \tag{5.36}$$

5.5   Interconnections.   If two or more 2-ports are interconnected in such a manner that the over-all combination is another 2-port, the parameters or matrices of the resulting 2-port can easily be established from the matrices of the individual ones.   For example, the feedback amplifier shown in Fig. 5.2 is the parallel combination of two 2-ports, one a cascaded amplifier and the other a passive feedback network.   It is assumed that both networks are grounded 2-ports; i.e., each 2-port has a common input and output terminal.   The short-circuit admittance matrix is the logical one to determine for the over-all feedback amplifier, because the voltages of the ports are common to the individual 2-ports,

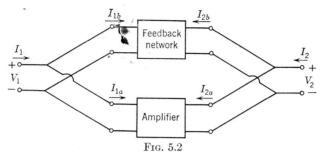

Fig. 5.2

and the input and output currents are the sums of the input currents and output currents of the individual 2-ports.

$$
\begin{aligned}
V_1 &= V_{1a} = V_{1b} \\
V_2 &= V_{2a} = V_{2b} \\
I_1 &= I_{1a} + I_{1b} \\
I_2 &= I_{2a} + I_{2b}
\end{aligned}
\tag{5.37}
$$

For each 2-port, the following matrix equations hold:

$$
\begin{bmatrix} I_{1a} \\ I_{2a} \end{bmatrix} = [\mathbf{Y}_a] \begin{bmatrix} V_{1a} \\ V_{2a} \end{bmatrix} \\
\begin{bmatrix} I_{1b} \\ I_{2b} \end{bmatrix} = [\mathbf{Y}_b] \begin{bmatrix} V_{1b} \\ V_{2b} \end{bmatrix}
\tag{5.38}
$$

Therefore the $[\mathbf{Y}]$ matrix for the over-all feedback amplifier can be obtained by combining (5.37) and (5.38); it is simply the sum of the admittance matrices of the individual networks.

$$
\begin{bmatrix} I_1 \\ I_2 \end{bmatrix} = [\mathbf{Y}_a] \begin{bmatrix} V_{1a} \\ V_{2a} \end{bmatrix} + [\mathbf{Y}_b] \begin{bmatrix} V_{1b} \\ V_{2b} \end{bmatrix} = \big\{ [\mathbf{Y}_a] + [\mathbf{Y}_b] \big\} \begin{bmatrix} V_1 \\ V_2 \end{bmatrix}
\tag{5.39}
$$

The over-all admittance matrix of two or more general 2-ports in parallel is not necessarily the sum of the admittance matrices of the individual 2-ports. Unless all individual 2-ports are grounded 2-ports, the direct interconnection disturbs one or more of them, e.g., by shorting out some elements.* The admittance matrix of the disturbed 2-ports is thus different from the matrix of the 2-ports in isolation. To parallel general 2-ports, the interconnections must be made with ideal transformers† of unity turns ratio if the above difficulty is to be avoided. This is illustrated in Fig. 5.3.

* The direct interconnection of 2-ports may upset the basic definition of a port. That is, the current going into one terminal of a port may not be the same as the current coming out of the other terminal of the same port, because of the interconnection. See Ref. 13.

† Ideal transformers are discussed in Chap. 8. For now it should be noted that an ideal transformer of unity turns ratio provides ideal transmission together with isolation of the input and output over the entire frequency range, including d-c.

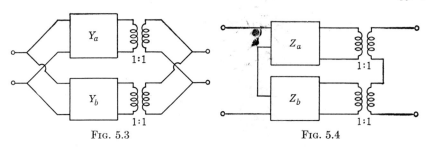

FIG. 5.3   FIG. 5.4

In a similar manner, the over-all impedance matrix for two or more 2-ports in series, if they are properly connected with ideal transformers, is the sum of the impedance matrices of the individual 2-ports. The series connection of two 2-ports is shown in Fig. 5.4. The over-all impedance matrix is

$$[\mathbf{Z}] = [\mathbf{Z}_a] + [\mathbf{Z}_b] \tag{5.40}$$

An important special case is that of an amplifier with series feedback, as shown in Fig. 5.5. A direct series connection can be made without

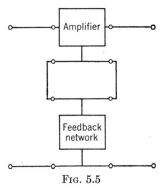

FIG. 5.5

ideal transformers if the amplifier is a grounded 2-port and the feedback network is a 1-port. It should be noted that the 2-port impedance matrix of a 1-port which is connected as in Fig. 5.5 and which has a driving-point impedance Z_1 is

$$\begin{bmatrix} Z_1 & Z_1 \\ Z_1 & Z_1 \end{bmatrix}$$

If several grounded 2-ports are connected in tandem, as shown in Fig. 5.6, the over-all transmission matrix of the combination can easily be obtained. In the tandem connection the output voltage of the first 2-port is equal to the input voltage of the second 2-port, whereas the output current of the first 2-port is the negative of the input current of the second 2-port

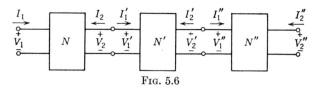

FIG. 5.6

$$\begin{aligned} V_2 &= V_1' \\ -I_2 &= +I_1' \end{aligned} \tag{5.41}$$

If the transmission matrices of the two 2-ports are

$$\begin{bmatrix} V_1 \\ I_1 \end{bmatrix} = \begin{bmatrix} A & B \\ C & D \end{bmatrix} \begin{bmatrix} V_2 \\ -I_2 \end{bmatrix}$$

$$\begin{bmatrix} V_1' \\ I_1' \end{bmatrix} = \begin{bmatrix} A' & B' \\ C' & D' \end{bmatrix} \begin{bmatrix} V_2' \\ -I_2' \end{bmatrix} \qquad (5.42)$$

the over-all transmission matrix is obtained by combining (5.41) and (5.42).

$$\begin{bmatrix} V_1 \\ I_1 \end{bmatrix} = \begin{bmatrix} A & B \\ C & D \end{bmatrix} \begin{bmatrix} A' & B' \\ C' & D' \end{bmatrix} \begin{bmatrix} V_2' \\ -I_2' \end{bmatrix} \qquad (5.43)$$

Thus the over-all transmission matrix of a tandem combination is the product of the transmission matrices of the individual 2-ports. If ungrounded 2-ports are to be included, isolation transformers must be used.

5.6 Unilateral 2-ports. In the tandem connection of 2-ports, if a certain number of the individual 2-ports are unilateral, the properties of the over-all 2-port, and particularly the transfer function, can be obtained rather simply.   Multiplication of the transmission matrices is not necessary.   A unilateral 2-port is defined as one in which transmission can occur in only one direction.   An illustration of a unilateral 2-port is a pentode in which the grid-plate capacitance and the cathode-lead inductance can be assumed negligible.   If a source is applied at the input of such a pentode, an output response is obtained.   If a source is applied at the output, no response appears at the input.   If reference is made to the various forward-transfer functions in Sec. 4.5, the parameter z_{21} or y_{21} always appears in the numerator.   The corresponding reverse-transfer functions have the parameter z_{12} or y_{12} in the numerator.   An investigation of the transfer functions under any kind of load and source indicates that for a unilateral 2-port with forward transmission the reverse-transfer parameters of a 2-port must be equal to zero; $z_{12} = y_{12} = 0$.   Thus $z_{12} = y_{12} = 0$ are the necessary conditions for a unilateral 2-port with forward transmission only.   If only backward transmission is possible, $y_{21} = z_{21} = 0$.

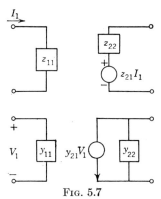

FIG. 5.7

The equivalent circuits of a unilateral 2-port in terms of the open and short circuits become those of Fig. 5.7.   Clearly, for a unilateral 2-port, $z_{11} = 1/y_{11}$ and $z_{22} = 1/y_{22}$.   If any load impedance is connected to the 2-port, the input impedance remains invariant.   Similarly, any source impedance at the input leaves the output impedance invariant. In cascading a unilateral 2-port with other 2-ports, such as those shown in Fig. 5.8, this last property leads one to incorporate the input and output admittances (impedances) into the adjacent 2-ports, as shown in Fig. 5.8b. The over-all transfer function, e.g., the transfer impedance, is then the product of the individual transfer functions of the modified 2-ports.

$$Z_{21} = \frac{V_2}{I_1} = \frac{V_2'}{I_1}\frac{V_2}{V_2'} = Z_{21a}Z_{21b}(-y_{21}) \qquad (5.44)$$

This product type of over-all transfer function is used to advantage in the design example of Sec. 3.5. When pentodes are used as the unilateral

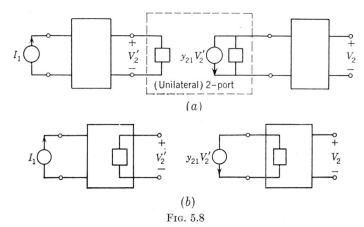

(a)

(b)

Fig. 5.8

2-port, y_{21} is the constant g_m; and the over-all complicated transfer function can be factored into simple groups, each of which can be assigned as a transfer function of a more elementary 2-port.

5.7 Further 2-port Descriptions. In the previous sections of this chapter, all six of the possible parameter sets based on terminal voltage and current variables have been discussed. This does not, however, exhaust the possible methods of 2-port description. Two other widely used 2-port descriptions are the image parameters and the scattering parameters or matrix.

The image-parameter description constitutes a special case of the more general scattering-matrix description. The scattering parameters are described not in terms of the actual terminal voltages and currents; rather the individual currents and voltages are treated as the superposition of two components. One component of each voltage and current is that which would occur for a matched reference source and load condition. The other component of the voltage or current is the difference between the above component and the actual voltage or current that exists for any source and load. The scattering parameters are obtained by taking the ratios of the two components of the same or alternate ports. In the image-parameter description, the reference source and load are determined from the given configuration of the 2-port rather than arbitrarily. Both the scattering and the image parameters are introduced and used in Chaps. 13 and 14.

PROBLEMS

5.1. Given two matrices

$$[A] = \begin{bmatrix} 1 & 2 \\ 3 & 4 \end{bmatrix} \quad \text{and} \quad [B] = \begin{bmatrix} 2 & 3 \\ 1 & 4 \end{bmatrix}$$

Find $[A] + [B]$, $[A][B]$, $[B][A]$, $[A]^{-1}$, $[B]^{-1}$, and $[A][A]^{-1}$.

5.2. Evaluate

$$[1 \ 3 \ 5] \begin{bmatrix} 2 \\ 4 \\ 6 \end{bmatrix}$$

$$\begin{bmatrix} 1 & 0 \\ 2 & 3 \end{bmatrix} \begin{bmatrix} 2 \\ -1 \end{bmatrix}$$

$$\begin{bmatrix} a_{11} & a_{12} & a_{13} \\ a_{21} & a_{22} & a_{23} \end{bmatrix} \begin{bmatrix} b_{11} & b_{12} \\ b_{21} & b_{22} \\ b_{31} & b_{32} \end{bmatrix}$$

5.3. From the determination of an inverse matrix, check the z and y parameters of Prob. 4.4.

5.4. Determine the $ABCD$ matrices of the circuits in Fig. P5.4.

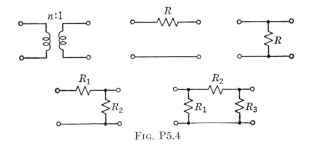

FIG. P5.4

5.5. Determine the g and h matrices of the circuits in Fig. P5.4.

5.6. Derive the relationship between the g parameters and the z and y parameters.

5.7. The results of a set of low-frequency measurements of a transistor are as follows:

(a) With the output shorted, the input impedance is 45 ohms.

(b) With the input an open circuit and for a voltage source at the output, the ratio of the input voltage to the output voltage is 5×10^{-4}.

(c) With the output shorted for a current source at the input, the ratio of the output current to the input current is -0.98.

(d) If the input is open, the output admittance is 10^{-6} mhos.

Develop one-generator T- and π-equivalent circuits.

5.8. Determine the over-all z, y, or $ABCD$ matrices of the circuits in Fig. P5.8, using the techniques of Sec. 5.5.

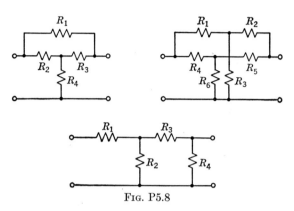

FIG. P5.8

5.9. Show that the over-all 2-port matrix after interconnection cannot be obtained from an addition of the z matrices. Determine the currents I_{1a} and I_{1b} of the input port of the first network before and after interconnection (Fig. P5.9).

5.10. Analyze the one-stage feedback transistor amplifier (Fig. P5.10), using the interconnection of 2-ports. Determine V_2/V_o.

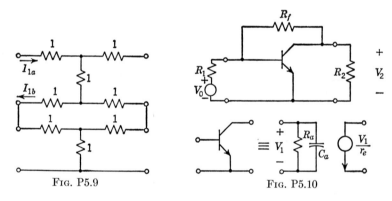

FIG. P5.9   FIG. P5.10

5.11. Analyze and determine V_2/V_1 of the cathode-follower circuit in Fig. P5.11.

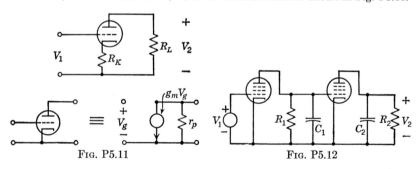

FIG. P5.11   FIG. P5.12

5.12. Determine the transfer voltage ratio V_2/V_1 of the circuit in Fig. P5.12. Using the technique of equating coefficients, synthesize

$$\frac{V_2}{V_1} = \frac{H}{(p+1)(p+2)}$$

5.13. Determine the possible 2-port descriptions of each of the circuits in Fig. P5.13.

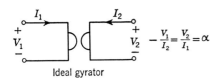

Ideal gyrator

$$-\frac{V_1}{I_2} = \frac{V_2}{I_1} = \alpha$$

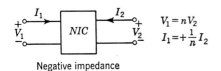

Negative impedance converter

$$V_1 = nV_2$$
$$I_1 = +\frac{1}{n}I_2$$

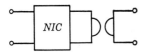

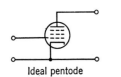

Ideal pentode

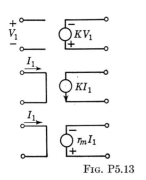

KV_1

KI_1

$r_m I_1$

Fig. P5.13

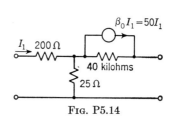

Fig. P5.14

5.14. Determine the transmission matrices $ABCD$ and $\mathfrak{ABCD}$ and the g and h matrices for the common emitter transistor shown in Fig. P5.14.

5.15. Find the constraint for a reciprocal 2-port in terms of the g and h parameters.

5.16. The circuit-element normalization procedure given in Chap. 3 can be developed simply by using matrix algebra. Justify the following derivation, and apply to a simple two-mesh network containing R, L, and C.

Given an arbitrary passive RLC circuit with n meshes and driven by a single voltage source, the mesh equations in the frequency domain can be written in matrix form.

$$\left[\left(R_{ij} + pL_{ij} + \frac{1}{pC_{ij}}\right)\right]\begin{bmatrix} I_1 \\ I_2 \\ \cdot \\ \cdot \\ \cdot \\ I_n \end{bmatrix} = \begin{bmatrix} V_1 \\ 0 \\ \cdot \\ \cdot \\ \cdot \\ 0 \end{bmatrix}$$

$$[\mathbf{Z}][\mathbf{I}] = [\mathbf{V}]$$

The equality is unchanged if $[\mathbf{Z}]$ is multiplied by a constant $1/r_n$ and $[\mathbf{I}]$ is multiplied by r_n.

$$\frac{1}{r_n}[\mathbf{Z}]\, r_n[\mathbf{I}] = [\mathbf{V}]$$

From the rule of the multiplication of a matrix by a constant, each element of Z and each element of I are multiplied by the appropriate constant.

$$\left[\frac{\mathbf{Z}}{r_n}\right][r_n\mathbf{I}] = [\mathbf{V}]$$

Thus, if R_{ij}/r_n, L_{ij}/r_n, and r_nC_{ij} are defined as the new self and mutual elements, all mesh currents are changed by the resistance-normalization factor r_n. To frequency-normalize the elements and the network, a linear change of frequency variable $p = p'\Omega_n$ is introduced, as in Chap. 3.

$$\left[\left(\frac{R_{ij}}{r_n} + p'\frac{L_{ij}\Omega_n}{r_n} + \frac{1}{p'C_{ij}\Omega_n r_n}\right)\right][r_n\mathbf{I}(p')] = [\mathbf{V}(p')]$$

Since the matrix equality is unchanged, the relative electric behavior of the circuit is unchanged.

CHAPTER 6

1-PORT LC NETWORKS

6.1 Introduction. A typical realization problem is that illustrated in Fig. 6.1. A coupling network between an antenna and an amplifier with a specified transfer voltage ratio is to be developed. Minimum signal loss is desired; hence the coupling network should contain only lossless elements, i.e., L and C. The source impedance of the antenna is assumed to be purely resistive and of value R_s. The input capacitance of the pentode is incorporated as an element of the coupling network. From

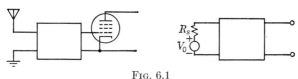

FIG. 6.1

Table 4.1 the relationship between the open-circuit parameters of the coupling network and the specified over-all transfer voltage ratio is

$$N(p) = \frac{V_2}{V_0} = \frac{z_{21}}{R_s + z_{11}}$$

The next chapter deals with a method of determining z_{21} and z_{11} from the specified network function $N(p)$, if it is of the proper form. The network is then developed by a realization of z_{11} which incorporates the properties of z_{21}. In order to understand and use this synthesis procedure, it is first necessary to establish the properties of the input impedance of an LC network, then to develop realization techniques for 1-port LC networks. These are the topics of this chapter.

Before a restriction is made to 1-port networks containing only L and C, a basic property of the input impedance of a general 1-port is taken up in the next section. This basic property is that every driving-point impedance of a passive network is a *positive real function*. All realization techniques stem from this property. After this development the necessary properties of LC 1-ports are established. This is followed by development of several realization techniques for these networks. The successful development of general realization techniques from functions which satisfy the necessary properties demonstrates that the properties are also sufficient.

79

6.2   Positive Real Functions.   The input impedance (and its reciprocal, the input admittance) of a passive network consisting of R, L, and C
(see Fig. 6.2) is shown in this section to be a positive

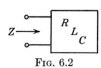

FIG. 6.2

real function. This property, which is explained
below, can be established by various means. The
method used here stems from stability and power
considerations. Another method of development is
presented in Appendix 2.   Brune has shown that if an arbitrary rational
function is positive real, a physical network can be found, the input
impedance of which is the given function.*   Thus the positive real property is both a necessary and a sufficient property.

As mentioned in Chap. 2, the input impedance Z is a rational function
with real coefficients

$$Z(p) = \frac{P(p)}{Q(p)} = \frac{\displaystyle\prod_{i=1}^{m} H(p - z_i)}{\displaystyle\prod_{i=1}^{n} (p - p_i)} \tag{6.1}$$

Clearly, if the variable is real, $p = \sigma + j0$; then $Z(\sigma)$ is real.

$$Z(p) \text{ is real if } p \text{ is real} \tag{6.2}$$

This constitutes the first part of the positive real property.

Next, it should be remembered that both the poles and zeros must lie
in the left half plane (LHP) or on the $j\omega$ axis.   Any poles and zeros on
the $j\omega$ axis must be simple.   These properties follow from stability considerations.   If the source to the network is a current source, the natural
frequencies are the poles of $Z(p)$, which must lie in the left half plane or
be simple if they lie on the $j\omega$ axis.   For a voltage source the natural
frequencies are the poles of $Y(p) = 1/Z(p)$; i.e., the zeros of $Z(p)$ must
satisfy the same conditions.   Since no poles and zeros lie in the right
half plane (RHP), the function $Z(p)$ and its reciprocal are analytic in
the interior of the right half plane.

Because the network is passive, the average power into the network
from a sinusoidal generator of any frequency ω is nonnegative.   In terms
of the input current and the input impedance†

$$P_{\text{in}} = \tfrac{1}{2}|I|^2 \operatorname{Re}[Z(j\omega)] \geq 0 \tag{6.3}$$

* O. Brune, Synthesis of a Finite Two Terminal Network Whose Driving Point
Impedance Is a Prescribed Function of Frequency, *J. Math. and Phys.*, vol. 10, p. 191,
1931.

† It is assumed for the present that $Z(p)$ has no poles on the $j\omega$ axis.   At a $j\omega$-axis
pole, the real part of Z is indeterminate.   That is, a sustained sinusoidal oscillation is
obtained at a frequency of a $j\omega$-axis pole without the necessity of any sustained input
power.

$|I|^2$ is always positive; therefore the real part of the input impedance for $p = j\omega$ is always nonnegative.

$$\text{Re}\,[Z(j\omega)] \geq 0 \qquad (6.4)$$

From (6.4) and the fact that $Z(p)$ is analytic in the right half plane, it can now be shown that the real part of $Z(p)$ in the right half plane must be nonnegative.

In proving this, use is made of the maximum modulus theorem of complex function theory.[7]   This theorem states that if a function $f(p)$ is

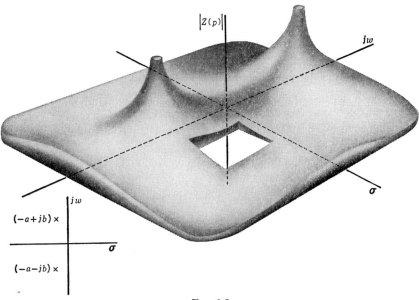

FIG. 6.3

analytic inside and on the boundary of a region, the maximum value of the magnitude of the function must appear on the boundary. This can be illustrated with the use of a three-dimensional plot, such as that in Fig. 6.3. For the region as shown, which includes no poles, the magnitude is clearly a maximum on the boundary. An extension of this theorem can be made if the region contains no zeros. The minimum of the magnitude then also occurs on the boundary, as illustrated in the figure. Similar arguments can be made for the function $e^{f(p)}$. If $f(p)$ is analytic in a region, $e^{f(p)}$ not only is analytic but contains no zeros in this region. Therefore both the maximum and the minimum of the magnitude of $e^{f(p)}$ occur on the boundary. Since

$$\left|e^{f(p)}\right| = e^{\text{Re}[f(p)]} \qquad (6.5)$$

it can also be concluded that the maximum and the minimum values of the real part of $f(p)$ must occur on the boundary.

For the case at hand, $Z(p)$ is analytic within the interior of the right half plane. The boundary is the $j\omega$ axis, including the point at infinity. If for the moment it is assumed that the function $Z(p)$ has no poles on the $j\omega$ axis, the minimum value of the real part of $Z(p)$ occurs on the $j\omega$ axis. From (6.4) the real part of Z on the $j\omega$ axis is nonnegative. Therefore the real part of $Z(p)$ in the entire right half plane must also be nonnegative. This statement can be concisely written as

$$\text{Re}\,[Z(p)] \geq 0 \qquad \text{in the RHP} \tag{6.6}$$

If $Z(p)$ has poles on the $j\omega$ axis, which of course must be simple, the same conclusion can be drawn except at the $j\omega$ pole locations proper. The maximum modulus theorem can be modified to deal with the case where the contour is closed except for a finite number of points. The proper conclusion is then that the maximum modulus of the function on the contour is not exceeded at any points within the contour. Equation (6.6) can also be obtained in a similar manner.

From the above developments, the driving-point impedance of a passive network must have the following two properties:

$$Z(p) \text{ is real if } p \text{ is real}$$
$$\text{Re}\,[Z(p)] \geq 0 \qquad \text{for Re}\,[p] \geq 0 \tag{6.7}$$

Any function that satisfies (6.7) is called a positive real function, or is said to be p-r. A similar development starting from (6.4) can also be made for $Y(p)$, and a similar conclusion can be drawn, namely: $Y(p)$ is p-r. Hence the general statement can be made that if a function is p-r its reciprocal is also p-r.

6.3   Further Properties and Tests of Driving-point Impedance Functions. From the p-r property of $Z(p)$ an important subsidiary property can be derived: that the residues of the function at the $j\omega$-axis poles must be real and positive. To prove this, assume $Z(p)$ has a pole at $j\omega_1$. The Laurent series expansion of $Z(p)$ about $j\omega_1$ has the form

$$Z(p) = \frac{k_{-1}}{p - j\omega_1} + k_0 + k_1(p - j\omega_1) + \cdots \tag{6.8}$$

The coefficient k_{-1} is by definition the residue. In the immediate neighborhood of $j\omega_1$ the first term of the series is dominant. That is,

$$Z(p)|_{p \sim j\omega_1} \approx \frac{k_{-1}}{p - j\omega_1} \tag{6.9}$$

In this neighborhood, $p - j\omega_1$ can be expressed in polar coordinates about $j\omega_1$, as illustrated in Fig. 6.4.

$$p - j\omega_1 = \rho e^{j\phi} \tag{6.10}$$

The residue k_{-1} can also be expressed in polar form.

$$k_{-1} = |k|e^{i\theta} \qquad (6.11)$$

The function and its real part in the neighborhood of $j\omega_1$ can then be written

$$Z(p) = \frac{|k|}{\rho} e^{j(\theta-\phi)} \qquad (6.12)$$

$$\text{Re}\,[Z(p)] = \frac{|k|}{\rho} \cos(\theta - \phi) \qquad (6.13)$$

It should now be noted that a point in the right half plane corresponds to $-\pi/2 \leq \phi \leq \pi/2$. Since $\text{Re}\,[Z(p)]$ must be positive in the right half plane,

$$\cos(\theta - \phi) \geq 0$$

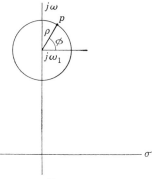

Therefore θ must be equal to zero. That is, the residue k_{-1} must be real and positive.

Further properties of a driving-point impedance together with a testing procedure can be established. It should be kept in mind that if any necessary condition is not satisfied the function is not a driving-point impedance. Because poles and zeros must be simple on the $j\omega$ axis and infinity is a point on the $j\omega$ axis, the relative degrees of the numerator and denominator polynomials can at most differ by one. In general

FIG. 6.4

$$Z(p) = H \frac{p^m + \cdots + a_1 p + a_0}{p^n + \cdots + b_1 p + b_0} \qquad (6.14)$$

At very high frequencies

$$Z(p) \rightarrow Hp^{m-n} \qquad (6.15)$$

Since a zero or a pole at infinity must be simple, the only possibilities are

$$m - n = \begin{cases} 1 \\ 0 \\ -1 \end{cases} \qquad (6.16)$$

From (6.15) and the p-r properties, the constant H can be shown to be always positive. If $m - n = \pm 1$, either $Z(p)$ or $1/Z = Y(p)$ has a pole at infinity with a residue equal to H or $1/H$ respectively, which must be positive. If m is equal to n, H must also be positive, since it is equal to $\text{Re}\,[Z(j\omega)]$ at infinity.

Similarly, since the origin is a point on the $j\omega$ axis, any poles or zeros at the origin must be simple. Thus in (6.14) the lowest degree of the numerator polynomial can differ at most by one from the lowest degree of the denominator polynomial. At very low frequencies $Z(p)$ may have the following three forms:

$$Z(p) \rightarrow \begin{cases} \dfrac{a_0}{b_0} \\[2ex] \dfrac{a_0}{b_1 p} \\[2ex] \dfrac{a_1 p}{b_0} \end{cases} \tag{6.17}$$

If either the numerator or denominator polynomial has negative or missing coefficients, there must be poles or zeros in the right half plane. This can be seen by inspecting representative factors of polynomials with zeros in the left half plane. A zero on the negative real axis, e.g., $-a$, has the factor $(p + a)$. Complex zeros in the left half plane occur in conjugate pairs, e.g., $-a + jb$, $-a - jb$; and the product of the factors due to each is $p^2 + 2ap + a^2 + b^2$. For both types of factors the coefficients are positive. Therefore a polynomial which is the product of these components must have only positive coefficients and no missing terms. An exception to this rule occurs if all the zeros of the polynomials lie on the $j\omega$ axis. The factor for a conjugate pair on the imaginary axis is $(p + jb)(p - jb) = p^2 + b^2$. In this type of polynomial the coefficients for either all odd powers or all even powers are missing. The absence of all the odd powers occurs if there is no zero at the origin. It is important to keep in mind one point. If a polynomial has only positive coefficients and no missing terms, there still may be zeros in the right half plane.

In order to determine whether a given function $F(p)$ is p-r, further testing is necessary. It is easiest first to check for the above properties. If these simple tests fail to indicate that the function lacks the p-r property, the presence of this property can be established by showing that the following three conditions are fulfilled. (1) The function must be analytic in the right half plane. This property of the function is checked by determining whether the denominator polynomial is Hurwitz. A simple test is introduced at the end of this chapter to ascertain whether a polynomial is Hurwitz. (2) Any $j\omega$-axis poles must of course be simple, and the residues at these poles must be positive and real. (3) If the function satisfies these two conditions, the final step is to ascertain that Re $[F(j\omega)]$ is not negative.

A straightforward method of determining whether the real part is non-negative is to investigate the zeros of Re $[F(j\omega)]$. In general, the function can be written

$$F(p) = \frac{A_1 + pB_1}{A_2 + pB_2} \tag{6.18}$$

From (2.29) through (2.32)

$$\text{Re}\,[F(j\omega)] = \text{Ev}\,F(p)|_{p=j\omega} = \frac{A_1 A_2 + \omega^2 B_1 B_2}{A_2{}^2 + \omega^2 B_2{}^2} \qquad (6.19)$$

where A_1, A_2, B_1, and B_2 are functions of ω^2. The denominator of (6.19) is always positive. Therefore only the numerator need be investigated. The crucial step is to determine whether there are any real zeros in the numerator of (6.19) of odd multiplicity. If there are zeros of odd multiplicity, the numerator must change from positive to negative or from negative to positive values. This is illustrated in Fig. 6.5a. If there are zeros of even multiplicity, the function can stay positive, as shown in Fig. 6.5b.

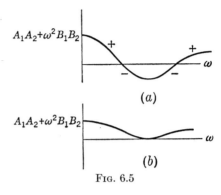

(a)

(b)

Fig. 6.5

As a final point, an alternate condition for $\text{Re}\,[Z(j\omega)] \geq 0$ can be made.

$$Z(j\omega) = \text{Re}\,[Z(j\omega)] + j\,\text{Im}\,[Z(j\omega)] \qquad (6.20)$$

$$\text{Arg}\,Z(j\omega) = \tan^{-1}\frac{\text{Im}\,[Z(j\omega)]}{\text{Re}\,[Z(j\omega)]} \qquad (6.21)$$

Since $\text{Re}\,[Z(j\omega)] \geq 0$

$$-\frac{\pi}{2} \leq \text{Arg}\,Z(j\omega) \leq \frac{\pi}{2} \qquad (6.22)$$

Equation (6.22) is thus an equivalent condition.

6.4 Properties of LC Driving-point Impedances. The material in the last two sections can be used and specialized for the case where the 1-port contains only L and C. In this section the properties of this kind of network are developed. In the remaining sections of the chapter these properties are used as a basis for realization procedures.

For a network that contains no resistance, no real power can be supplied to the network and

$$\text{Re}\,[Z(j\omega)] = 0 \qquad (6.23)$$

For a $Z(p)$ having the general form

$$Z(p) = \frac{A_1 + pB_1}{A_2 + pB_2} \qquad (6.24)$$

(6.23) can be rewritten as

$$A_1 A_2 - p^2 B_1 B_2|_{p=j\omega} = 0 \qquad (6.25)$$

The product $A_1 A_2$ is a polynomial as is the product $p^2 B_1 B_2$. These two product polynomials are equal for $p = j\omega$; hence their corresponding coefficients must be equal.   Clearly, then, (6.25) must be true for all p, and

$$\frac{A_1}{pB_1} = \frac{pB_2}{A_2} \tag{6.26}$$

Combining (6.24) and (6.26)

$$Z(p) = \frac{pB_1 (A_1/pB_1 + 1)}{A_2 (pB_2/A_2 + 1)} = \frac{pB_1}{A_2} \tag{6.27}$$

or

$$Z(p) = \frac{A_1 (1 + pB_1/A_1)}{pB_2 (A_2/pB_2 + 1)} = \frac{A_1}{pB_2} \tag{6.28}$$

Thus the driving-point impedance of an LC network must be an odd rational function, i.e., the ratio of an even to odd polynomial or the ratio of an odd to even polynomial.

From the general properties of a driving-point function and because $Z(p)$ for an LC network is an odd function, one can prove that all poles and zeros lie on the $j\omega$ axis.   This is seen by investigating the even polynomials A and B.   As indicated in Chap. 2, the zeros of the even polynomial are symmetrical about both the real and the imaginary axes. Since poles and zeros of $Z(p)$ cannot lie in the right half plane, the only possibility for the poles and zeros of (6.27) or (6.28) to be symmetric with regard to the $j\omega$ axis is to lie on the $j\omega$ axis.   Because the poles and zeros lie on the $j\omega$ axis, they must be simple.   In addition, since $Z(p)$ is an odd function, there must be either a pole or a zero at the origin and at infinity.

In the last section it is shown that the residues of $Z(p)$ at $j\omega$-axis poles must be real and positive.   This leads to the conclusion that the poles and zeros must alternate along the $j\omega$ axis.   The partial fraction expansion of an LC impedance function has the form

$$Z(p) = \frac{k_0}{p} + \frac{k_1}{p - j\omega_1} + \frac{\bar{k}_1}{p + j\omega_1} + \cdots + k_\infty p \tag{6.29}$$

It has been assumed for generality that $Z(p)$ has poles at both the origin and infinity.   Since the residues are real and positive, $k_1 = \bar{k}_1$.   The contribution of a pair of conjugate poles is

$$\frac{k_1}{p - j\omega_1} + \frac{\bar{k}_1}{p + j\omega_1} = \frac{2k_1 p}{p^2 + \omega_1^2} \tag{6.30}$$

Equation (6.29) can therefore be written

$$Z(p) = \frac{k_0}{p} + \frac{2k_1 p}{p^2 + \omega_1^2} + \cdots + k_\infty p \tag{6.31}$$

For $p = j\omega$, (6.31) becomes

$$Z(j\omega) = -j\frac{k_0}{\omega} + j\frac{2k_1\omega}{\omega_1^2 - \omega^2} + \cdots + jk_\infty\omega = jX(\omega) \tag{6.32}$$

where $X(\omega)$ is called the *reactance function*. If the derivative of $X(\omega)$ is taken with respect to ω

$$\frac{dX(\omega)}{d\omega} = \frac{k_0}{\omega^2} + \frac{2k_1(\omega_1^2 + \omega^2)}{(\omega_1^2 - \omega^2)^2} + \cdots + k_\infty > 0 \qquad \text{for all } \omega \quad (6.33)$$

Since $\dfrac{dX}{d\omega}$ is always positive, the poles and zeros must alternate on the $j\omega$ axis, as shown in Fig. 6.6. (An alternate method of proving that the poles and zeros alternate on the $j\omega$ axis is to use the Cauchy-Riemann conditions.) Because of the four different possibilities with regard to the poles and zeros at the origin and infinity, four basic pole-zero configurations for $Z(p)$ are possible, as shown in Fig. 6.6. For a typical pole-zero arrangement of Fig. 6.6, $Z(p)$ is

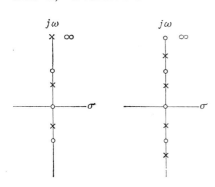

$$Z(p) = H \frac{p(p^2 + \omega_2^2)(p^2 + \omega_4^2)}{(p^2 + \omega_1^2)(p^2 + \omega_3^2)} \quad (6.34)$$

where

$$0 < \omega_1 < \omega_2 < \omega_3 < \cdots \quad (6.35)$$

The plot of $X(\omega)$ is shown in Fig. 6.7.

The reciprocal of the LC driving-point impedance function, the LC

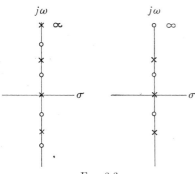

FIG. 6.6

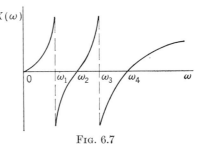

FIG. 6.7

admittance function, has the same mathematical form as the impedance function. Hence the above properties also hold for the admittance function. Corresponding to the reactance function one has the *susceptance function* $B(\omega)$, where

$$Y(j\omega) = jB(\omega) \quad (6.36)$$

6.5 Realization through Partial Fraction Expansions. From the properties of the last section, it is possible to determine whether a given function is an LC impedance function. These properties can be expressed in several ways.

1. The function must be an odd rational function that is p-r.

or

2. The function must have poles only on the $j\omega$ axis that are simple. The residues of the function at the poles must be positive and real.

or

3. The function must have poles and zeros lying only on the $j\omega$ axis that are simple. The poles and zeros must alternate, and there must be either a pole or zero at the origin and infinity.

If the function has these properties, a physical realization can be obtained quite simply. In this section a realization technique using the partial fraction expansion is discussed. In the next section a continued fraction expansion is used to achieve a realization.

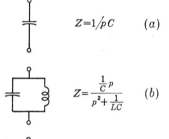

$$Z = 1/pC \qquad (a)$$

$$Z = \frac{\frac{1}{C}p}{p^2 + \frac{1}{LC}} \qquad (b)$$

$$Z = pL \qquad (c)$$

FIG. 6.8

Consider the partial fraction expansion of $Z(p)$ in (6.31). The first term of the expansion in (6.31), k_0/p, has the same mathematical form and can be identified as the impedance of a capacitor having a value of $C = 1/k_0$, as shown in Fig. 6.8a. An interior term of this expansion can be identified as the impedance of a parallel LC circuit, as shown in Fig. 6.8b. The proper values of L and C for the network that is to realize a particular term of (6.31) are obtained by equating coefficients as follows:

$$Z(p) = \frac{(1/C)p}{p^2 + 1/LC} = \frac{2k_ip}{p^2 + \omega_i^2}$$

$$C = \frac{1}{2k_i} \qquad L = \frac{2k_i}{\omega_i^2} \qquad (6.37)$$

In a similar manner, the contribution due to the pole at infinity can be identified as the impedance of an inductance of value $L = k_\infty$, as shown in Fig. 6.8c. Since all the residues are real and positive, the network realization of each term consists of positive elements. The complete realization of (6.31) is thus the series combination of a set of simple networks, as in Fig. 6.8. The combination is shown in Fig. 6.9. The single capacitance is not present if the function has no pole at the origin. The single inductance is not present if the function has no pole at infinity. There is a parallel LC network for each conjugate pair of poles of the impedance function. Clearly, there are as many elements in the reali-

zation of the impedance as there are poles of the impedance. Notice in (6.31) that the number of coefficients $(k_0, \omega_i, k_i, \ldots k_\infty)$ is equal to the number of poles. This set of coefficients completely specifies the imped-
ance function, and the number of the coefficients represents the degrees of freedom. Since this number is equal to the number of elements in the above realization, no smaller number of elements in a realization is possible for a given impedance function. A configuration which has only this minimum number of elements, such as that in Fig. 6.9, is called a *canonical form*.

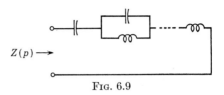

$Z(p) \longrightarrow$

FIG. 6.9

An alternate realization can be obtained by taking the partial fraction expansion of the reciprocal of $Z(p)$, $Y(p) = 1/Z(p)$. The partial fraction expansion of $Y(p)$ has the same form as (6.31).

$$Y(p) = \frac{k_0'}{p} + \frac{2k_1'p}{p^2 + \omega_1'^2} + \cdots + k_\infty'p \tag{6.38}$$

For generality, poles of $Y(p)$ at both the origin and infinity are included. In a manner similar to that used for the impedance function, each term in (6.38) is identified as the admittance of one of the three elementary networks shown in Fig. 6.10. The single inductance has an admittance $Y(p) = 1/pL$, which equals the contribution due to the pole at the origin if $L = 1/k_0'$. The single capac-
itance can be used to represent the contribution due to the pole at infinity if $C = k_\infty'$. The series LC net-
work can be used to realize the contribution of a conjugate-pole pair if

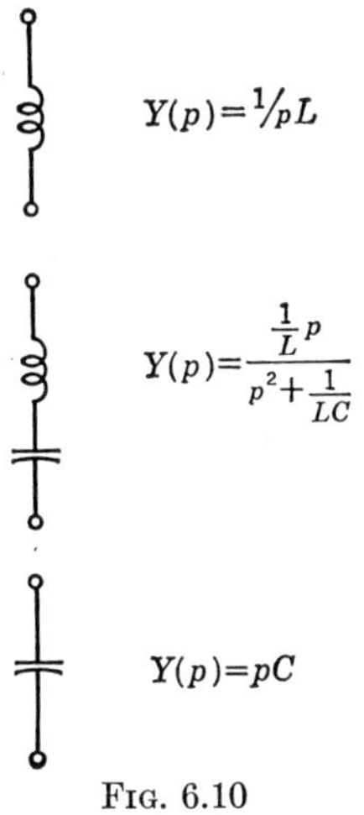

$$Y(p) = \frac{1}{pL}$$

$$Y(p) = \frac{\frac{1}{L}p}{p^2 + \frac{1}{LC}}$$

$$Y(p) = \frac{(1/L)p}{p^2 + 1/LC} = \frac{2k_i'p}{p^2 + \omega_i'^2}$$
$$L = \frac{1}{2k_i'} \qquad C = \frac{2k_i'}{\omega_i'^2} \tag{6.39}$$

$$Y(p) = pC$$

FIG. 6.10

The total realization of (6.38), shown in Fig. 6.11, is a parallel combination of the simple networks. The number of elements in the realization is equal to the number of poles of the admittance function. For any given function the total numbers of poles and zeros are equal. Therefore both types of realization have the same number of elements. The above two canonical forms were first developed by Foster and are known as the Foster's canonical forms.*

* R. M. Foster, A Reactance Theorem, *Bell System Tech. J.*, vol. 3, p. 259, 1924.

As an example of these two realizations, consider the function

$$Z(p) = \frac{p(p^2 + 4)}{(p^2 + 1)(p^2 + 9)} \tag{6.40}$$

This function satisfies the third set of conditions at the beginning of this

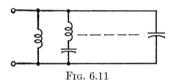

section. Hence the function is an LC impedance function. The partial fraction expansion of $Z(p)$ is

FIG. 6.11

$$Z(p) = \frac{\frac{3}{8}p}{p^2 + 1} + \frac{\frac{5}{8}p}{p^2 + 9} \tag{6.41}$$

The network realization is shown in Fig. 6.12a. The partial fraction expansion of $Y(p)$ is

$$Y(p) = \frac{9}{4p} + \frac{\frac{15}{4}p}{p^2 + 4} + p \tag{6.42}$$

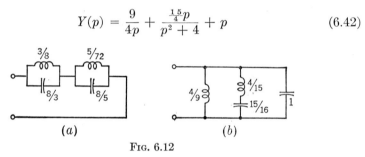

(a) (b)

FIG. 6.12

The network realization is shown in Fig. 6.12b.

6.6 Realization through Continued Fraction Expansions. The realization procedures in the last section can be considered a sequential process;

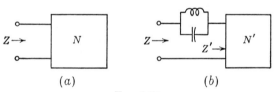

(a) (b)

FIG. 6.13

that is, the partial fraction expansion is accomplished in steps. The contribution is removed from one pole or one conjugate-pole pair at a time. This can be visualized with the help of Fig. 6.13, where the given impedance is represented by the unknown structure, network N. The contribution in the partial fraction expansion of $Z(p)$ due to a given pole pair is realized as an elementary network and removed from the unknown structure (see Fig. 6.13b). The input impedance Z' of the remaining network N' is of reduced complexity; it also must be an LC driving-point impedance function, because the impedance Z' has poles on the $j\omega$ axis with positive and real residues, as can be seen from a complete partial fraction expansion. Z', of course, does not contain the pole pair which has been removed.   This process can be continued in an iterative manner until the final remainder is zero.

This iterative removal technique need not be accomplished with successive impedances only.   One can at any step make a removal from an admittance remainder function rather than from an impedance remainder function. An impedance removal leads to a series network while an admittance removal leads to a shunt network, as shown in Fig. 6.14. A special and very simple case is that where only poles at infinity are removed from either $Z(p)$ or $Y(p)$ or the remainders.   For example, assume that the given impedance has a pole at infinity.   It can be removed with a series inductance, as shown in Fig. 6.15a.   The remainder

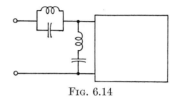

FIG. 6.14

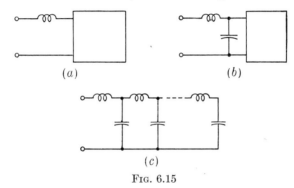

(a) (b)

(c)

FIG. 6.15

impedance function $Z'(p)$ has a zero at infinity.   The reciprocal remainder therefore has a pole at infinity, which can be removed as a shunt capacitance, as shown in Fig. 6.15b.   If this process is iterated, the network realization of $Z(p)$ has the form shown in Fig. 6.15c.   If $Z(p)$ does not have a pole at infinity, the first inductance is absent.   If $Z(p)$ does not have a pole at the origin, the final shunt capacitance is replaced by a short circuit, corresponding to a zero-impedance final remainder.

The network shown in Fig. 6.15c is a simple ladder network.   The input impedance of this network can be expressed as follows:

$$Z(p) = L_1 p + \cfrac{1}{C_2 p + \cfrac{1}{L_3 p + \cfrac{1}{\genfrac{}{}{0pt}{}{\cdot}{\genfrac{}{}{0pt}{}{\cdot}{\genfrac{}{}{0pt}{}{\cdot}{C_n p}}}}}$$

(6.43)

The mathematical form of (6.43) is known as a finite continued fraction. Because of this, the above realization technique leading to a ladder-network configuration is called a continued fraction expansion.

To illustrate this procedure, the same impedance function as that used in the last section is realized.

$$Z(p) = \frac{p(p^2 + 4)}{(p^2 + 1)(p^2 + 9)} \tag{6.44}$$

$Z(p)$ does not have a pole at infinity; therefore the initial removal is made from $Y(p)$. The residue of $Y(p)$ at infinity is one. Thus a capacitance of 1 farad is removed, leaving a remainder

$$Y'(p) = Y(p) - p = \frac{6p^2 + 9}{p^3 + 4p} \tag{6.45}$$

The reciprocal of $Y'(p)$, $Z'(p)$, has a pole at infinity with a residue of $\frac{1}{6}$. A series inductance of $\frac{1}{6}$ henry is removed. The remainder is

$$Z''(p) = Z'(p) - \frac{1}{6}p = \frac{\frac{5}{2}p}{6p^2 + 9} \tag{6.46}$$

The residue of $Y''(p) = 1/Z''(p)$ at infinity is $\frac{12}{5}$. This pole is removed as a shunt capacitance of $\frac{12}{5}$ farads. The remainder is

$$Y'''(p) = Y''(p) - \frac{12}{5}p = \frac{18}{5p} \tag{6.47}$$

The pole of the reciprocal is removed as a series inductance of $\frac{5}{18}$ henry, leaving a final impedance remainder of zero, which corresponds to a short circuit. The network realization is shown in Fig. 6.16.

The numerical procedure of obtaining the network elements can be accomplished more simply. The residue of the function at infinity is equal to the ratio of the leading coefficients of the numerator and the denominator polynomials.

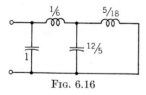

FIG. 6.16

One step of division removes the pertinent term at infinity and provides the proper remainder function. Likewise, one step of division of the inverted remainder function provides the next residue and remainder. This successive division and inversion can be consolidated as follows for the above example:

Remove poles at ∞

$$p^3 + 4p \overline{\big)\, p^4 + 10p^2 + 9} \;\big|\; p\text{—}Y \text{ division}$$
$$\underline{\;p^4 + \;4p^2}$$
$$6p^2 + 9 \overline{\big)\, p^3 + 4p} \;\big|\; \tfrac{1}{6}p\text{—}Z \text{ division}$$
$$\underline{\;p^3 + \tfrac{3}{2}p}$$
$$\tfrac{5}{2}p \overline{\big)\, 6p^2 + 9} \;\big|\; \tfrac{12}{5}p\text{—}Y \text{ division}$$
$$\underline{\;6p^2}$$
$$9 \overline{\big)\, \tfrac{5}{2}p} \;\big|\; \tfrac{5}{18}p\text{—}Z \text{ division}$$
$$\underline{\;\tfrac{5}{2}p}$$
$$0\text{—Short-circuit remainder}$$

A different ladder network can be developed if successive poles at the origin instead of poles at infinity are removed. The element removed from an impedance function to remove a pole at the origin is a series capacitance, while the element removed from an admittance function is a shunt inductance. The network realization has the ladder-network configuration shown in Fig. 6.17. The initial capacitance is absent if $Z(p)$ does not have a pole at the origin. The last shunt inductance is absent if $Z(p)$ does not have a pole at infinity. The input impedance of this ladder network is again a finite continued fraction expansion of the following form:

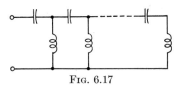

FIG. 6.17

$$Z(p) = \frac{1}{C_1 p} + \cfrac{1}{\cfrac{1}{L_2 p} + \cfrac{1}{\cfrac{1}{C_3 p} + \cdot}}$$

$$\cdot$$
$$\cdot$$
$$\frac{1}{L_n p}$$

(6.48)

The numerical procedure to obtain the network element values, i.e., the above continued fraction expansion, again is very simple. The residue of a function at a pole at the origin is equal to the ratio of the coefficient of the lowest power of the numerator polynomial to the coefficient of the lowest power of the denominator polynomial. One step of division again provides the pole factor together with the proper remainder. However, this division process must be made with respect to the lowest powers of the polynomials and not the highest. To illustrate this, consider the impedance function used previously:

$$Z(p) = \frac{p(p^2 + 4)}{(p^2 + 1)(p^2 + 9)}$$

(6.49)

The reciprocal of this function $Y(p)$ has a pole at the origin. It is convenient to rewrite the polynomials with the lowest degrees first.

$$Y(p) = \frac{9 + 10p^2 + p^4}{4p + p^3} \tag{6.50}$$

One step of division is now made to eliminate the lowest power of the numerator.

$$Y(p) = \frac{9 + 10p^2 + p^4}{4p + p^3} = \frac{9}{4p} + \frac{\frac{31}{4}p^2 + p^4}{4p + p^3} \tag{6.51}$$

The remainder function $Y'(p)$ is inverted and the process continued. Comparably to the numerical procedure used previously, the entire expansion can be written

Remove
Poles at
origin

$$4p + p^3 \overline{\smash{\big)}\, 9 + 10p^2 + p^4} \;\Big|\; \frac{9}{4p} \;—Y \text{ division}$$

$$\underline{9 + \tfrac{9}{4}p^2}$$

$$\tfrac{31}{4}p^2 + p^4 \overline{\smash{\big)}\, 4p + \;\;\; p^3} \;\Big|\; \frac{16}{31p} \;—Z \text{ division}$$

$$\underline{4p + \tfrac{16}{31}p^3}$$

$$\tfrac{15}{31}p^3 \overline{\smash{\big)}\, \tfrac{31}{4}p^2 + p^4} \;\Big|\; \frac{(31)^2}{60p} \;—Y \text{ division}$$

$$\underline{\tfrac{31}{4}p^2}$$

$$p^4 \overline{\smash{\big)}\, \tfrac{15}{31}p^3} \;\Big|\; \frac{15}{31p} \;—Z \text{ division}$$

$$\underline{\tfrac{15}{31}p^3}$$

$$0 \text{ Short-circuit remainder}$$

The network realization is shown in Fig. 6.18.

It is helpful in clarifying the above procedure to introduce a variable transformation in $Z(p)$. For $s = 1/p$, the pole at the origin in the p plane transforms into the pole at infinity in the s plane. In this transformation

$$Y(p)\Big|_{p=1/s} = \frac{9s^4 + 10s^2 + 1}{4s^3 + s} \tag{6.52}$$

If a normal continued fraction expansion is now made in s, i.e., if successive poles at infinity are removed, a ladder network in the new variable is obtained. If in this network $s = 1/p$ is substituted, the inductances are changed to capacitances and vice versa, and the network of Fig. 6.18 is again obtained. The above transformation of variables is the familiar low-pass to high-pass transformation.

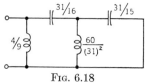

FIG. 6.18

If Figs. 6.17 and 6.18 are compared with Fig. 6.12a and b, it is seen that the networks developed through the continued fraction expansions have the same number of elements as the Foster's canonical forms, which indicates that the ladder networks are also canonical forms. That this is true in general is seen by noting the number of the division steps in the expansion to obtain a zero remainder. This number is equal to the highest power of the initial dividend, which in turn is equal to the total number of poles or zeros of the impedance function.

The development of these networks from continued fraction expansions was first done by Cauer, and the two ladder network realizations are often referred to as the Cauer canonical forms.*

6.7 Generalization and a Design Example.   In the last two sections four canonical realizations are developed from functions that satisfy the necessary properties given in Sec. 6.5.   Since physically realizable networks can be developed for functions having these properties, the properties are thus sufficient.

As indicated at the beginning of the last section, it is not necessary to follow the exact procedure leading to the Foster and Cauer forms.   At any step in the realization one can re-move any number of poles (at the origin and/or infinity) or pole pairs, from the pertinent impedance function or its reciprocal.   Thus for any given $Z(p)$ there exists a multiplicity of possible network realizations.

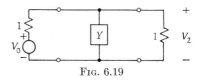

Fig. 6.19

This is a good illustration of the fact that network synthesis leads to nonunique solutions.

A practical use of the LC 1-port is illustrated in the example that follows.   Assume that the source V_0 in Fig. 6.19 is a vacuum-tube oscillator having an output with a fundamental frequency of 1 radian/sec together with second and fourth harmonics.   It is desired to minimize the presence of these harmonics in the load as well as to block d-c.   This can be accomplished by the insertion of an LC 1-port, as shown in the figure.   For unit source and load resistances the transfer voltage ratio is

$$\frac{V_2}{V_0} = \frac{1}{2 + Y} \tag{6.53}$$

The specification of the 1-port is determined by the requirements of the transfer voltage ratio.   Zero transmission is desired at d-c, $\omega = 2$, and $\omega = 4$.   From (6.53) it can be seen that this is accomplished if Y has poles at these frequencies.   The fundamental should pass through to the load, unaffected by the insertion filter.   Thus Y should have a zero at $\omega = 1$.   If Y is to be an LC function it must have an additional zero

---

* W. Cauer, Die Verwirklichung von Wechselstromwiderständen vorgeschriebener Frequenzabhängigkeit, *Arch. Elektrotech.*, vol. 17, p. 355, 1926.

between $\omega = 2$ and $\omega = 4$. For convenience, $\omega = 3$ is chosen as the zero location. $Y(p)$ then has the form

$$Y(p) = H \frac{(p^2 + 1)(p^2 + 9)}{p(p^2 + 4)(p^2 + 16)} \tag{6.54}$$

In (6.54) a multiplier H is included, since pole and zero locations do not completely specify a network function. The value of H can be used as

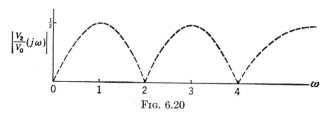

Fig. 6.20

a degree of freedom to alter the shape of the transfer function between critical frequencies. If H is chosen as 10, the magnitude of the transfer function for $p = j\omega$ is that shown in Fig. 6.20. One possible network realization is shown in Fig. 6.21.

6.8 Hurwitz Polynomials. The synthesis procedures in Sec. 6.6 can be used to determine whether or not a given polynomial is Hurwitz; for the ratio of the even part to the odd part of a Hurwitz polynomial has the property of being a p-r odd function.[6] That is, the ratio has the same properties as a driving-point impedance of an LC network.

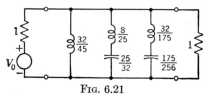

Fig. 6.21

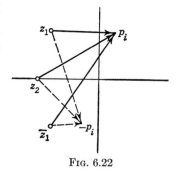

Fig. 6.22

As a starting point, it is assumed that the given polynomial $P(p)$ is Hurwitz. The even and odd parts of the polynomial are separated, as done previously.

$$P(p) = A + pB \tag{6.55}$$

Since all the zeros of $P(p)$ are in the left half plane, the magnitude of the function for any value of the variable p_i in the right half plane is larger than the magnitude of the function at $-p_i$, which is in the left half plane. This is easily seen from a vector interpretation of the magnitude function, as shown in Fig. 6.22. For a three-zero polynomial as illustrated

$$|P(p_i)| = |p_i - z_1|\,|p_i - \bar{z}_1|\,|p_i - z_2|$$
$$\geq |-p_i - z_1|\,|-p_i - \bar{z}_1|\,|-p_i - z_2| = |P(-p_i)| \tag{6.56}$$

Generalizing this idea, one obtains

$$|P(p)| > |P(-p)| \quad \text{in the RHP} \tag{6.57}$$

or
$$|\psi(p)| = \frac{|P(p)|}{|P(-p)|} > 1 \quad \text{in the RHP} \tag{6.58}$$

where the ratio of $P(p)/P(-p)$ is defined for convenience as $\psi(p)$. The new function $\psi(p)$ can be related simply to the even and odd parts of $P(p)$. From (6.55)

$$2A = P(p) + P(-p) \tag{6.59}$$
$$2pB = P(p) - P(-p)$$

The ratio of the last two equations is

$$\frac{A}{pB} = \frac{P(p) + P(-p)}{P(p) - P(-p)} = \frac{\psi(p) + 1}{\psi(p) - 1} \tag{6.60}$$

If ψ is expressed in terms of its real and imaginary components

$$\psi(p) = U + jV \tag{6.61}$$

Equation (6.58) can be rewritten

$$|\psi(p)| = \sqrt{U^2 + V^2} > 1 \quad \text{in the RHP} \tag{6.62}$$

A/pB can now be shown to be p-r by investigating its real part in the right half plane in terms of the last three equations.

$$\mathrm{Re}\left[\frac{A}{pB}\right] = \mathrm{Re}\left[\frac{U + 1 + jV}{U - 1 + jV}\right] = \frac{U^2 + V^2 - 1}{(U - 1)^2 + V^2} > 0 \quad \text{in the RHP} \tag{6.63}$$

This constitutes a proof that A/pB is p-r. If the above development is studied, it is seen that the converse is also true. Namely, if A/pB is p-r, $A + pB$ is Hurwitz. The realization procedures of this chapter can thus be used to determine whether a given polynomial is Hurwitz. For example, a continued fraction expansion can be made of the ratio of the even to odd parts of the given polynomial. If all the coefficients of the expansion are positive, there is a physically realizable LC network whose input impedance is the above ratio. Therefore the ratio is p-r and the polynomial is Hurwitz. If any coefficient of the expansion is negative, the polynomial is not Hurwitz.

There is one possible exception to the applicability of the above test. If A and pB have common factors, these factors cancel out, and the continued fraction expansion terminates prematurely. Common factors arise if the given polynomial has a set or sets of zeros symmetrical about the origin. The presence of these common factors is easily noted, however, and the polynomial is then known to be non-Hurwitz. As a final

point, polynomials with both zeros in the left half plane and simple
zeros on the $j\omega$ axis are important in network theory. Thus, one should
investigate whether the symmetrical zeros above are purely imaginary
conjugate sets.

PROBLEMS

6.1. Which of the functions are p-r?

(a) $\dfrac{p + \alpha}{p + \beta}$ (b) $\dfrac{p}{p^2 + 3}$ (c) $\dfrac{p + 0.2}{(p + 1)^2}$ (d) $\sqrt{p^2 + 1}$

(e) $\dfrac{(p + 1)^2}{p^3 + 2p^2 + 2p + 1}$ (f) $\dfrac{p^2 + p + 1}{p^2 + 3.6p + 1.6}$ (g) $\dfrac{p^2 + 1}{(p^2 + 4)(p + 1)}$

(h) $\dfrac{p + 4}{p^2 + 2p + 3}$

6.2. A rational function $F(p)$ has the value 1 at $p = 0$ and has the following finite
zeros and poles:

Pole location	Order	Zero location	Order
-1	1	$-1 + j1$	1
-3	1	$-1 - j1$	1

(a) Construct the function $F(p)$.
(b) What is the behavior of $F(p)$ at $p = \infty$?
(c) Find the partial fraction expansion of $F(p)$.
(d) Is this function p-r?

6.3. The network shown in Fig. P6.3 is driven by a voltage source $v(t) = V_0 e^{\sigma_1 t} \cos \omega_1 t$ where $\sigma_1 > 0$. (Yes, an exponentially increasing wave!) V_0 is a real, positive
number.

(a) Find the current $i(t)$ if $v(t)$ is applied at $t = 0$ and if $i(0) = 0$.
(b) If one considers only very large values of t, one may drop the exponentially
decreasing term(s). Show that under this assumption

$$i(t) = V_0 |Y(p_1)| e^{\sigma_1 t} \cos (\omega_1 t + \phi_1)$$

where $|Y_1|$ and ϕ_1 are defined by

$$Y(\sigma_1 + j\omega_1) = |Y(p_1)| e^{j\phi_1}$$

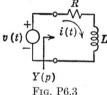

$Y(p)$

FIG. P6.3

(c) Compute the instantaneous power flow *into* the net-
work and sketch the curve $v(t)i(t)$. Indicate on the sketch both the envelopes and
the average.

(d) Since the network is passive, what can you tell about (1) ϕ_1; (2) Re $Y(p_1)$;
(3) the behavior of Re $Y(p)$ everywhere inside the right half plane?

(e) Could this reasoning be applied in the case of a more complicated network for
the purpose of establishing

$$\text{Re } Y(p) \geq 0 \qquad \text{for} \qquad \text{Re } p \geq 0$$

6.4. Given

$$F(p) = \frac{p + a}{p^2 + b_1 p + b_0}$$

what constraints on the coefficients make $F(p)$ p-r?

6.5. Given a rational function with all poles and zeros in the left half plane, can a positive constant be added to this function to obtain a new function which is p-r?

6.6. Determine which of the following polynomials are Hurwitz:

(a) $p^3 + 3p^2 + 3p + 2$ (b) $p^4 + 9p^3 + 3p^2 + 1$
(c) $p^5 + 5p^3 + 3p + 3$ (d) $p^4 + p^3 + 2p^2 + p + 1$
(e) $p^3 + p^2 - 1$

6.7. Determine a test to establish that all the zeros of a polynomial lie in the right half plane.

6.8. For the following functions, determine which are LC driving-point functions:

(a) $\dfrac{p^3 + p}{p^4 + 6p^2 + 8}$ (b) $\dfrac{p^4 + 3p^2 + 2}{p^3 + 3p}$ (c) $\dfrac{p^4 + 4p^2 + 3}{p^3 + 2p}$

(d) $\dfrac{p}{p^4 + p^2 + 1}$ (e) $\dfrac{(p^2 + 1)(p^2 + 3)}{(p^2 + 2)}$ (f) $\dfrac{p^3 + p^2 + p + 1}{p^2 + p}$

6.9. Develop all four canonical forms for each of the realizable functions in Prob. 6.8.

6.10. (a) Determine from the network in Fig. P6.10 $Y(p)$, and find the natural frequencies of the network.

(b) Find the other Foster's canonical form of the network.

(c) Plot the reactance function $X(\omega)$ vs. ω, where $Z(j\omega) = jX(\omega)$.

(d) Draw the corresponding network configurations (no element values) of the two Cauer's canonical forms.

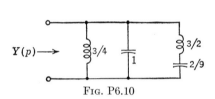

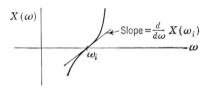

FIG. P6.10   FIG. P6.11

6.11. An LC driving-point impedance $Z(p)$ has a zero at $p = j\omega_i$. Hence the admittance, $Y(p) = 1/Z(p)$, has a pole at $j\omega_i$. Determine the relationship between the residue of $Y(p)$ at $j\omega_i$ and the slope of the reactance plot at ω_i, as shown in Fig. P6.11.

6.12. Given a p-r function $Z(p)$, what properties of $Z(p)$ are necessary so that $Z(p) - [p/(p^2 + 1) + 1]$ is again a p-r function?

6.13. A pulse-forming network can be obtained with a length of shorted transmission line, as shown in Fig. P6.13. After the switch is closed, $v(t)$ has the wave form shown. The pulse length T is twice the delay time of the transmission line l/c, where l is the length of the transmission line and c is the velocity of the electromagnetic propagation.

$$T = 2\frac{l}{c}$$

The input impedance of the shorted transmission line is a transcendental function,

$$Z_{in}(j\omega) = jZ_0 \tan \frac{l}{c}\omega$$

where Z_0 is the characteristic impedance of the line. It is desired to approximate the line with a lumped network. The problem, then, is to approximate the tangent function with a rational p-r function. One method is to express the tangent function as an infinite product.

$$\tan x = \frac{x \prod\limits_{n=1}^{\infty} (1 - x^2/n^2\pi^2)}{\prod\limits_{n=1}^{\infty} [1 - x^2/(n - \frac{1}{2})^2\pi^2]}$$

$$= \frac{x(1 - x^2/\pi^2) \cdots}{\left[1 - \dfrac{x^2}{(\pi/2)^2}\right]\left[1 - \dfrac{x^2}{(3\pi/2)^2}\right] \cdots}$$

A finite number of poles and zeros can be chosen to approximate tan x. As an example, take the first two terms from both the numerator and the denominator. For the problem at hand, the resulting function can be used to approximate $Z_{in}(j\omega)$ of the transmission line. Show that this approximation is an LC driving-point function, and develop a canonical realization for $T = 1$ μsec and $Z_0 = R = 1,000$ ohms.

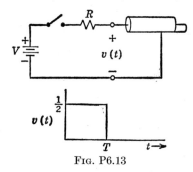

FIG. P6.13

6.14. Show how the magnitude of the transfer function changes with the choice of H for the design example of Sec. 6.7.

6.15. If the configuration of the example in Sec. 6.7 is changed to that of Fig. P6.15, develop a realization for Z.

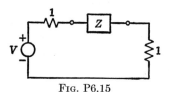

FIG. P6.15

6.16. Show that the alternation of poles and zeros for an LC driving-point function can be deduced directly from the fact that the poles lie on the $j\omega$ axis and the residues must be real and positive.

6.17. Realize the following functions as networks having only positive elements. Use successive removals of R_{min} [$= \min$ Re $Z(j\omega)$], G_{min}[$= \min$ Re $Y(j\omega)$], and/or $j\omega$-axis poles of Z or Y

(a) $\dfrac{3p + 2}{3p + 3}$　　　　(b) $\dfrac{2(p^2 + 3p + 1)}{p + 1}$　　　　(c) The function of Prob. 6.4

CHAPTER 7

THE REALIZATION OF LOSSLESS 2-PORTS—PART I

7.1 Introduction to Transfer-function Realization. For a driving-point impedance function the p-r property is a necessary and sufficient condition to ensure the physical realization of the impedance function. This is demonstrated for LC 1-ports in the last chapter. However, no such powerful restrictive criterion exists to ensure the physical realizability of a given transfer function. Certain necessary conditions must be satisfied if the function is to be a transfer function of a physical passive network. For example, from stability considerations one knows that the poles of the transfer function must lie in the left half plane or be simple if on the $j\omega$ axis. For some types of networks other necessary properties must be present. If a function has these necessary properties, a realization can be achieved. Thus the general and special properties for these types of networks are both necessary and sufficient.

A very useful class of networks is a lossless 2-port terminated at one or both ends in resistance. The realization of this class of networks is the subject of the next three chapters. In this chapter the realization of LC 2-ports with resistance loading at only one end is taken up. First, special properties of transfer functions of this type of network are determined. Then, as the initial step in the realization procedure, methods of obtaining a set of 2-port parameters are developed from a given transfer function of proper form. The development of the physical network stems from the development of these parameters.

7.2 Transmission Zeros. The poles of a transfer function defined on the basis of output over input are usually the natural frequencies of the network (see Sec. 2.3). The zeros of a transfer function are usually referred to as transmission zeros, since at a complex frequency equal to the value of a zero no transmission to the output occurs.* For a general network, not just an LC 2-port, the transmission zeros may lie anywhere in the complex-frequency plane. If all the zeros lie in the left half plane, including the $j\omega$ axis, the transfer function is said to be a *minimum-phase*

---

* It is sometimes convenient to work with the input over output function rather than with the transfer function above; the use of the terms *natural frequencies* and *transmission zeros* instead of *poles* and *zeros* prevents confusion.

101

function.[9,10]   This definition can be understood with the aid of the following example.   The two pole-zero sets shown in Fig. 7.1 are the natural frequencies and the transmission zeros of two transfer functions.   The poles of both transfer functions are the same, while the finite zero of one is the negative of the other.   The transfer functions are given by

$$T_1(p) = \frac{p + a}{(p + p_1)(p + p_2)} \tag{7.1}$$

$$T_2(p) = \frac{p - a}{(p + p_1)(p + p_2)} \tag{7.2}$$

The magnitude functions are equal.

$$|T_1(j\omega)| = \frac{|a + j\omega|}{|p_1 + j\omega|\,|p_2 + j\omega|} = \frac{|-a + j\omega|}{|p_1 + j\omega|\,|p_2 + j\omega|} = |T_2(j\omega)| \tag{7.3}$$

The phase functions, however, are different.

$$\text{Arg } T_1(j\omega) = \tan^{-1}\omega/a - \tan^{-1}\omega/p_1 - \tan^{-1}\omega/p_2$$
$$\text{Arg } T_2(j\omega) = \tan^{-1}\omega/-a - \tan^{-1}\omega/p_1 - \tan^{-1}\omega/p_2$$
$$= \pi - \tan^{-1}\omega/a - \tan^{-1}\omega/p_1 - \tan^{-1}\omega/p_2 \tag{7.4}$$

The two phase functions have the form shown in Fig. 7.2.   Notice that the phase of $T_2(j\omega)$ is greater than the corresponding value of $T_1(j\omega)$ at

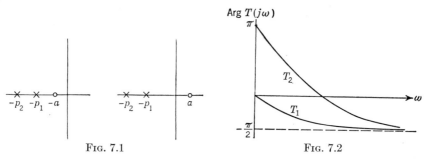

FIG. 7.1   FIG. 7.2

all positive finite frequencies.   Thus any transfer function with one or more transmission zeros in the right half plane has an excess phase in comparison with a corresponding function with only zeros in the left half plane.

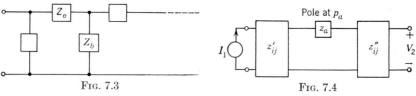

FIG. 7.3   FIG. 7.4

A simple ladder network with no-node bridging, as shown in Fig. 7.3, must have a minimum-phase transfer function.   The transmission zeros can occur in either of two ways.   Consider first a series branch z_a which has a pole at a frequency p_a, as shown in Fig. 7.4. The network to the left of z_a is characterized by the open-circuit impedance parameters z'_{ij}. The network to the right of z_a is characterized by the impedance parameters z''_{ij}. The over-all transfer function can then be written using Thévenin's theorem.

$$\frac{V_2}{I_1} = z_{21} = \frac{z'_{21} z''_{21}}{z'_{22} + z_a + z''_{11}} \tag{7.5}$$

If p_a is a pole of z_a but not a pole of the open-circuit parameters, $z_{21}(p_a) = 0$; i.e., p_a is a transmission zero. However, if p_a is also a pole of z'_{21} and/or z''_{21}, p_a is not a transmission zero; this is because of a cancellation. The same conclusions are drawn if the input is a voltage source. In a similar manner, a shunt branch y_b which has a pole at p_b, as shown in Fig. 7.5, produces a transmission zero at this frequency, provided that y'_{21} and/or y''_{21} do not also have the same pole. Since z_a and y_b are p-r functions, the poles of z_a and y_b cannot lie in the right half plane. Hence

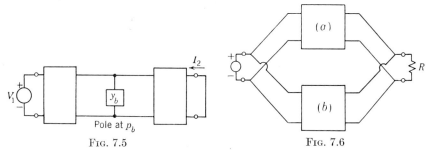

Pole at p_b

Fig. 7.5   Fig. 7.6

the transmission zeros produced in this manner cannot lie in the right half plane.

If the ladder consists of only L and C, the poles and zeros of the series and shunt networks of the ladder lie on the $j\omega$ axis. Hence all transmission zeros for this type of ladder network also lie on the $j\omega$ axis. This fact is of key importance in the realization procedure developed in this chapter. Any series or shunt LC branch of the ladder of Fig. 7.3 can produce only simple transmission zeros. However, it is possible for different series or shunt networks to have common poles and/or zeros; thus multiple-order transmission zeros on the $j\omega$ axis are possible. Infinity is a point on the $j\omega$ axis; and because multiple-order zeros are allowed on the $j\omega$ axis, the degree of a numerator of the transfer function can be any degree less than the degree of the denominator polynomial.

For a general network there is one other way in which transmission zeros can occur. If there is more than one path in the network from input to output, the transmission of one path at some frequency may be equal in magnitude but opposite in phase to that of the other path. At this frequency a transmission zero occurs, as can be seen more definitely by referring to the transfer function of the parallel combination of two 2-ports loaded at the output with resistance. This is shown in Fig. 7.6. From Table 4.1, the transfer function is

$$Y_{21} = \frac{y_{21}/R}{y_{22} + 1/R} \qquad (7.6)$$

where
$$y_{21} = y_{21a} + y_{21b}$$
$$y_{22} = y_{22a} + y_{22b} \qquad (7.7)$$

A zero of y_{21} is a zero of Y_{21}. Thus at a frequency where $y_{21a} + y_{21b} = 0$, a transmission zero occurs. Only in the case of multiple paths from input to output can transmission zeros in the right half plane be obtained. However, it should be noted that multiple paths do not always produce right half plane transmission zeros.

7.3   The Realization of a Lossless Ladder Terminated at One End in a Resistance.   Attention is now restricted to the development of a realiza-

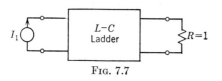

tion procedure for the configuration in Fig. 7.7. The 2-port network is a lossless ladder of the type shown in Fig. 7.3, with no-node bridging. The load resistance is set equal to unity for convenience. From

FIG. 7.7

Table 4.1, the transfer function is the transfer impedance, which is related to the open-circuit parameters as follows:

$$Z_{21} = \frac{z_{21}}{1 + z_{22}} = \frac{g(p)}{h(p)} \qquad (7.8)$$

In the last section it is shown that the transmission zeros of an LC ladder must lie on the $j\omega$ axis. The over-all transmission zeros occur at the zeros of z_{21} and at the poles of z_{22}, which are not common with poles of z_{21}. The numerator polynomial $g(p)$ must be either an even or an odd polynomial, as is shown below; $h(p)$ must be a Hurwitz polynomial of degree equal to or greater than the degree of $g(p)$. If a given transfer impedance satisfies these two properties, a physical realization can always be determined.

In order to obtain expressions for z_{22} and z_{21} from the given transfer impedance Z_{21}, one should first note from the last chapter that the ratio of the even to the odd parts of a Hurwitz polynomial is an LC impedance function. Thus if

$$h = A + pB \qquad (7.9)$$

(7.8) can be rewritten as

$$Z_{21} = \frac{g/pB}{1 + A/pB} \quad \text{or} \quad \frac{g/A}{1 + pB/A} \qquad (7.10)$$

z_{22} can be identified as either A/pB or pB/A. The question now arises whether z_{21} of the LC ladder can be either g/pB or g/A.

To determine the necessary properties of z_{21}, a general LC 2-port is considered.   From Chaps. 2 and 4, the poles of z_{21} are the natural frequencies of the open-circuit 2-port.   The poles of z_{11} and z_{22} must include the natural frequencies but may have extra poles which are due to series branches at the input and the output, as shown in Fig. 7.8. The poles due to these series branches are clearly not natural frequencies of the open-circuit 2-port.   Thus the poles of z_{21} must be included in the poles of z_{11} and z_{22}, but the converse is not true.

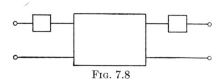

FIG. 7.8

Finally, it is shown that z_{21} must be an odd function.   A partial fraction expansion of z_{21} is of the form

$$z_{21}(p) = \frac{k_0}{p} + \frac{k_1}{p - j\omega_1} + \frac{\bar{k}_1}{p + j\omega_1} + \cdots + k_\infty p \qquad (7.11)$$

Poles at the origin and infinity are included for completeness.   For an LC network, all currents in the network must be in phase with one another and all voltages must be in quadrature phase.*   Hence, for a current input I_1,

$$\text{Arg} \left. \frac{V_2}{I_1} \right|_{p=j\omega} = \text{Arg } z_{21}(j\omega) = \pm \frac{\pi}{2}$$

or

$$\text{Re } [z_{21}(j\omega)] = 0 \qquad (7.12)$$

If the real part of (7.11) is taken, the contribution from a typical conjugate pair is

$$\text{Re} \left[\frac{k_1}{p - j\omega_1} + \frac{\bar{k}_1}{p + j\omega_1} \right] = \text{Re} \left[\frac{(k_1 + \bar{k}_1)p + j\omega_1(k_1 - \bar{k}_1)}{p^2 + \omega_1^2} \right]$$

$$= \text{Re} \left[\frac{j\omega(k_1 + \bar{k}_1)}{\omega_1^2 - \omega^2} + \frac{j\omega_1(k_1 - \bar{k}_1)}{\omega_1^2 - \omega^2} \right] = \frac{-2\omega_1 \text{ Im } k_1}{\omega_1^2 - \omega^2} \qquad (7.13)$$

From (7.12) and (7.13) it is seen that the residue k_1 must be real.   The typical conjugate pair becomes

$$\frac{2k_1 p}{p^2 + \omega_1^2}$$

---

* This statement is simply proved from a general analysis of an LC network in the sinusoidal steady state.   For example, the determinant of a set of nodal equations has only imaginary elements.   The value of the determinant is either purely imaginary or purely real.   Any cofactors of the determinant are therefore purely real or purely imaginary.   Hence any voltage in the network is in quadrature phase with the current source.   Any branch current must be in phase or out of phase with the current source.

which is an odd function. Therefore from (7.11) z_{21} must be an odd function. Note that the residues need not be positive. This is in contrast to the situation for a driving-point LC function.

Returning now to (7.10), one can make a proper choice to obtain the necessary properties of z_{21} and z_{22}. If $g(p)$ is an odd function the choice must be

$$z_{21} = \frac{g}{A} \qquad z_{22} = \frac{pB}{A} \qquad\qquad (7.14)$$

If $g(p)$ is an even function

$$z_{21} = \frac{g}{pB} \qquad z_{22} = \frac{A}{pB} \qquad\qquad (7.15)$$

In (7.14) and (7.15) the z_{21} and z_{22} have the same poles unless a cancellation occurs and the z_{21} in both cases are odd.

In the realization of the transfer impedance for this type of network, z_{11} is not specified. The problem is therefore to develop a 2-port which has the specified z_{22} and z_{21}. This is accomplished through a realization of z_{22} by a pole-removal technique. The zeros of z_{21} are transmission zeros, which in turn correspond to the poles of the series-impedance branches or the poles of the shunt-admittance branches of the ladder. Hence at each step in the development of z_{22} a pole is removed which corresponds to a zero of z_{21}. As shown in a later section, it may be necessary to introduce surplus elements in order to obtain the desired poles in the remainders of the z_{22} development.

7.4 Examples of Z_{21} Synthesis. For an example of the realization procedure developed in the last section, a transfer impedance is realized which is to have a three-pole low-pass maximally flat magnitude characteristic. From Chap. 3

$$Z_{21} = \frac{H}{p^3 + 2p^2 + 2p + 1} \qquad\qquad (7.16)$$

which has three transmission zeros at infinity. Since $g(p) = H$, which is even, (7.15) is used to obtain z_{21} and z_{22}.

$$z_{21} = \frac{H}{p^3 + 2p}$$
$$z_{22} = \frac{2p^2 + 1}{p^3 + 2p} \qquad\qquad (7.17)$$

z_{21} has three zeros at infinity. Hence in the development of z_{22} three poles at infinity must be removed. It should be remembered that in the first type of continued-fraction-expansion realization in the last chapter only poles at infinity are removed. Therefore this expansion is used to develop z_{22}. The network is as shown in Fig. 7.9.

In this realization no cognizance is taken of the value of H, since it does not appear in z_{22}.   For a specified load resistance, a specified value of H cannot be realized unless an ideal transformer is used. As a practical matter, however, the value of H obtained is not important, since only the form of Z_{21} is of major interest.

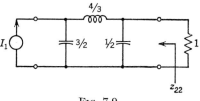

Fig. 7.9

For a transfer impedance which is to have a three-pole maximally flat magnitude characteristic at infinite frequency

$$Z_{21} = \frac{Hp^3}{p^3 + 2p^2 + 2p + 1} \tag{7.18}$$

(This function can be obtained from the previous example by making a variable transformation $p = 1/p'$, where p' is the low-pass variable.) Z_{21} in this case has three transmission zeros at the origin and none at infinity.   Hence it is called a high-pass function.   Since $g(p)$ is an odd function, (7.14) is used to obtain z_{21} and z_{22}.

$$z_{21} = \frac{Hp^3}{2p^2 + 1}$$
$$z_{22} = \frac{p^3 + 2p}{2p^2 + 1} \tag{7.19}$$

Three poles at the origin must be removed from z_{22} or the remainders to obtain the proper transmission zeros.   Pole removal at the origin is used in the second continued-fraction-expansion realization in the last chapter.   The network realization is shown in Fig. 7.10.

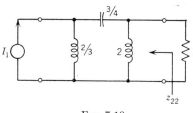

Fig. 7.10

The conventional continued fraction expansions cannot be used if the given transfer impedance has transmission zeros at both the origin and infinity.   For example, let

$$Z_{21} = \frac{Hp}{p^3 + 2p^2 + 2p + 1} \tag{7.20}$$

The necessary open-circuit impedances are

$$z_{21} = \frac{Hp}{2p^2 + 1}$$
$$z_{22} = \frac{p^3 + 2p}{2p^2 + 1} \tag{7.21}$$

It should be noticed that z_{21} has one zero at the origin and one zero at infinity, while Z_{21} has one transmission zero at the origin and two at infinity. The extra transmission zero at infinity is produced by the pole of z_{22} at infinity which is not present in z_{21}. The extra pole in z_{22} not present in z_{21} indicates that there is a series impedance at the output side

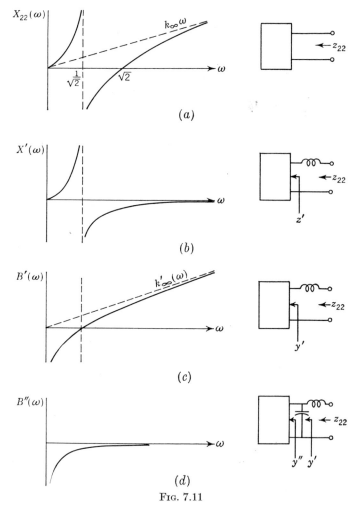

Fig. 7.11

of the 2 port, i.e., a private branch. In developing the physical realization, it is helpful to use a sequence of reactance plots of z_{22} and its remainders. With these plots it is easy to visualize which poles are to be removed to provide the desired transmission zeros. In the case at hand, it is necessary to remove from z_{22} or its remainders two poles at infinity and one pole at the origin.

The reactance plot of $z_{22}(j\omega) = jX_{22}(\omega)$ is shown in Fig. 7.11a.   There is a pole at infinity which can be removed as a series inductance having a value equal to the residue of z_{22} at infinity.   The reactance plot corresponding to this inductance is shown as the dashed line in Fig. 7.11a. The remainder function is

$$z' = z_{22} - k_\infty p = \frac{p^3 + 2p}{2p^2 + 1} - \frac{1}{2}p = \frac{\frac{3}{2}p}{2p^2 + 1} \tag{7.22}$$

The reactance plot of $z'(j\omega) = jX'(\omega)$ is given in Fig. 7.11b.   This same plot is obtained if the dashed curve is subtracted from the solid curve of Fig. 7.11a. z' does not contain a pole either at the origin or at infinity. But its reciprocal $y' = 1/z'$ contains poles at both the origin and infinity. The susceptance plot of $y'(j\omega) = jB'(\omega)$ is given in Fig. 7.11c.   Another pole at infinity can be removed, since two transmission zeros at infinity are needed.   This can be accomplished in a manner similar to that used above and results in a shunt capacitance.

$$y'' = y' - k'_\infty p = \frac{2p^2 + 1}{\frac{3}{2}p} - \frac{4}{3}p = \frac{2}{3p} \tag{7.23}$$

The susceptance plot of the remainder $y''(j\omega) = jB''(\omega)$ is shown in Fig.

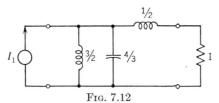

FIG. 7.12

7.11d.   The remaining function has only a pole at the origin, which can be removed as a shunt inductance to complete the realization.   The network is shown in Fig. 7.12.

A numerical procedure comparable to that used in the conventional continued fraction expansion follows:

$$2p^2 + 1 \,\overline{\big)\, p^3 + 2p} \;\big|\; \tfrac{1}{2}p \text{—Pole removal at infinity}$$

$$\underline{p^3 + \tfrac{1}{2}p}$$

$$\tfrac{3}{2}p \,\overline{\big)\, 2p^2 + 1} \;\big|\; \tfrac{4}{3}p + \frac{2}{3p} \text{—Pole removal at origin}$$

$$\underline{2p^2 + 1} \qquad \text{Pole removal at infinity}$$

$$0\text{—Open-circuit remainder}$$

The last example to be taken up in this section is the realization of a transfer impedance with two transmission zeros at the origin and one at infinity.

$$Z_{21} = \frac{Hp^2}{p^3 + 2p^2 + 2p + 1}$$

$$z_{21} = \frac{Hp^2}{p^3 + 2p} = \frac{Hp}{p^2 + 2} \qquad (7.24)$$

$$z_{22} = \frac{2p^2 + 1}{p^3 + 2p}$$

If the same process is used as in the previous example, the network in Fig. 7.13 is obtained.

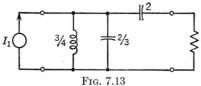

FIG. 7.13

7.5 Zero-shifting Realization Technique. For a ladder network the numerator $g(p)$ of the given $Z_{21}(p)$ is restricted to having zeros on the $j\omega$ axis. If the zeros do not all occur at infinity and the origin, the procedure followed in the last section must be modified. To produce transmission zeros on the finite $j\omega$ axis (e.g., $\pm j\omega_i$), a pair of conjugate poles at $\pm j\omega_i$ must be removed. This removal takes the form

$$\frac{2k_i p}{p^2 + \omega_i^2} \qquad (7.25)$$

and leads to a series-tuned circuit for removal from an admittance and a parallel-tuned circuit for removal from an impedance. A problem arises because the poles of z_{22} or any of its remainders usually do not occur at the desired transmission zeros. The desired pole locations are provided by introducing redundant elements and a technique known as zero shifting. This type of realization is shown in the following example.

Let the specified transfer impedance be

$$Z_{21} = H \frac{p^2 + 4}{p^3 + 2p^2 + 2p + 1} \qquad (7.26)$$

There are transmission zeros at $p = \pm j2$ and infinity. Since the numerator is an even function,

$$z_{22} = \frac{2p^2 + 1}{p^3 + 2p} \qquad \text{and} \qquad z_{21} = \frac{p^2 + 4}{p^3 + 2p} \qquad (7.27)$$

The reactance plot of z_{22} and its development are shown in Fig. 7.14. z_{22} does not have either poles or zeros at $\pm j2$; however, the reciprocal of z_{22} has a pole at infinity. The removal of this pole with a shunt capacitance is allowable, since a transmission zero must be produced at infinity. The value of the capacitance is $\frac{1}{2}$. The remainder function y' is

$$y' = \frac{\frac{3}{2}p}{2p^2 + 1} \qquad (7.28)$$

y' does not have poles at the transmission zeros $\pm j2$. Neither does its reciprocal z'. The reactance plot $z'(j\omega) = jX'$ is shown in Fig. 7.14d. z' has a pole at infinity with a residue equal to $\frac{4}{3}$. If an inductance with a value less than $\frac{4}{3}$ is removed, the pole at infinity is not removed; how-

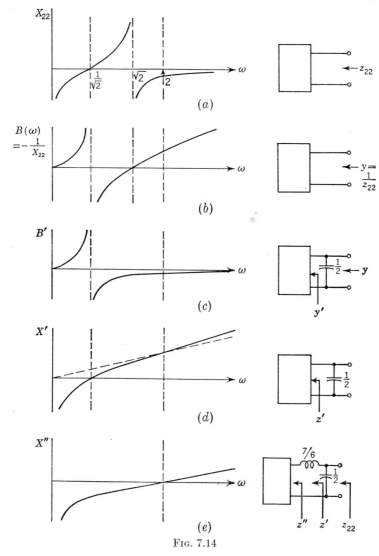

FIG. 7.14

ever, the zero at $j1/\sqrt{2}$ is shifted to the right. For the case at hand, it is desirable to shift the zero to $+j2$. The reciprocal of the new remainder then has a pole at this frequency, which can be removed to produce the desired transmission zeros. The value of the inductance necessary to produce the above shift can be determined as follows:

$$pL|_{p=j2} = z'(p)|_{p=j2}$$
$$L = \frac{z'(j2)}{j2} = \frac{7}{6} \tag{7.29}$$

The above equation corresponds to the crossover point of the reactance plots of $X'(\omega)$ and ωL, shown in Fig. 7.14d. The remainder function is

$$z'' = z' - \frac{7}{6}p = \frac{p^2 + 4}{6p} \tag{7.30}$$

Its reactance plot is shown in Fig. 7.14e. Notice that z'' has the desired

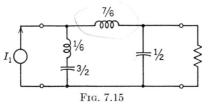

FIG. 7.15

zeros at $p = \pm j2$. The reciprocal of z'' has a pole pair at $\pm j2$ and is removed as a series LC network. The value of L is $\frac{1}{6}$ and the value of C is $\frac{3}{2}$. The final remainder is zero on the admittance basis, which is compatible with the presence of a current source for the 2-port. The complete network is shown in Fig. 7.15.

Attention is now redirected to the series-inductance removal, i.e., the zero-shifting step. The pole at infinity of z' is only "partially" removed. That is, an impedance function $\frac{7}{6}p$ is removed whose residue at the pole at infinity is less than the residue, $\frac{4}{3}$, of z' at infinity. Thus z'' also has a pole at infinity. From the arguments of Sec. 7.2 [see Eq. (7.5)], pL does not produce a transmission zero at infinity. This follows because z'' also has a pole at the same frequency as does z_{21} (the transfer imped- ance of the remaining network).

Another network realization can be obtained if the shifting step is taken directly with $1/z_{22}$. The shifting step consists in a "partial" removal of the pole at infinity with a shunt capacitance. The value of the capacitance should be such as to produce zeros of the remainder function at $\pm j2$. Transmission zeros at these frequencies are pro- duced by a total pole removal from the reciprocal. This takes the form

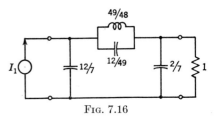

FIG. 7.16

of the LC series branch shown in Fig. 7.16. The final step is the removal of a pole at infinity with a shunt capacitance.

In the above examples, and in general, the zero being shifted always moves toward the pole being "partially" removed.* This is understand-

* If negative elements in the shifting branch are used, the zero can be shifted away from the pole. The negative inductive element can often be realized with perfectly coupled inductances (see Prob. 8.8).

able, since a total removal of the pole produces for an LC network a zero at the pole location.   A partial removal, then, takes the zero only part way.

With the above in mind, it is possible and often necessary to make a partial removal from interior poles. As an example, assume that the desired transmission zeros (7.26) are at $\pm j1$ and not at $\pm j2$.   One network realization has the form of Fig. 7.15.   However, an all-positive element realization in the form of Fig. 7.16 is not possible.   If the shift-

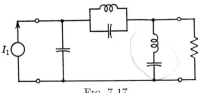

FIG. 7.17

ing step is to be the initial step in the development of $1/z_{22}$, a partial removal must be made from the poles at $p = \pm j1/\sqrt{2}$.   This shifting branch is the series LC network shown in Fig. 7.17, which has a resonant frequency $\pm j1/\sqrt{2}$.   The admittance of this branch at $\pm j1$ must have a value equal to $1/z_{22}(j1)$.

$$\left. \frac{p/L}{p^2 + 1/LC} \right|_{p=j1} = \frac{1}{z_{22}}(j1) \qquad (7.31)$$

where $1/LC = \frac{1}{2}$.   Thus the L and C can be determined.   The succeeding steps in the realization are total removal steps to produce the desired transmission zeros.

7.6   General Remarks.   The examples in the last two sections illustrate that a transfer-function realization is possible in the form of a lossless ladder terminated at one end in resistance.   The necessary and sufficient conditions that must be satisfied are

(a) The poles of Z_{21} all lie in the left half plane.

(b) The zeros of Z_{21} lie only on the $j\omega$ axis.   If the restriction to simple ladders is removed, condition (b) is replaced by the statement:

(b') The numerator polynomial must be either odd or even.   In this case the zeros may lie in the complex plane provided that the zeros have quadrangle symmetry with respect to the σ and $j\omega$ axes.   The realization of these transfer impedances is not taken up here but in general involves the use of mutual inductances and ideal transformers.*   In certain special cases the realization may take the practical form of simple ladders in parallel.

It is left as an exercise for the reader to duplicate the realization procedure of this chapter for a transfer-admittance (Y_{21}) specification.   It should also be noted that the developments in Sec. 4.5 can be used for the realization of the situations illustrated in Fig. 7.18.

---

* S. Darlington, Synthesis of Reactance Four-poles Which Produce Prescribed Insertion Loss Characteristics, *J. Math. and Phys.*, vol. 18, pp. 257–353, September, 1939.

In the configurations of Figs. 7.7 and 7.18 it is assumed that the sources are ideal current and voltage sources and the loads are open circuit, short circuit, or furnished by a single resistance.   In practice a much greater application can be made.   First, the actual source may have a finite resistance or conductance.   These finite source resistances can be used to furnish, totally or in part, the required terminating resistances of the lossless 2-port, as in Fig. 7.18a, b, d, and e.   In addition, a source may contain a single inductance, a single capacitance, a resistance and an inductance, or a resistance and a capacitance. For these types of sources the reactive elements can be associated with the LC 2-port. The realization procedure must then ensure that these elements are present.   The same holds true for the load.   That is, the load may consist of single resistance and/or reactive elements.   As an example, in the design of pentode-amplifier coupling networks, the input and output capacitances furnished by the pentode can be incorporated into lossless coupling networks.   This is done in the example in Sec. 3.5.

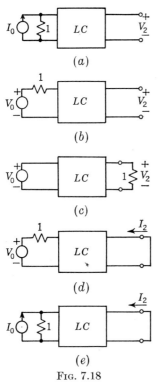

(a)

(b)

(c)

(d)

(e)

Fig. 7.18

It should be remembered that the plate resistance of a pentode is finite.   However, its value is so large that most often it can be ignored.   That is, the pentode can be approximated as an ideal current source in parallel with capacitance.   This type of approximation can also be used for other source and load situations, where the source or load resistance is several orders of magnitude greater than the specified terminating resistance. Going to the other extreme, an actual source or load resistance may be neglected if it is several orders of magnitude smaller than the specified terminating resistance.

7.7   Incidental Dissipation.   In the practical realization of an LC network, resistance (i.e., dissipation) is unavoidable.   Primarily, this is due to the presence of resistance in any actual inductance.   The loss of modern capacitors is usually negligible.   The presence of this resistance distorts the transfer function of the actual network realization in comparison with the lossless design.   Often this distortion is small enough to be neglected.   However, in many cases, e.g., in very narrow band filters, the distortion is intolerable.   In this section a predistortion method is introduced which may compensate for the unavoidable resistances.[10]

To see the effect of incidental dissipation, consider first an LC network
to which is added a series resistance
with each inductance and a parallel
conductance to each capacitance.
This is shown in Fig. 7.19 for the
circuit of Fig. 7.9. Added for each
original element is a resistance or
conductance such that the ratio of

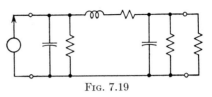

FIG. 7.19

R/L or G/C is equal to the same constant d. The impedance of an
original inductance becomes the impedance of a series R, L branch:

$$Lp \rightarrow Lp + R = L(p + d) \tag{7.32}$$

The admittance of an original capacitance becomes the admittance of a
shunt G, C branch:

$$Cp \rightarrow Cp + G = C(p + d) \tag{7.33}$$

Note that (7.32) and (7.33) involve a transformation of variable. Thus
the original $Z_{21}(p)$ becomes $Z_{21}(p + d)$ with the addition of the resistances. In terms of the locations of the poles, a translation of $-d$ is
obtained as resistances are added. This is shown in Fig. 7.20. This
uniform shift of the poles with
dissipation leads to a predistortion
technique. It should be noted that
the Q of a coil is related to the
constant d.

$$Q = \frac{\omega L}{R} = \frac{\omega}{d} \tag{7.34}$$

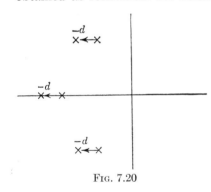

FIG. 7.20

Data on the Qs are readily available in many handbooks.* In most
practical inductors, Q is not linear
with frequency. However, over a
given bandwidth, the deviation from linearity may not be too severe
and a linear approximation can be made. Thus for a certain type of coil
construction and the band-edge frequencies of the transfer-function
specification, one can find an appropriate value of Q, hence d, for this
frequency range. In the predistortion technique, the pole-zero locations
that result from an approximation problem are shifted to the right by
the amount d. A lossless network design is realized from the shifted
pole-zero locations. In the actual construction of the network, the
loss of the inductances and the capacitances is adjusted by adding
resistances as appropriate to achieve a uniform d. Hence, the actual

* F. E. Terman, "Radio Engineers' Handbook," pp. 74–77, McGraw-Hill Book
Company, Inc., New York, 1943.

network provides the desired pole-zero locations as obtained from the approximation problem.

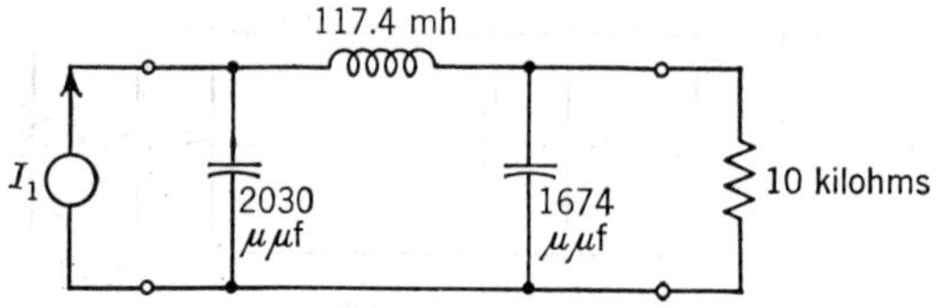

117.4 mh

I_1

2030 $\mu\mu f$

1674 $\mu\mu f$

10 kilohms

FIG. 7.21

As an example, a three-pole equal-ripple low-pass magnitude transfer impedance is desired to have a 3-db tolerance bandwidth at 15.9 kc and a d-c level of approximately 10 kilohms. From Chap. 3, the pole locations are

$$p = \frac{-0.2986 \times 10^5}{(-0.1493 \pm j0.9038) \times 10^5} \qquad (7.35)$$

The network realization for ideal elements is shown in Fig. 7.21. Assume now that Q of the coil at the upper band edge is 20. With dissipation the magnitude response is distorted. In the passband the magnitude does not have an equal-ripple behavior. In Fig. 7.22 the original and the distorted magnitude curves are plotted on the decibel scale as curves (1) and (2), respectively.

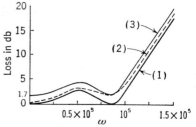

FIG. 7.22. Curve (1) no dissipation; (2) coil with $Q = 20$ at $w = 10^5$; (3) redesign using predistortion.

To compensate for the coil Q, a redesign using predistortion is made. For a Q of 20 at $\omega = 10^5$ the value of d is 5×10^3. The predistorted pole locations are

$$\begin{array}{c} -(0.2986 - 0.05) \times 10^5 \\ [-(0.1493 - 0.05) \pm j.9038] \times 10^5 \end{array} \qquad (7.36)$$

The new network design is shown in Fig. 7.23. The added shunt resistances are determined from the new values of the capacitances and the value of d above. For example,

$$\frac{G_1}{C_1} = \frac{G_2}{C_2} = d \qquad G_1 = 10.28 \; \mu\text{mhos} \qquad G_2 = 11.18 \; \mu\text{mhos} \qquad (7.37)$$

With this redesign using the predistortion technique, the magnitude behavior becomes equal ripple again. However, owing to the added resistances, a flat loss of about 1.7 db is introduced. This is shown in

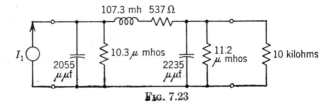

107.3 mh   537 Ω

I_1

2055 $\mu\mu f$

10.3 μ mhos

2235 $\mu\mu f$

11.2 μ mhos

10 kilohms

FIG. 7.23

curve (3) of Fig. 7.22.   It should also be noted that the value of d is chosen for the original network.   Since d depends on the value of the inductance and the value of the inductance has changed, the value of d used is only approximately correct.

Often the flat loss and the number of additional elements are too expensive in relation to the amount of distortion to be corrected.   In this case an approximate form of the predistortion technique is used. The actual coils of a circuit have approximately the same Q, i.e., the same d factor.   The actual capacitances introduce no loss, i.e., zero d factor. If no additional loss is added, an approximate predistortion is achieved, provided the average value $d/2$ is used to shift the poles and zeros.

PROBLEMS

7.1. Determine the location and the order of the transmission zeros of the networks in Fig. P7.1.   Indicate which have transfer functions that are minimum phase.

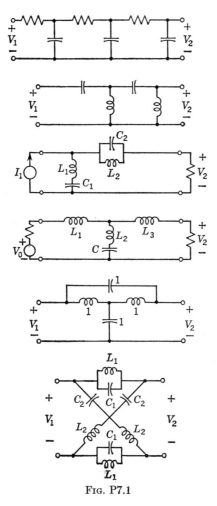

FIG. P7.1

7.2. Determine Z_{21} for the networks in Fig. P7.2a and b. Plot the locations of the transmission zeros. Are these minimum-phase networks? (Note that network b is a ladder network.)

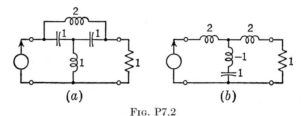

(a)   (b)

FIG. P7.2

7.3. Given

$$(a)\ Z_{21} = \frac{Hp^4}{(p+1)^4} \quad \text{and} \quad (b)\ Z_{21} = \frac{H}{(p+1)^4}$$

where are the transmission zeros? Determine z_{21} and z_{22}. Synthesize the functions as ladder networks terminated at the output by 1-ohm resistances. Determine the constant multipliers. If the H for both networks is specified to be equal to 2, how can realizations be achieved?

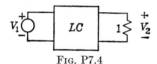

FIG. P7.4

7.4. If the functions in Prob. 7.3 are the voltage transfer ratio V_2/V_1, as shown in Fig. P7.4, realize the networks and determine H.

7.5. Synthesize a network to realize

$$Y_{21} = \frac{Hp^2}{(p+1)^4}$$

7.6. Which of the following sets of specifications can be realized as a lossless 2-port either terminated at one end in resistance or unterminated?

$$(a)\ Z_{21} = \frac{p^2+1}{p^2+ap+b} \qquad (b)\ Z_{21} = \frac{p+1}{p^2+ap+b} \qquad (c)\ z_{21} = \frac{p}{p^2+1}$$

$$(d)\ z_{21} = \frac{1}{p^2+1} \qquad\qquad (e)\ z_{21} = \frac{p^3+2p}{p^2+1} \qquad (f)\ Z_{21} = \frac{p^2-1}{p^2+ap+b}$$

$$z_{22} = \frac{p^2+\frac{1}{2}}{p(p^2+1)} \qquad\qquad z_{22} = \frac{2p}{p^2+1}$$

$$(g)\ z_{21} = \frac{p^2-a}{p}$$

$$z_{22} = \frac{p^2+a}{p}$$

7.7. Given the function

$$F(p) = \frac{p^2+2}{p^4+3p^3+4p^2+3p+1}$$

(a) Show that $F(p)$ can be realized as the transfer impedance Z_{21} of a lossless ladder terminated at one end in a resistance of 1 ohm.

(b) Develop three configurations which will realize $F(p) = Z_{21}$ with all elements positive. For each development show reactance and susceptance plots.

7.8. Given

$$y_{22} = \frac{5p^4 + 5p^2 + 1}{3p^3 + 2p}$$

develop a lossless ladder which has second-order transmission zeros at $p = \pm j1$.

7.9. Given

$$f(p) = \frac{p^2 + 2}{(p + 1)(p^2 + 2p + 2)}$$

can $f(p)$ be realized as the transfer function of a lossless ladder terminated at one end in 1 ohm? If so, realize the function in the two forms shown in Fig. P7.9a and b. If the zeros of $f(p)$ are changed to lie at $\pm j\frac{1}{2}$, realize the new $f(p)$, as shown in Fig. P7.9c. Determine the constant H for each realization.

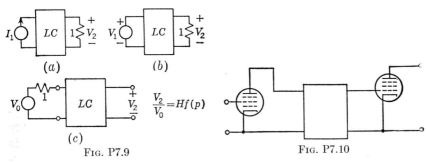

Fig. P7.9   Fig. P7.10

7.10. An interstage network (Fig. P7.10) is desired to realize a three-pole maximally flat delay response. The network must incorporate the input and output capacitances of the pentode. Realize the interstage to achieve a 3-db bandwidth of 1 Mc and with $C_{\text{out}} = 5\mu\mu f$ and $C_{\text{in}} = 10\mu\mu f$. Some capacitance padding is necessary. Determine the d-c gain $(V_{g2}/V_{g1})(0)$ and the gain-bandwidth product for a g_m of 0.005 mho. Show that the maximum gain-bandwidth product is obtained if padding capacitance is added at one end only.

7.11. For the circuit of Prob. 7.10 assume that the inductance has a $Q = 50$ at 1 Mc. Determine the new transfer impedance and the pole locations. What is the d-c gain $(V_{g2}/V_{g1})(0)$?

7.12. Use the predistortion technique to redesign the circuit of Fig. 7.10. Add shunt conductances to achieve uniform dissipation. The Q of the coil at 1 Mc is again 50.

CHAPTER 8

TOPICS IN THE SYNTHESIS OF BANDPASS LADDERS

8.1 Introduction: Low-pass to High-pass Transformation. The realization procedures developed in the last chapter are applicable to low-pass, bandpass, and high-pass specifications. However, the approximation criteria introduced in Chap. 3 are restricted to the low-pass situation. In this chapter it is shown how to transform low-pass criteria so that they can be applied to either the high-pass or the bandpass situation. In addition, it is shown that low-pass networks can be transformed into high-pass or bandpass networks.

The low-pass to high-pass transformation is introduced in earlier chapters. In the high-pass case, the passband extends from some frequency ω_c to infinity. As in the low-pass case, the band-edge frequency ω_c is defined as that frequency where the response is down to a certain percentage of the maximum value in the passband, e.g., the -3-db frequency. A low-pass criterion can be transformed to a high-pass criterion through the use of the transformation

$$s = \frac{\omega_c^2}{p} \tag{8.1}$$

where $p = \sigma + j\omega$ represents the frequency variable in the high-pass situation and $s = u + jv$ is the frequency variable in the low-pass. Notice that the origin in the low-pass plane corresponds to infinity in the high-pass. In addition, the imaginary axis jv in the s plane transforms into the imaginary axis $j\omega$ in the p plane. From (8.1)

$$u + jv = \frac{\omega_c^2}{\sigma + j\omega} = \omega_c^2 \left(\frac{\sigma}{\sigma^2 + \omega^2} - j \frac{\omega}{\sigma^2 + \omega^2} \right) \tag{8.2}$$

For $u = 0$, $\sigma = 0$,

$$jv = -j \frac{\omega_c^2}{\omega} \tag{8.3}$$

The negative sign in (8.3) indicates that the positive jv axis transforms into the negative $j\omega$ axis. For a given network function in the low-pass domain $N(jv)$, the transformed magnitude and phase functions are, using (8.3),

$$|N(j\omega)| = \left| N\left(-j\frac{\omega_c^2}{v}\right) \right| = \left| N\left(j\frac{\omega_c^2}{v}\right) \right|$$

$$\beta(\omega) = \beta\left(-\frac{\omega_c^2}{v}\right) = -\beta\left(\frac{\omega_c^2}{v}\right)$$

(8.4)

Thus a low-pass function having certain properties on the positive jv axis about the origin transforms into a high-pass function having the same properties on the negative $j\omega$ axis about infinity.

A low-pass function with a maximally flat magnitude characteristic at the origin transforms into a high-pass function with a maximally flat characteristic at infinity. The constant ω_c can be chosen to transform from a given low-pass band edge v_a to a specified high-pass band edge ω_b. From (8.3) and (8.4)

$$\omega_c^2 = \omega_b v_a$$

(8.5)

In the actual design of a high-pass network it is usually convenient to develop a low-pass prototype directly from the low-pass specification. The transformation (8.1) is applied directly to the impedances and admittances of the low-pass network to obtain the high-pass network. The impedance of an inductance in the low-pass network sL transforms into $\omega_c^2 L/p$, i.e., the impedance of a capacitance in the high-pass network of value $C_h = 1/\omega_c^2 L$. Similarly, capacitance of value C in the low-pass network is transformed into inductance of value $L_h = 1/\omega_c^2 C$. Resistances are not functions of frequency; hence they are invariant in the transformation. As an illustration of these procedures, the reader should compare the networks in Figs. 7.9 and 7.10. Both networks have 3-db frequencies $\omega_c = 1$.

8.2 Low-pass to Bandpass Transformation. In a manner similar to that just used, bandpass criteria and/or bandpass networks can be obtained from a suitable transformation. The transformation is illustrated by a simple example. The admittance of a parallel GLC circuit is

$$Y(p) = pC + \frac{1}{pL} + G$$

(8.6)

By a simple manipulation

$$Y(p) = C\omega_0\left(\frac{p}{\omega_0} + \frac{\omega_0}{p}\right) + G$$

(8.7)

In (8.7), $\omega_0 = 1/\sqrt{LC}$ is the resonance frequency of the circuit and is the frequency where the magnitude $|Y(j\omega)|$ is a minimum. If a transformation of variables is used:

$$s = \omega_0\left(\frac{p}{\omega_0} + \frac{\omega_0}{p}\right)$$

(8.8)

(8.7) becomes

$$Y = Cs + G$$

(8.9)

This can be recognized as the admittance of a shunt RC circuit in a new frequency domain; the s domain $= u + jv$. Since the GLC circuit constitutes the bandpass situation and the RC circuit a low-pass situation, (8.8) effects a low-pass to bandpass transformation. It is convenient to normalize the frequency variable p with respect to ω_0, i.e., $\omega_0 = 1$. Equation (8.8) becomes

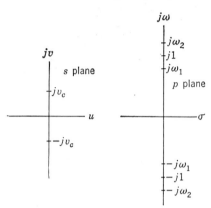

FIG. 8.1

$$s = p + \frac{1}{p} \qquad (8.10)$$

It can now be shown that the low-pass interval $-v_c$ to $+v_c$ in the s plane is transformed into the two bandpass intervals ω_1 to ω_2 and $-\omega_2$ to $-\omega_1$ in the p plane, as shown in Fig. 8.1. Solving for p in (8.10) in terms of s, one obtains

$$p = \frac{s}{2} \pm \sqrt{\left(\frac{s}{2}\right)^2 - 1} \qquad (8.11)$$

The imaginary axis in the s plane, $s = jv$, is transformed to the imaginary axis in the p plane, $p = j\omega$.

$$p = j\left[\frac{v}{2} \pm \sqrt{1 + \left(\frac{v}{2}\right)^2}\right] = 0 + j\omega \qquad (8.12)$$

$$\omega = \frac{v}{2} \pm \sqrt{1 + \left(\frac{v}{2}\right)^2}$$

Any point v_1 is transformed into two points on the $j\omega$ axis. For example

v	ω
0	± 1
v_c	$\omega_2 = \frac{v_c}{2} + \sqrt{1 + \left(\frac{v_c}{2}\right)^2}$
	and
	$-\omega_1 = \frac{v_c}{2} - \sqrt{1 + \left(\frac{v_c}{2}\right)^2}$
$-v_c$	$\omega_1 = -\frac{v_c}{2} + \sqrt{1 + \left(\frac{v_c}{2}\right)^2}$
	and
	$-\omega_2 = -\frac{v_c}{2} - \sqrt{1 + \left(\frac{v_c}{2}\right)^2}$
∞	0
	and
	∞ [seen most easily from (8.10)]

Note that there exists a one-to-one correspondence between the low-pass interval $-v_c$ to v_c and either of the bandpass intervals in the p plane. For practical reasons one always deals with the interval in the upper half plane. From the above example it is seen that the product of the transformed frequencies ω_1 and ω_2 is equal to unity; i.e., the geometric mean of the transformed frequencies is the center frequency. In unnormalized form

$$\omega_0 = \sqrt{\omega_1 \omega_2} \qquad (8.13)$$

The difference $\omega_2 - \omega_1$ is equal to v_c. Thus the low-pass bandwidth is equal to the bandpass bandwidth. Because of the one-to-one correspondence it should be clear that if a low-pass function has a value at a particular frequency v_1, the transformed function will have the same value at the frequency corresponding to v_1.

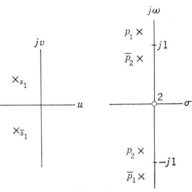

FIG. 8.2

To generalize: any point in the s plane transforms into two points in the p plane. If the point in the s plane is in the neighborhood of the origin, the transformed points are in the neighborhood of $\pm j1$ in the p plane. Thus a pole-zero set in s in the vicinity of the origin ($|s| < 1$) transforms into a pole-zero set in the neighborhood of $+j1$ and a pole-zero set in the neighborhood of $-j1$. A complex pair of poles or zeros in the s plane transforms into complex conjugate pairs of poles or zeros in the p plane, as shown in Fig. 8.2. It should be pointed out that zeros at infinity in s transform into an equal number at both the origin and infinity in the p plane. It is thus possible to find the poles and zeros of a bandpass function corresponding to a low-pass transmission criterion, e.g., the maximally flat magnitude characteristic. From this function and the methods of the last chapter a bandpass network can be realized. However, a simpler method is to realize a low-pass network initially and then transform the reactive elements of this network through Eq. (8.8). A capacitance in the

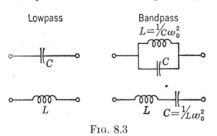

FIG. 8.3

low-pass circuit transforms into a shunt LC combination, and an inductance transforms into a series LC combination, as shown in Fig. 8.3.

As an example, assume that a bandpass network is desired which will have a two-pole maximally flat magnitude response with -3-db frequencies at 80 and 125 kc. The term *bandpass two-pole* denotes that two poles are desired in the vicinity of $j\omega_0$ (there also are, of course, the conjugate poles; therefore the transfer function has four poles). The center frequency f_0 is the geometric mean of the band-edge frequencies. $f_0 = 100$ kc. If the frequency specifications are normalized with respect to the center frequency, the lower band-edge frequency is $\omega_1 = 0.8$ and the upper band-edge frequency is $\omega_2 = 1.25$. The normalized bandwidth is $\omega_2 - \omega_1 = 0.45$. This value of bandwidth must also hold for the corresponding low-pass situation. Thus in the low-pass situation the problem becomes one of developing a network that has a two-pole maximally flat magnitude response with a 3-db bandwidth at 0.45. From the discussion

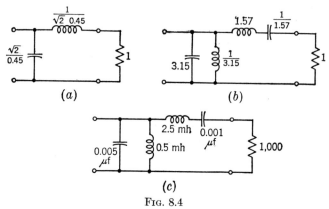

FIG. 8.4

in Chaps. 3 and 7, such a network is as shown in Fig. 8.4a. This network is now transformed into a bandpass network having a center frequency ω_0 of unity. Note that radian measure is used here. The network is shown in Fig. 8.4b. Finally, the network can be frequency-denormalized with respect to $\Omega_n = 2\pi \times 10^5$. In addition, a resistance denormalization can be introduced to achieve a desired resistance level. For a resistance level of 1,000 ohms, the final network is shown in Fig. 8.4c.

8.3 Narrow-band Approximation. Very often the specification of a bandpass filter is such that the bandwidth is a small percentage of the center frequency. In this case a simple approximation of the low-pass to bandpass transformation can be made, which permits an easy use of low-pass transmission criteria. In addition, these criteria can be used in the synthesis of bandpass configurations other than those that result from the conventional transformation.[*]

[*] G. E. Valley, Jr., and H. Wallman (eds.), "Vacuum Tube Amplifiers," MIT Radiation Laboratory Series, vol. 18, McGraw-Hill Book Company, Inc., New York, 1948.

For a center frequency that is normalized to unity, attention is restricted to the neighborhood of $p = +j1$. A new variable is then defined as follows:

$$p = p' + j1 \qquad (8.14)$$

The origin of the p' plane is $j1$ in the p plane. In the neighborhood of $p = +j1$

$$|p'| \ll 1 \qquad (8.15)$$

Equation (8.14) is now substituted into (8.10).

$$s = (p' + j1) + \frac{1}{p' + j1} \qquad (8.16)$$

Because of (8.15), the second member of (8.16) can be expanded by the binomial expansion and only the first terms retained.

$$s = p' + j1 - j\left(1 - \frac{p'}{j} + \cdots\right) \simeq 2p' \qquad (8.17)$$

Equation (8.17) indicates that in the vicinity of the center frequency the bandpass domain has the same properties as the low-pass domain, but it is shrunk by a factor 2. Thus a transformed pole set in the vicinity of $j1$ in the p plane has the same geometric relation to $j1$ as the low-pass pole set in the vicinity of the origin of the s plane. The poles in the p plane have a radial distance from $j1$ of one-half the pole radius in the s plane. For example, if a two-pole bandpass network with a maximally flat magnitude is desired,

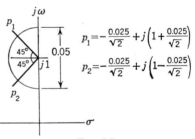

$$p_1 = -\frac{0.025}{\sqrt{2}} + j\left(1 + \frac{0.025}{\sqrt{2}}\right)$$

$$p_2 = -\frac{0.025}{\sqrt{2}} + j\left(1 - \frac{0.025}{\sqrt{2}}\right)$$

Fig. 8.5

the poles can be located about $j\omega_0$, just as they would be located about the origin for a low-pass situation. This is illustrated in Fig. 8.5 for a bandwidth which is 5 per cent of the center frequency $\omega_0 = 1$. In constructing a transfer function that is to have the desired poles in the neighborhood of $p = +j\omega_0$, a conjugate set of poles must also be included. If the transfer function is a transfer impedance, where for the moment it is assumed that there are two transmission zeros at the origin and two at infinity, it has the form

$$Z_{21}(p) = \frac{Hp^2}{(p - p_1)(p - p_2)(p - \bar{p}_1)(p - \bar{p}_2)} \qquad (8.18)$$

The pole-zero set is shown in Fig. 8.6. For a narrow-band situation

$$p_1 = -\alpha_1 + j\omega_1 \qquad p_2 = -\alpha_2 + j\omega_2$$

where
$$\alpha_1 \ll \omega_1 \qquad \omega_1 \approx \omega_0$$
$$\alpha_2 \ll \omega_2 \qquad \omega_2 \approx \omega_0$$

Now for $p = j\omega$, and only in the neighborhood of $j\omega_0$, the factor $p - \bar{p}_1$ in (8.18) can be approximated as follows:

$$p - \bar{p}_1|_{p=j\omega\approx j\omega_0} = j\omega + \alpha_1 + j\omega_1 \approx 2j\omega \qquad (8.19)$$

Similarly

$$p - \bar{p}_2|_{p=j\omega\approx j\omega_0} \approx 2j\omega$$

Equation (8.18) becomes

$$Z_{21}(j\omega)|_{p\approx j\omega_0} \approx \frac{H(j\omega)^2}{(j\omega - p_1)(j\omega - p_2)(2j\omega)^2} = \frac{H/4}{(j\omega - p_1)(j\omega - p_2)} \qquad (8.20)$$

Equation (8.20) expresses what is already known, i.e., that the transfer function has the same form as a low-pass function. The poles near $j\omega_0$ are dominant. The contributions of the transmission zeros at the origin and of the conjugate-pole set are negligible in the passband.

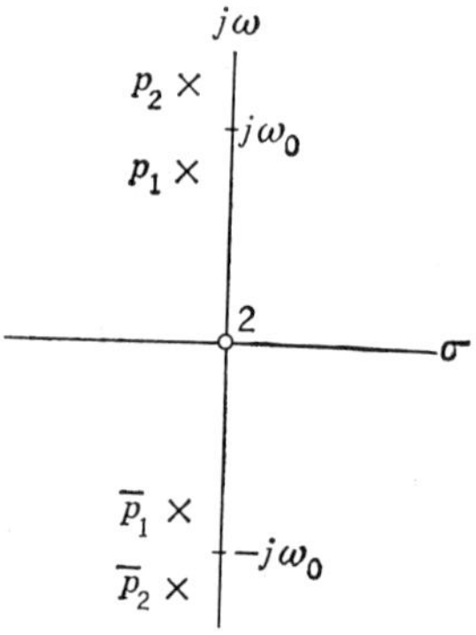

The example just used has the same number of transmission zeros at the origin and at infinity. However, the transfer function can be chosen to have a different number of zeros at the origin and at infinity. The above four-pole example has the following transfer impedance if there is one zero at the origin and there are three zeros at infinity.

FIG. 8.6

$$Z_{21}(j\omega) = \frac{Hj\omega}{(j\omega - p_1)(j\omega - p_2)(2j\omega)^2} = \frac{j(H/4)}{\omega(j\omega - p_1)(j\omega - p_2)} \qquad (8.21)$$

Because of the presence of the ω factor in the denominator of (8.21), a small distortion is introduced over and above the narrow-band approximation. In comparison with (8.20), the actual passband magnitude has a tilt from the lower band edge to the upper band edge, as illustrated in an exaggerated manner in Fig. 8.7. This tilt is usually not noticeable until the percentage bandwidth exceeds 10 per cent. Alternately, if there are three zeros at

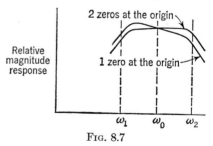

FIG. 8.7

the origin and one zero at infinity, the tilt increases from lower to upper band edges.

The advantage of not having an equal number of transmission zeros at the origin and infinity lies in the possibility of obtaining a desired network configuration. For a design illustration, the maximally flat magnitude two-pole response shown in Fig. 8.5 is realized with one transmission zero at the origin. The desired transfer impedance is

$$Z_{21}(p) = \frac{Hp}{(p^2 + 0.0354p + 1.036)(p^2 + 0.0354p + 0.965)} \quad (8.22)$$

Using the realization procedure of the last chapter, one obtains the two networks shown in Fig. 8.8. In the realization care must be taken to

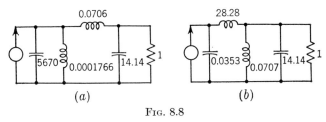

FIG. 8.8

maintain numerical accuracy at each step. The premature rounding off of numbers to less significant places leads to high error in the resulting element values. This is a direct result of the narrow-band situation and is common to all narrow-band problems. The tilt introduced by the dissymmetry of the transmission zeros is approximately equal to the percentage bandwidth for the problem in question.

$$\text{Tilt} = \frac{\text{upper band edge}}{\text{lower band edge}} - 1 = \frac{1.025}{0.975} - 1 = 0.05$$

8.4 Transformers in Bandpass Circuits. For bandpass coupling networks in amplifiers, it is desirable for at least two reasons to use transformers, i.e., coupled circuits, in the physical realization. The need for d-c blocking is one reason. The other is to achieve different impedance levels in different parts of the network. In this section it is shown how circuits such as the two-pole circuits of Fig. 8.8 can be realized, as shown in Fig. 8.9. The latter circuit is often referred to as a double-tuned circuit. Clearly, d-c blocking is obtained. In addition, the freedom of setting the impedance levels of the two parts of the network at different values permits, for example, the capacitances of pentodes to be used

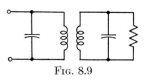

FIG. 8.9

as the total capacitances of the network without additional padding. It can be shown that if no capacitance is added maximum gain for a given bandwidth is obtained.*   The procedure to obtain a circuit such as the one shown in Fig. 8.9 involves inserting an ideal transformer into the original configuration.

An ideal transformer such as that shown in Fig. 8.10a is defined as follows:

$$\frac{V_1}{V_2} = \frac{-I_2}{I_1} = n \tag{8.23}$$

Its transmission matrix is

$$\begin{bmatrix} n & 0 \\ 0 & \dfrac{1}{n} \end{bmatrix} \tag{8.24}$$

Referring to Chap. 5, one can see that the impedance and admittance matrices are indeterminate.   However, a shunt inductance in tandem

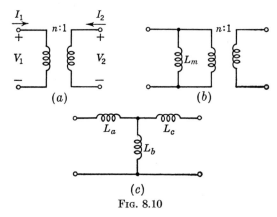

(a)   (b)

(c)

FIG. 8.10

with an ideal transformer, such as that shown in Fig. 8.10b, has an impedance matrix

$$[\mathbf{Z}] = \begin{bmatrix} pL_m & \dfrac{pL_m}{n} \\ \dfrac{pL_m}{n} & \dfrac{pL_m}{n^2} \end{bmatrix} \tag{8.25}$$

The common p factor in (8.25) can be removed as a multiplier.

$$[\mathbf{Z}] = p[\mathbf{L}] = p \begin{bmatrix} L_m & \dfrac{L_m}{n} \\ \dfrac{L_m}{n} & \dfrac{L_m}{n^2} \end{bmatrix} \tag{8.26}$$

The [L] matrix is called the inductance matrix.   In general, an inductance matrix has the form

$$[\mathbf{L}] = \begin{bmatrix} l_{11} & l_{12} \\ l_{21} & l_{22} \end{bmatrix} \tag{8.27}$$

* *Ibid.*

where l_{11} and l_{22} are called self-inductances and $l_{12} = l_{21}$ is the mutual inductance. Note that the l_{ij} are the open-circuit inductance parameters. Often the mutual inductance is specified in terms of a coefficient of coupling.

$$k = \frac{|l_{12}|}{\sqrt{l_{11}l_{22}}} \tag{8.28}$$

An equivalent T circuit shown in Fig. 8.10c can be obtained from the results of Chap. 4. Its inductance matrix is

$$\begin{bmatrix} L_a + L_b & L_b \\ L_b & L_b + L_c \end{bmatrix} \tag{8.29}$$

The individual inductances are related to those of (8.26) by

$$L_a = L_m\left(1 - \frac{1}{n}\right)$$

$$L_b = \frac{L_m}{n} \tag{8.30}$$

$$L_c = \frac{L_m}{n}\left(\frac{1}{n} - 1\right)$$

Note that either L_a or L_c is negative for a positive n, depending upon whether n is smaller or larger than one. If n is negative, L_a and L_c are positive and L_b is negative. The coefficient of coupling is equal to unity.

$$k = \frac{|L_m/n|}{\sqrt{L_m(L_m/n^2)}} = 1 \tag{8.31}$$

Because $k = 1$, the circuit in Fig. 8.10b or its equivalent in Fig. 8.10c is called a set of perfectly coupled coils.

A practical transformer has a coefficient of coupling less than unity ($k < 1$). The transformer has finite leakage inductances. It follows, then, that if series inductances are added to the configuration of Fig. 8.10b, the circuit in Fig. 8.11 is a valid equivalent circuit for a practical transformer. The equivalent T for a practical transformer differs from a set of perfectly coupled coils by the additional two series inductances (or by only one on either side).

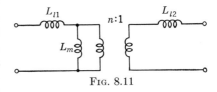

FIG. 8.11

Another very useful matrix is the reciprocal-inductance matrix $[\mathbf{\Gamma}]$. This matrix is the inverse of the inductance matrix.

$$[\mathbf{\Gamma}] = \begin{bmatrix} \Gamma_{11} & \Gamma_{12} \\ \Gamma_{21} & \Gamma_{22} \end{bmatrix} = [\mathbf{L}]^{-1} \tag{8.32}$$

In terms of the [L] matrix parameters

$$\Gamma_{11} = \frac{l_{22}}{|L|} \qquad \Gamma_{22} = \frac{l_{11}}{|L|} \qquad \Gamma_{12} = \frac{-l_{12}}{|L|} = \Gamma_{21} \qquad |L| = l_{11}l_{22} - l_{12}^2 \quad (8.33)$$

The Γ_{ij} are the short-circuit reciprocal-inductance parameters. If an inductance L is placed in series with an ideal transformer, as in Fig. 8.12a, the [Γ] matrix is

$$[\Gamma] = \begin{bmatrix} \dfrac{1}{L} & -\dfrac{n}{L} \\ -\dfrac{n}{L} & \dfrac{n^2}{L} \end{bmatrix} \qquad (8.34)$$

The coefficient of coupling of this combination is unity. A π-equivalent circuit, shown in Fig. 8.12b, is related to L and n as follows:

$$\Gamma_a = \frac{1}{L}(1 - n)$$

$$\Gamma_b = \frac{n}{L} \qquad (8.35)$$

$$\Gamma_c = \frac{n}{L}(n - 1)$$

Notice that if a shunt inductance is added to either side of the circuits of Fig. 8.12a and b, the coefficient of coupling is less than one. Either

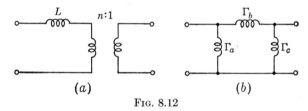

(a)   (b)

FIG. 8.12

configuration with the additional inductance is then an equivalent circuit of a practical transformer.

   With the above information as a background, attention is once more drawn to the realization of bandpass circuits. In order to introduce a practical transformer, an ideal transformer is first inserted into the original network. A simple grouping of inductance elements with the ideal transformer provides a practical transformer. Starting with the two-pole bandpass circuit of Fig. 8.8b, one can insert an ideal transformer, as shown in Fig. 8.13a. The value of the element C_1 is modified by n^2, as shown in the figure. This maintains the impedance relationships within the network and also the same poles and zeros of the transfer function. The constant multiplier of the transfer function of the new network is n times the constant of the original transfer function. The ideal transformer together with the elements L_1 and L_2 can now be realized as a practical transformer, such as that shown in Fig. 8.13b. The reciprocal-inductance matrix of this combination is

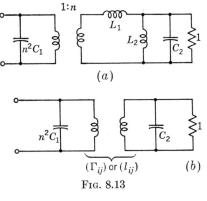

$$[\mathbf{\Gamma}] = \begin{bmatrix} \dfrac{n^2}{L_1} & -\dfrac{n}{L_1} \\[2ex] -\dfrac{n}{L_1} & \left(\dfrac{1}{L_1} + \dfrac{1}{L_2}\right) \end{bmatrix}$$

(8.36)

(a)

The coefficient of coupling is

$$k = \frac{1}{\sqrt{1 + (L_1/L_2)}}$$

(8.37)

(Γ_{ij}) or (l_{ij}) (b)

Fig. 8.13

8.5 Illustrative Example. As an example of the procedure in the last section, a bandpass interstage is designed. The specifications are

$$f_0 = 60 \text{ Mc}$$
$$Bw|_{3\,db} = 3 \text{ Mc}$$

The response is to have a double-tuned maximally flat magnitude. Typical pentode characteristics are

$$C_{\text{out}} = 5 \ \mu\mu\text{f}$$
$$C_{\text{in}} = 10 \ \mu\mu\text{f}$$
$$g_m = 0.005 \text{ mho}$$

A double-tuned response is the same as the previous two-pole bandpass response. Since the bandwidth is 5 per cent of the center frequency, the normalized poles are those of Fig. 8.5 and the normalized prototype network is that shown in Fig. 8.8a or b. The network of Fig. 8.8b is used.

Before applying denormalization, note that the ratio C_1/C_2 of normalized capacitances is equal to 0.0025. This is much smaller than the ratio of capacitances supplied by the pentodes $(C_{1,act}/C_{2,act} = \frac{1}{2})$. A large value of capacitance must be added to C_{in}, therefore, if the network of Fig. 8.8b is to be realized. It can easily be shown that this capacitance padding leads to a loss of gain. An ideal transformer can be added, as in the last section, to eliminate the need for padding. The necessary value of n is found from the actual ratio of capacitances.

$$\frac{C_{1,\text{new}}}{C_2} = \frac{C_{1,act}}{C_{2,act}} = \frac{1}{2}$$

$$C_{1,\text{new}} = n^2 C_{1,\text{original}} = 7.07$$

$$n^2 = \frac{7.071}{0.0353} = 200 \tag{8.38}$$

$$n = 14.14$$

The normalized network including a transformer is shown in Fig. 8.14a.

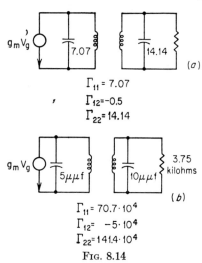

To denormalize the network, remember from Chap. 3 that the normalized and actual element values are related as follows:

$\Gamma_{11} = 7.07$

$\Gamma_{12} = -0.5$

$\Gamma_{22} = 14.14$

$$L_{act} = \frac{r_n}{\Omega_n} L_n$$

$$C_{act} = \frac{1}{r_n \Omega_n} C_n \tag{8.39}$$

$$R_{act} = r_n R_n$$

The frequency normalization factor is

$$\Omega_n = 2\pi \times 60 \times 10^6$$

$\Gamma_{11} = 70.7 \cdot 10^4$

$\Gamma_{12} = -5 \cdot 10^4$

$\Gamma_{22} = 141.4 \cdot 10^4$

Fig. 8.14

The resistance normalization factor r_n is determined by the actual capacitance specification of C_{out} or C_{in}, since for the network of Fig. 8.14a $C_{out} = C_{1,act}$ and $C_{in} = C_{2,act}$. From the value for C_{in} and from (8.39)

$$r_n = \frac{1}{\Omega_n} \frac{C_2}{C_{2,act}} = \frac{14.14}{(2\pi \times 60 \times 10^6)(10 \times 10^{-12})} = 3.75 \text{ kilohms} \tag{8.40}$$

The actual element values of the network are shown in Fig. 8.14b. The gain of the stage at center frequency can be shown to be

$$\text{Gain } (f_0) = g_m \left(\frac{L_1}{n}\right) r_n = 37.5 \tag{8.41}$$

PROBLEMS

8.1. Design a high-pass filter with a three-pole equal-ripple magnitude characteristic. The filter is to be a lossless ladder terminated at one end in a resistance of 600 ohms. The allowable tolerance in the passband is $\frac{1}{2}$ db. The tolerance band-edge frequency is 20 kc. Determine the attenuation at one-half the band-edge frequency. Sketch the magnitude and phase functions.

8.2. If a low-pass function is transformed by the low-pass to high-pass transformation, the magnitude of the low-pass function at $s = jv_1$ is equal to the magnitude of the high-pass function at the transformed frequency $p = j\omega_1$. What is the relationship between the value of the derivative of the magnitude of the low-pass function at v_1 and the value of the derivative of the magnitude of the high-pass function at ω_1?

8.3. A bandpass network N, which is part of a microwave link, is to be designed (Fig. P8.3). The information is in the form of RF pulses. After being received by the antenna, these pulses are mixed with a local oscillator and the signal across AB consists of carrier pulses with a carrier frequency of 30 Mc ($\omega_0 = 2\pi \times 3 \times 10^7$ radians/sec). The network N must have enough bandwidth so that, if the input signal is a carrier pulse whose envelope is a step function, the output carrier pulse will have a 10 to 90 per cent envelope rise time of $\frac{1}{2}$ μsec. System studies have shown that extraneous RF signals will be sufficiently rejected if the low-pass equivalent of N is a third-order rational function. Furthermore, a maximally flat delay characteristic is desirable to obtain a smoothly rising envelope for the output pulses.

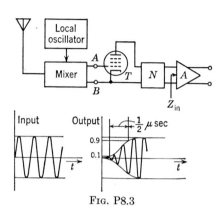

Fig. P8.3

Assume that the input capacitance of N is large enough to absorb the output capacitance of the pentode T so that for design purposes N is driven by a current source. The input impedance Z_{in} of the amplifier A is designed to be purely resistive and equal to 200 ohms.

(a) Determine the required bandwidth of the bandpass network together with the 3-db frequencies. (Note from the solution of Prob. 3.9 that the product of the 10 to 90 per cent rise time and the 3-db bandwidth is equal to approximately 0.7 for a bandpass situation.)

(b) Specify the normalized low-pass specifications that can be used. [From Chap. 3 the radial 3-db bandwidth for a low-pass maximally flat delay function is approximately $\sqrt{(2n - 1) \ln 2}$ for unit delay.]

(c) Synthesize the low-pass network.

(d) Apply the low-pass to bandpass transformation and proper denormalization to obtain the bandpass network.

8.4. The transfer function of a bandpass filter is desired. The magnitude function is to have a maximally flat magnitude characteristic at the center frequency. The 1-db passband is from 100 to 200 kc. At one-half the lower band-edge frequency and twice the upper band-edge frequency, the attenuation is to be at least 40 db.

8.5. Determine the pole locations for a bandpass two-pole maximally flat magnitude function for a 20 per cent 3-db bandwidth, using (a) the narrow-band approximation and (b) the low-pass to bandpass transformation. Compare the resulting magnitude functions.

8.6. For certain bandpass networks, the narrow-band technique can be used in both the analysis and design of the networks. Consider the circuit shown in Fig. P8.6. The nodal equations of this network can be written

$$\begin{bmatrix} \left(pC_1 + \dfrac{\Gamma_{11}}{p}\right) & \dfrac{\Gamma_{12}}{p} \\ \dfrac{\Gamma_{12}}{p} & \left(pC_2 + \dfrac{\Gamma_{22}}{p} + G\right) \end{bmatrix} \begin{bmatrix} V_1 \\ V_2 \end{bmatrix} = \begin{bmatrix} I_1 \\ 0 \end{bmatrix}$$

C_1 and C_2 can be assumed to be resonant at ω_0 with the input and output short-circuit reciprocal inductances Γ_{11} and Γ_{22}.

$$\frac{\Gamma_{11}}{C_1} = \frac{\Gamma_{22}}{C_2} = \omega_0^2$$

In addition, for a small bandwidth, the mutual-admittance term can be approximated as $\Gamma_{12}/j\omega_0$. Show, using Eq. (8.14) or (8.17), that under these conditions

$$Z_{21}(p') = \frac{(1/4C_1C_2)(\Gamma_{12}/j\omega_0)}{p'^2 + (G/2C_2)p' + (k\omega_0/2)^2}$$

where

$$k = \frac{|\Gamma_{12}|}{\sqrt{\Gamma_{11}\Gamma_{22}}}$$

Plot the pole locations in the p plane under this assumption. Using the above transfer impedance and pole locations, design the network that satisfies the specification of Sec. 8.5.

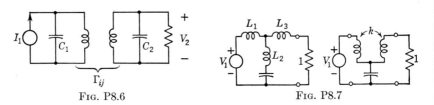

FIG. P8.6   FIG. P8.7

8.7. Realize the transfer admittance

$$Y_{21} = \frac{-1 + p^2}{p^3 + 2p^2 + 2p + 1}$$

using the zero-shifting procedure of Chap. 7. Note that L_2 in Fig. P8.7 must be negative for transmission zeros at $p = \pm 1$ to be obtained. Determine the coefficient of coupling and the polarity of the transformer. Plot the magnitude and phase of $Y_{21}(j\omega)$.

8.8. If a negative element is used in the shifting step in the realization of a transfer admittance

$$Y_{21} = \frac{-(p^2 + 1)}{p^3 + 2p^2 + 2p + 1}$$

develop the network configuration shown in Fig. P8.8. Note that L_3 is negative, and show that it can be realized with coupled coils. What is the coefficient of coupling?

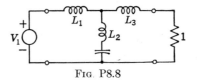

FIG. P8.8

8.9. For a T of inductances show that $L_1L_2 + L_2L_3 + L_3L_1 = 0$ is equivalent to $k = 1$.

8.10. Show that the two 2-ports in Fig. P8.10 are equivalent if $k = 1$ for both networks. This implies for the second network that $C_aC_b + C_bC_c + C_cC_a = 0$.

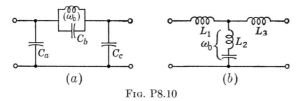

(a)   (b)

Fig. P8.10

8.11. The two circuits in Fig. P8.11 can be obtained by inserting ideal transformers into the circuits of Fig. 8.8. Show that these two configurations can also be obtained by using a partial removal step in the realization of Z_{21}.

$$Z_{21} = \frac{Hp}{p^4 + a_3p^3 + a_2p^2 + a_1p + a_0}$$

That is, L_3 in both circuits can be obtained from a partial removal. Use reactance and susceptance plots in your development.

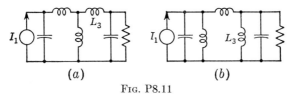

(a)   (b)

Fig. P8.11

8.12. Using the procedure and the tube information of Sec. 8.5, develop a double-tuned interstage circuit having an approximate maximally flat magnitude response with a center frequency of 30 Mc. The bandwidth is 10 Mc. Find the pole locations from the bandpass to low-pass transformation. Include only one transmission zero at the origin. Determine the tilt in the passband due to this approximation.

8.13. Show that the low-pass two-pole network shown in Fig. P8.13 can be transformed into the bandpass circuit through use of the low-pass to bandpass transformation and the inclusion of an ideal transformer. If the output voltage is taken across

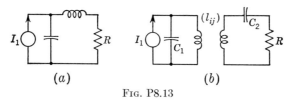

(a)   (b)

Fig. P8.13

C_2 rather than R, show that the transfer function of Prob. 8.11 is obtained. For equal capacitances and for a maximally flat magnitude response with a 10 per cent bandwidth, determine the center-frequency transfer-impedance magnitude. Compare this value with that which can be obtained with the circuit of Fig. 8.9 for the same capacitances and the same response.

CHAPTER 9

THE REALIZATION OF LOSSLESS 2-PORTS—PART II

9.1 Lossless Ladders Terminated at Both Ends in Resistances. In many design situations resistances are present at both the input and the output, i.e., the source and the load. For example, a filter or equalizer may be required which must operate between matched transmission lines without the need of additional amplification. Such a situation is illustrated in Fig. 9.1. In this chapter a technique is presented for realizing lossless 2-ports terminated at both ends in resistances. For simplicity's sake, a restriction is made to the low-pass situation, where all transmission zeros lie at infinity. The transformations described in Chap. 8 can of course be used to extend the applications to high-pass and bandpass situations.

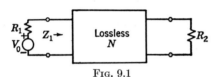

Fig. 9.1

The realization to be developed stems directly from the lossless character of the 2-port. The power into the network must be equal to the power transmitted to the load.

$$P_{in} = |I_1|^2 \text{ Re } [Z_1(j\omega)] \qquad (9.1)$$
$$= P_{out} = |V_2|^2/R_2$$

Z_1 is the input impedance of the 2-port terminated in R_2. Thus

$$\left|\frac{V_2}{I_1}\right|^2 = R_2 \text{ Re } [Z_1(j\omega)] \qquad (9.2)$$

Equation (9.2) cannot be used directly, since the specified transfer function is usually given in terms of the transfer voltage ratio V_2/V_0 or the comparable definition, the insertion voltage gain [see Eq. (4.34)]. From Fig. 9.1 it is evident that

$$I_1 = \frac{V_0}{R_1 + Z_1} \qquad (9.3)$$

Combining (9.2) and (9.3), one obtains

$$\left|\frac{V_2}{V_0}\right|^2 = \frac{R_2 \text{ Re } [Z_1(j\omega)]}{|R_1 + Z_1|^2} \qquad (9.4)$$

The problem now is to obtain the impedance Z_1 from the specified transfer function. Once Z_1 is found, a removal realization technique can be used to obtain the network. $Z_1(p)$ cannot be obtained directly from (9.4). It is necessary, as Darlington has shown, first to obtain a function known as the reflection coefficient $S_{11}(p)$.*† From this function, $Z_1(p)$ can be determined.

In developing the reflection coefficient, the actual power levels are normalized with respect to the maximum available power that can be obtained from the source. The latter is

$$\text{Available } P_{\text{in}} = \frac{|V_0|^2}{4R_1} \tag{9.5}$$

The normalized transmitted power is then

$$\frac{P_{\text{out}}}{\text{Available } P_{\text{in}}} = \frac{|V_2|^2/R_2}{|V_0|^2/4R_1} = \frac{4R_1}{R_2}\left|\frac{V_2}{V_0}\right|^2 = |S_{21}(j\omega)|^2 \tag{9.6}$$

where $S_{21}(p)$ is defined as the transmission coefficient. Clearly,

$$|S_{21}(j\omega)|^2 \leq 1 \tag{9.7}$$

The equality sign in (9.7) is satisfied if maximum power is transmitted to the load. If the equality is not satisfied, the difference can be viewed as a normalized power reflected by the network back to the source. This normalized reflected power is expressed as

$$|S_{11}(j\omega)|^2 = 1 - |S_{21}(j\omega)|^2 \tag{9.8}$$

Equations (9.4), (9.6), and (9.8) can now be combined to obtain

$$|S_{11}(j\omega)|^2 = 1 - \frac{4R_1 \text{ Re }[Z_1(j\omega)]}{|R_1 + Z_1|^2} \tag{9.9}$$

$Z_1(j\omega)$ can be expressed in terms of its real and imaginary parts.

$$Z_1(j\omega) = R + jX \tag{9.10}$$

Equation (9.9) becomes

$$|S_{11}(j\omega)|^2 = 1 - \frac{4R_1R}{(R_1 + R)^2 + X^2} = \frac{(R - R_1)^2 + X^2}{(R_1 + R)^2 + X^2} = \left|\frac{Z_1 - R_1}{Z_1 + R_1}\right|^2 \tag{9.11}$$

If the square root of (9.11) is taken and if the $j\omega$ variable is analytically continued to p, one obtains

$$S_{11}(p) = \pm\frac{Z_1 - R_1}{Z_1 + R_1} \tag{9.12}$$

* The notations S_{11} and S_{21} are used to conform with another 2-port description, the scattering matrix. This description is discussed in Chap. 14.

† S. Darlington, Synthesis of Reactance Four-poles Which Produce Prescribed Insertion Loss Characteristics, J. Math. and Phys., vol. 18, pp. 257–353, September, 1939.

The choice of sign in (9.12) results from the square root. The input impedance to the terminated 2-port is

$$Z_1 = R_1 \frac{1 \pm S_{11}}{1 \mp S_{11}} \tag{9.13}$$

In reviewing the development from (9.5) through (9.13), it should be recognized that the analytic continuation of the variable $j\omega$ can be accomplished in (9.6) and (9.8) as follows:

$$|S_{21}(p)|^2 = \frac{4R_1}{R_2} \left| \frac{V_2}{V_0} (p) \right|^2$$

or $\qquad S_{21}(p)S_{21}(-p) = 4 \frac{R_1}{R_2} \frac{V_2}{V_0} (p) \frac{V_2}{V_0} (-p) \tag{9.14}$

$$S_{11}(p)S_{11}(-p) = 1 - 4 \frac{R_1}{R_2} \frac{V_2}{V_0} (p) \frac{V_2}{V_0} (-p) \tag{9.15}$$

Equations (9.14) and (9.15) turn out to be easier to use in the realization procedure.

In practice, $S_{11}(p)$ cannot be obtained by merely solving (9.15). The technique of Sec. 2.5 is used. Clearly, from (9.12), the denominator polynomial of S_{11} must be Hurwitz. So, the poles of $(V_2/V_0)(p)$ in (9.15) are chosen as the poles of $S_{11}(p)$. There is freedom in choosing the zeros of $S_{11}(p)$. The zeros of $S_{11}(p)S_{11}(-p)$ are in quadrangle symmetry. For any quadrangle set, the conjugate set in either the left half plane or the right half plane can be chosen for zeros of $S_{11}(p)$. Similarly, for a symmetrical real set of zeros, either the right or the left half plane zeros can be chosen. With $S_{11}(p)$ established, Z_1 is found from (9.13).

9.2 Realization Procedure. A realization example is presented in this section to illustrate the actual procedure. A simple problem is that of realizing a lossless ladder which has a three-pole low-pass maximally flat magnitude response.

$$\frac{V_2}{V_0} = \frac{\frac{1}{2}}{p^3 + 2p^2 + 2p + 1} \tag{9.16}$$

Notice that the constant multiplier H has been set equal to $\frac{1}{2}$. The choice of H must be such that (9.7) is satisfied for all ω. For a low-pass maximally flat magnitude transfer function the maximum magnitude occurs at d-c. From (9.6) and for $R_1 = R_2$, H must be equal to or less than $\frac{1}{2}$.

It is assumed that the terminations are both equal to unity. Using the developments of the last section, one must first determine the input impedance $Z_1(p)$. From (9.15)

$$S_{11}(p)S_{11}(-p) = 1 - 4 \frac{\frac{1}{4}}{1 - p^6} = \frac{-p^6}{1 - p^6} \tag{9.17}$$

The poles of $S_{11}(p)$, as mentioned in the last section, are the same as the poles of $(V_2/V_0)(p)$. The zeros of (9.17) all occur at the origin; hence there is no choice.

$$S_{11}(p) = \frac{\pm p^3}{p^3 + 2p^2 + 2p + 1} \tag{9.18}$$

From (9.13)

$$Z_1 = \frac{2p^2 + 2p + 1}{2p^3 + 2p^2 + 2p + 1} \tag{9.19}$$

or

$$Z_1 = \frac{2p^3 + 2p^2 + 2p + 1}{2p^2 + 2p + 1} \tag{9.20}$$

The physical network is obtained from $Z_1(p)$ by a removal technique comparable to that used in Chap. 7. In the present example all the transmission zeros (the zeros of V_2/V_0 or of S_{21}) are at infinity. It seems reasonable that the network is a lossless ladder with series L and shunt C. As in Chap. 7, the successive removals can be accomplished by a continued fraction expansion of Z_1. The numerical expansion of either (9.19) or (9.20) is as follows:

$$
\begin{array}{l}
2p^2 + 2p + 1 \overline{\left| 2p^3 + 2p^2 + 2p + 1 \right.} \mid p \\
\qquad\quad\; 2p^3 + 2p^2 + \;\; p \\
\hline
\qquad\qquad\quad p + 1 \overline{\left| 2p^2 + 2p + 1 \right.} \mid 2p \\
\qquad\qquad\qquad\quad 2p^2 + 2p \\
\hline
\qquad\qquad\qquad\qquad\qquad 1 \overline{\left| p + 1 \right.} \mid p \\
\qquad\qquad\qquad\qquad\qquad\quad p \\
\hline
\qquad\qquad\qquad\qquad\qquad\qquad\qquad 1 \overline{\left| 1 \right.} \mid 1 \\
\qquad\qquad\qquad\qquad\qquad\qquad\qquad\quad 1 \\
\hline
\qquad\qquad\qquad\qquad\qquad\qquad\qquad\quad 0
\end{array}
$$

Notice that the next to the last remainder is a constant equal to unity, corresponding to a 1-ohm termination. The network realization of (9.19) is that shown in Fig. 9.2a, since the first step is a removal from an admittance. The network realization of (9.20) is shown in Fig. 9.2b.

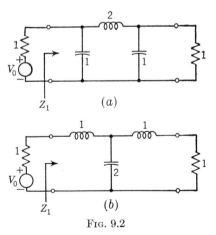

(a)

(b)

Fig. 9.2

9.3 Transmission-zero Realization. In the Z_1 development of the example in the last section the question arises: Why is the process valid? After the first pole removal to produce a transmission zero, why does the remainder impedance or admittance function pertain to a network that contains the remaining transmission zeros? These questions are answered by investigating the interrelations of the input impedance and the transmission zeros of a terminated lossless 2-port. In particular, the needed relationship is one in which the zeros of the even part of $Z_1(p)$ are the transmission zeros and their negatives. This can be seen from a generalization of the development in Sec. 9.1.

The transfer voltage ratio can be expressed as follows:

$$\frac{V_2}{V_0}(p) = \frac{V_2}{I_1}\frac{I_1}{V_0} = \frac{V_2}{I_1}\frac{1}{R_1 + Z_1} \tag{9.21}$$

Next, V_2/I_1 can be written

$$\left|\frac{V_2}{I_1}(p)\right|^2_{p=j\omega} = R_2 \operatorname{Re}[Z_1(p)]_{p=j\omega} = R_2 \operatorname{Ev}[Z_1(p)]_{p=j\omega} \tag{9.22}$$

Therefore, by analytic continuation,

$$\frac{V_2}{I_1}(p)\frac{V_2}{I_1}(-p) = R_2 \operatorname{Ev}[Z_1(p)] \tag{9.23}$$

From (9.21) and (9.23)

$$\frac{V_2}{V_0}(p)\frac{V_2}{V_0}(-p) = \frac{R_2 \operatorname{Ev} Z_1(p)}{[R_1 + Z_1(p)][R_1 + Z_1(-p)]} \tag{9.24}$$

It can now be shown that the transmission zeros and their negatives in (9.23) are precisely the zeros of $\operatorname{Ev}[Z_1(p)]$. This is done by showing that the denominator of $\operatorname{Ev}[Z_1(p)]$ is equal to the denominator of $[R_1 + Z_1(p)][R_1 + Z_1(-p)]$. If $Z_1(p)$ is written as

$$Z_1(p) = \frac{A_1 + pB_1}{A_2 + pB_2} \tag{9.25}$$

$$\operatorname{Ev}[Z_1(p)] = \frac{A_1A_2 - p^2B_1B_2}{A_2^2 - p^2B_2^2} \tag{9.26}$$

$$[R_1 + Z_1(p)][R_1 + Z_1(-p)] = \frac{Q(p^2)}{A_2^2 - p^2B_2^2} \tag{9.27}$$

where $Q(p^2)$ is an even polynomial. Clearly, then, the zeros of $\operatorname{Ev}[Z_1(p)]$ are the transmission zeros and their negatives. Since the zeros of $\operatorname{Ev} Z_1(p)$ are the same as the zeros of $\operatorname{Ev} Y_1(p)$, the above statement is also true on the admittance basis (see Chap. 2).

In the ladder development of $Z_1(p)$, when a transmission zero or a conjugate pair of zeros is produced by a branch removal, a zero or pair of zeros is removed from the even part of the impedance or admittance function. The remainder impedance or admittance function after this step pertains to a network which must have only the remaining transmission zeros. The realization of $Z_1(p)$ in this iterative procedure is concluded when all transmission zeros have been produced. The final remainder of the development has no zeros and thus must be a constant corresponding to a resistance termination.

The preceding paragraphs show that the development of $Z_1(p)$ leads to a correct network realization if the proper transmission zeros are produced. The example in the last section indicates the simplicity of the procedure if all transmission zeros are at infinity. Similarly, no difficulty is encountered if all transmission zeros are at the origin or if the transmission zeros occur at infinity and the origin. If some transmission zeros lie on the finite $j\omega$ axis, zero-shifting steps undoubtedly have to be used, as explained in Chap. 7. For this case one expects a simple ladder network realization. Typical sections of the network are shown in Fig. 9.3. In many cases the zero-shifting step demands the use of negative elements. However, it is possible to show that these negative elements can always be realized with a set of perfectly coupled coils. As indicated in Chap. 7, there are methods of realizing complex transmission zeros.[8,9]

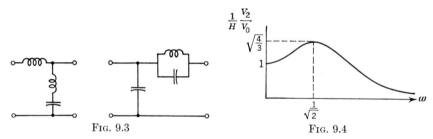

FIG. 9.3   FIG. 9.4

9.4 Unequal Terminations. A complication may arise if the maximum magnitude of the specified $|(V_2/V_0)(j\omega)|$ does not occur at d-c for the low-pass case (center frequency for the bandpass case). This is brought out in the following example, where

$$\frac{V_2}{V_0} = \frac{H}{p^2 + p + 1} \tag{9.28}$$

Equal terminations of unit resistance are used. The magnitude function for $p = j\omega$ is plotted in Fig. 9.4. The maximum occurs at $\omega = 1/\sqrt{2}$ and is equal to $\sqrt{\frac{4}{3}} H$. With reference to (9.6) and (9.7)

$$H \leq \frac{\sqrt{3}}{4} \tag{9.29}$$

Notice that the maximum value of H is less than $\frac{1}{2}$, where $\frac{1}{2}$ is the value of $(V_2/V_0)(0)$, i.e., the gain at d-c that can be expected for a low-pass ladder terminated in equal resistances. This immediately suggests that a realization with equal-resistance terminations is not possible without the use of ideal transformers or some other artifice. Choosing the maximum value of H, one can realize the network as follows:

$$S_{11}(p)S_{11}(-p) = 1 - \frac{4 \times \frac{3}{16}}{(p^2 + p + 1)(p^2 - p + 1)}$$

$$= \frac{(p^2 + \frac{1}{2})^2}{(p^2 + p + 1)(p^2 - p + 1)} \quad (9.30)$$

$$S_{11}(p) = \frac{p^2 + \frac{1}{2}}{p^2 + p + 1} \quad (9.31)$$

$$Z_1 = \frac{p + \frac{1}{2}}{2p^2 + p + \frac{3}{2}} \quad \text{or} \quad \frac{2p^2 + p + \frac{3}{2}}{p + \frac{1}{2}} \quad (9.32)$$

The network realizations of Z_1 are shown in Fig. 9.5. Note that the termination as developed is $\frac{1}{3}$ ohm for one case and 3 ohms for the other

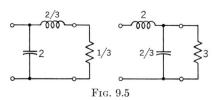

FIG. 9.5

case. Since the realization has been specified to be 1 ohm, ideal transformers of turns ratio $1/\sqrt{3}$ and $\sqrt{3}$, respectively, must be introduced, as shown in Fig. 9.6. An alternate procedure is to add either resistance or conductance to the load, as shown in Fig. 9.7. This last procedure eliminates the need for the ideal transformer; however, one pays for this in flat loss. The d-c voltage gain of both networks in Fig. 9.6 is $\sqrt{3}/4$, which is equal to H, as expected, since $(V_2/V_0)(0) = H$. The d-c voltage gain of both networks in Fig. 9.7 is $\frac{1}{4}$. Therefore the flat loss is $20 \log \sqrt{3} = 5$ db.

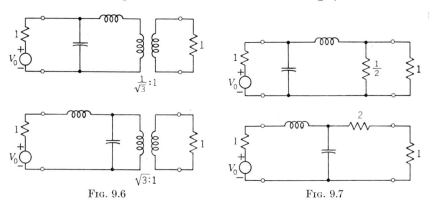

FIG. 9.6   FIG. 9.7

Often the specified terminations are not equal. An example illustrating this situation is the design of a network with a two-pole maximally flat delay response with $R_1 = 1$ and $R_2 = 2$.

$$\frac{V_2}{V_0} = \frac{H}{p^2 + \sqrt{3}\,p + 1} \quad (9.33)$$

The maximum magnitude of $(V_2/V_0)(j\omega)$ occurs at d-c.   The maximum value of H is found from (9.6) and (9.7).

$$4\,\frac{R_1}{R_2}\,H^2 \le 1$$

$$H_{\max} = \frac{1}{\sqrt{2}} \tag{9.34}$$

The network is found as follows:

$$S_{11}(p)S_{11}(-p) = 1 - \frac{1}{(p^2 + \sqrt{3}\,p + 1)(p^2 - \sqrt{3}\,p + 1)}$$
$$= \frac{p^2(p^2 - 1)}{(p^2 + \sqrt{3}\,p + 1)(p^2 - \sqrt{3}\,p + 1)}$$

The zeros of $S_{11}(p)S_{11}(-p)$ occur at $p = \pm 1$ and $p = 0$ (double). There are two possible sets of zeros for $S_{11}(p)$.

$$S_{11}(p) = \frac{p(p - 1)}{p^2 + \sqrt{3}\,p + 1} \tag{9.35}$$

$$S_{11}(p) = \frac{p(p + 1)}{p^2 + \sqrt{3}\,p + 1} \tag{9.36}$$

The possible input impedances are

$$Z_1(p) = \frac{(\sqrt{3} + 1)p + 1}{2p^2 + (\sqrt{3} - 1)p + 1} \quad \text{or its reciprocal} \tag{9.37}$$

$$Z_1(p) = \frac{(\sqrt{3} - 1)p + 1}{2p^2 + (\sqrt{3} + 1)p + 1} \quad \text{or its reciprocal} \tag{9.38}$$

The network realizations using ideal transformers are shown in Fig. 9.8. These transformers can be eliminated, for example, through the addition of a shunt conductance at the output, as shown in Fig. 9.9 for the first network.   The d-c voltage gain for all networks of Fig. 9.8 is $1/\sqrt{2}$. If resistance padding is used, the voltage gain is $\frac{1}{2}$.   The flat loss is 3 db.

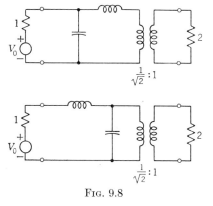

FIG. 9.8

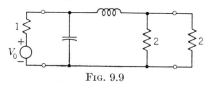

FIG. 9.9

The constant H does not have to be chosen as $H_{\max}$.   For the problem at hand, where the maximum magnitude occurs at d-c, a reasonable choice is

$$H = \frac{R_2}{R_1 + R_2} = \frac{2}{3} \tag{9.39}$$

The network realization is found as follows:

$$
\begin{aligned}
S_{11}(p)S_{11}(-p) &= 1 - \frac{\frac{8}{9}}{(p^2 + \sqrt{3}\,p + 1)(p^2 - \sqrt{3}\,p + 1)} \\
&= \frac{p^4 - p^2 + \frac{1}{9}}{(p^2 + \sqrt{3}\,p + 1)(p^2 - \sqrt{3}\,p + 1)} \\
&= \frac{(p + 0.94)(p - 0.94)(p + 0.37)(p - 0.37)}{(p^2 + \sqrt{3}\,p + 1)(p^2 - \sqrt{3}\,p + 1)}
\end{aligned}
\tag{9.40}
$$

One possible choice is

$$S_{11}(p) = \frac{(p + 0.94)(p + 0.37)}{p^2 + \sqrt{3}\,p + 1} = \frac{p^2 + 1.31p + 0.35}{p^2 + \sqrt{3}\,p + 1} \tag{9.41}$$

$$Z_1(p) = \frac{0.42p + 0.65}{2p^2 + 3.04p + 1.35} \tag{9.42}$$

The network is shown in Fig. 9.10. Notice that the final resistance of the development has the desired value of 2 ohms.

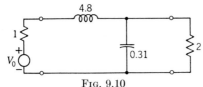

FIG. 9.10

The problems of why the desired resistance is obtained and under what conditions the technique of the last paragraphs can be used remain. The answers to these problems are established below by a consideration of the maximum power transfer to the load and of the transfer of power at d-c without transformers. A general transfer voltage ratio can be written as

$$\frac{V_2}{V_0} = HF(p) = H\,\frac{p^n + \cdots + a_0}{p^m + \cdots + b_0} \tag{9.43}$$

The maximum value of H, $H_{\max}$, is determined from the maximum power transfer, i.e., from the equality condition of (9.6) and (9.7).

$$|S_{21}(j\omega)|^2 = 4\,\frac{R_1}{R_2}\left|\frac{V_2}{V_0}(j\omega)\right|^2 = 1 \tag{9.44}$$

Combining the last two equations, one obtains

$$H_{\max}|F(j\omega)|_{\max} = \tfrac{1}{2}\sqrt{\frac{R_2}{R_1}} \tag{9.45}$$

The d-c value of the transfer voltage ratio, if there are no transformers in the network and if $a_0, b_0 \neq 0$, i.e., if there are no transmission zeros at the origin, is equal to the resistance ratio $R_2/(R_1 + R_2)$.   Therefore,

$$\frac{V_2}{V_0}(0) = H_0 F(0) = H_0 \frac{a_0}{b_0} = \frac{R_2}{R_1 + R_2} \tag{9.46}$$

In (9.46), H_0 is a specific value of H.   Should this value be less than H_{max}, it can be chosen for the realization procedure.   In terms of the given

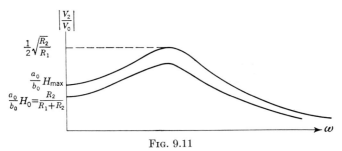

FIG. 9.11

transfer function and the terminating resistances, H_0 can be chosen if the following equation is satisfied.

$$\frac{2\sqrt{R_1 R_2}}{R_1 + R_2} \frac{|F(j\omega)|_{max}}{F(0)} \leq 1 \tag{9.47}$$

(9.47) is obtained directly from (9.45) and (9.46).   Illustrations are shown in Fig. 9.11 of a representative transfer voltage ratio with $H = H_{max}$ and $H = H_0 < H_{max}$.

If H_0 can be used and is chosen, either the desired value of R_2 or R_1^2/R_2 is obtained as the terminating resistor.   The second possibility is explained as follows.   From (9.46) the power transmitted to the load at d-c is specified:

$$P_{out}|_{d-c} = \frac{|V_2(0)|^2}{R_2} = |V_0(0)|^2 \frac{R_2}{(R_1 + R_2)^2} \tag{9.48}$$

This power transfer is implicit in the formulation of S_{21}, S_{11}, and Z_1. The physical realization of Z_1 provides a direct transmission of d-c from input to output, as shown in Fig. 9.12, since there are no transmission zeros at the origin.   Hence the final remainder in the development of Z_1 must be a resistance satisfying speci-fied power-transfer relationship of

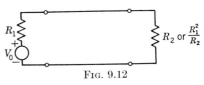

FIG. 9.12

(9.48).   The value can be either R_2 or R_1^2/R_2, since the power transfer is the same for both choices.   One-half of the possible realizations of Z_1 terminates in R_2, the other half in R_1^2/R_2.   This is the result of the plus and minus sign choice in (9.13), since for any pole-zero set of S_{11}, the sign choice leads to dual networks.

PROBLEMS

9.1. Determine the transmission coefficient S_{21} and the insertion voltage ratio of the networks in Fig. P9.1a and b.

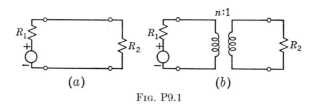

(a)   (b)

FIG. P9.1

9.2. Realize the transfer voltage ratio

$$\frac{V_2}{V_0} = \frac{\frac{1}{2}}{(p+1)^3}$$

with a lossless ladder terminated at both ends in 1-ohm resistances.

9.3. Given

$$S_{21} = \frac{Hp^3}{(p+1)^3}$$

determine H_{max} and develop two realizations of lossless ladders terminated at both ends with 1-ohm resistances.

9.4. Given

(a) $S_{21} = \dfrac{H}{p^2 + p + 1}$ (b) $S_{21} = \dfrac{Hp}{p^2 + p + 1}$

for terminations $R_1 = 1$ and $R_2 = 3$, determine H_{max}. Realize the transmission coefficients and the H_{max}, using ideal transformers.

9.5. Realize the transmission function of Prob. 9.4a without an ideal transformer.

9.6. Design a maximally flat magnitude bandpass filter operating between 600-ohm resistances. The 3-db bandwidth is from 2 to 4.5 kc and the required attenuation at 9 kc is at least 20 db.

9.7. The realization technique developed in this chapter can be extended to transfer functions with transmission zeros on the $j\omega$ axis other than zero and infinity. The zero-shifting procedure can be used in the development of the input impedance Z_1 of the terminated network. Negative elements may be necessary in the shifting steps. However, it can be shown that these negative elements can always be realized with perfectly coupled coils. Given

$$S_{21} = \frac{\frac{2}{3}(p^2 + 1)}{p^3 + \frac{4}{3}p^2 + p + \frac{2}{3}}$$

realize S_{21} as a lossless ladder terminated at both ends with 1-ohm resistances. For this function an all-positive element realization can be obtained.

9.8. Another way of designing networks with resistive termination at both ends is due to Norton.* Consider the network in Fig. P9.8. If Z_2 is the complementary impedance of Z_1, i.e., $Z_2 = 1 - Z_1$,

then
$$\frac{V_2}{V_0} = \frac{V_2}{2I_1} = \frac{Z_{21}}{2}$$

where Z_{21} is the transfer impedance of N_1. Thus the design of N_1 reduces to the method of Chap. 7. Network N_2 is realized from Z_2, which in turn is found from Z_1 of N_1. Z_2, of course, must be p-r and in special cases can be realized by the removal technique. An example is where the transfer-function specification is for a maximally flat magnitude function. Apply this method to develop networks N_1 and N_2 to realize a voltage transfer function V_2/V_0, which has a normalized two-pole maximally flat magnitude characteristic. Note that network N_2 is a high-pass network.

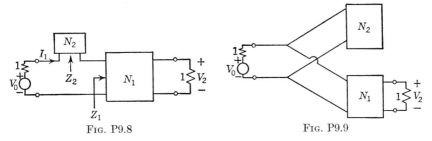

FIG. P9.8   FIG. P9.9

9.9. The dual situation of the network in Prob. 9.8 is shown in Fig. P9.9. Develop N_1 and N_2 for the same specification as Prob. 9.8.

* E. L. Norton, Constant Resistance Networks with Applications to Filter Groups, *Bell System Tech. J.*, vol. 16, pp. 178–193, April, 1937.

CHAPTER 10

SYNTHESIS OF 1-PORT RC NETWORKS

10.1 Introduction. In the design of circuits for low-frequency applications, inductances, if required, usually take on very large values. Consequently, the physical realization of these inductances becomes very impractical because of size, cost, and copper loss. In addition, where precise specifications are to be attained, the realization techniques described in the last few chapters cannot be used, because of the inherent resistances of the inductors. There is, however, a great need for precise network realization at low frequencies, especially in the field of control, where precise compensating networks are needed. Capacitances of large values can be obtained with low loss and for reasonable cost. Thus the use of networks containing only R and C is very important. The flat loss associated with such networks can be compensated with low-frequency amplifiers. In this chapter the properties and realization techniques of 1-port RC networks are developed. In the following chapter, the realization of RC 2-ports is treated.

10.2 Properties of RC Driving-point Impedances. In the development of the properties of LC networks the starting point can be the fact that LC networks consume no real average power. This approach is used in Chap. 6. Similarly, the properties of RC networks can be developed from the basic starting point that RC networks clearly consume power (the input power to an RC network is nonnegative). This approach is used in Appendix 2. The development in Appendix 2 can be used as an alternate to the presentation in this section.

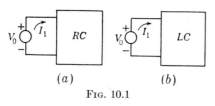

(a)   (b)

Fig. 10.1

The properties of an RC driving-point impedance can also be deduced directly from the known properties of LC driving-point impedances. Consider the two networks shown in block diagram form in Fig. 10.1. The RC network is passive and has an arbitrarily complicated configuration. The LC network is constructed to have precisely the same configuration as the RC network, with the resistances of Fig. 10.1a replaced

148

by inductances. The value of each inductance is equal to the value of
the resistance corresponding to it in the parent RC network. As is shown
below, from the known properties of the input impedance of the LC network, the properties of the input impedance of the RC network can be
established.

If a mesh analysis is made of each network, the input impedances can
be written

$$Z\big|_{RC} = \frac{\Delta^R}{\Delta_{11}{}^R} \tag{10.1}$$

$$Z\big|_{LC} = \frac{\Delta^L}{\Delta_{11}{}^L} \tag{10.2}$$

The superscripts R and L denote the RC and LC network determinants.
In (10.1) and (10.2) it is assumed that the mesh containing the voltage
source is labeled the first mesh and that the determinants have n rows
and n columns; i.e., there are n independent meshes in the networks.
The determinant of the equations of the RC network has elements of
the form

$$R_{ij} + \frac{1}{C_{ij}p} = \frac{1}{p}\left(R_{ij}p + \frac{1}{C_{ij}}\right) \tag{10.3}$$

The elements of the determinant of the LC network are of the form

$$L_{ij}p + \frac{1}{C_{ij}p} = \frac{1}{p}\left(L_{ij}p^2 + \frac{1}{C_{ij}}\right) \tag{10.4}$$

If each column (or each row) of Δ^R and $\Delta_{11}{}^R$ in (10.1) and Δ^L and $\Delta_{11}{}^L$ is
multiplied by p, the elements of the new determinants are simple poly-
nomials. Thus

$$\Delta^R = \frac{1}{p^r} P(p)$$

$$\Delta_{11}{}^R = \frac{1}{p^{r-1}} Q(p)$$

$$\Delta^L = \frac{1}{p^r} P(p^2) \tag{10.5}$$

$$\Delta^L = \frac{1}{p^{r-1}} Q(p^2)$$

It should be noted that the coefficient of p^{2k} in $P(p^2)$ or $Q(p^2)$ is equal to
the corresponding coefficient p^k in $P(p)$ or $Q(p)$, respectively, because
the inductances of the LC network have the same values as the corresponding resistances of the RC network. The input impedances then are

$$Z\big|_{RC} = \frac{1}{p}\frac{P(p)}{Q(p)} \tag{10.6}$$

$$Z\big|_{LC} = \frac{1}{p}\frac{P(p^2)}{Q(p^2)} \tag{10.7}$$

From Chap. 6, the poles and zeros of $Z|_{LC}$ lie on the $j\omega$ axis, alternate, and are simple. The numerator and denominator polynomials can be written

$$P(p^2) = H_1(p^2 + \omega_1{}^2)(p^2 + \omega_3{}^2) \cdots$$
$$Q(p^2) = H_2(p^2 + \omega_2{}^2)(p^2 + \omega_4{}^2) \cdots \tag{10.8}$$

where $0 < \omega_1 < \omega_2 < \omega_3 < \cdots$. Therefore the polynomials of $Z_{11}|_{RC}$ can be written

$$P(p) = H_1(p + \sigma_1)(p + \sigma_3)$$
$$Q(p) = H_2(p + \sigma_2)(p + \sigma_4) \tag{10.9}$$

where $\sigma_i = \omega_i{}^2 > 0 \qquad 0 < \sigma_1 < \sigma_2 < \sigma_3 \cdots$

The poles and zeros of $Z|_{RC}$ must therefore lie on the negative σ axis, be simple, and alternate with each other.

The behavior at zero and infinite frequency is compared next. If $2m$ is the degree of $P(p^2)$, the degree of $Q(p^2)$ is either $2m - 2$ or $2m$, and $Z|_{LC}$ has the following behavior:

$$\underset{p\to\infty}{Z|_{LC}} \to \frac{p^{2m}}{p(p^{2m-2})} \to p \quad \text{or} \quad \frac{p^{2m}}{p(p^{2m})} \to \frac{1}{p} \tag{10.10}$$

$$\underset{p\to 0}{Z|_{LC}} \to \frac{1}{p} \quad \text{or} \quad \frac{p^2}{p} \to p$$

From (10.6) and (10.7)

$$\underset{p\to\infty}{Z|_{RC}} \to \frac{p^m}{p(p^{m-1})} \to \text{const} \quad \text{or} \quad \frac{p^m}{p(p^m)} \to \frac{1}{p} \tag{10.11}$$

$$\underset{p\to 0}{Z|_{RC}} \to \frac{1}{p} \quad \text{or} \quad \frac{p}{p} \to \text{constant}$$

Hence $Z|_{RC}$ must either be a constant or have a zero at infinity, and at the origin $Z|_{RC}$ must either have a pole or be a constant.

Combining the properties of $Z|_{RC}$ at d-c and infinity with the fact that all poles and zeros lie on the negative real axis, one can establish four basic pole-zero diagrams, as illustrated in Fig. 10.2. Shown superimposed on the pole-zero diagrams are plots of $Z(\sigma)$. Clearly, from the plots,

$$\frac{dZ(\sigma)}{d\sigma} < 0 \tag{10.12}$$

Note that the critical frequency (a zero or a pole) nearest to or at the origin is a pole, while the critical frequency nearest to or at infinity is a zero. These facts follow directly from the inequalities of (10.8) and (10.9) together with (10.12).

The residues of $Z|_{RC}$ at the poles σ_i can be shown to be positive by similar reasoning. For the LC network, the residue of $Z|_{LC}$ at a pole $j\omega_i$ is real and positive.

$$k_i|_{LC} = (p - j\omega_i)Z(p)|_{p=j\omega_i}$$

$$= \frac{(p - j\omega_i)P(p^2)}{p(p^2 + \omega_i^2)Q_1(p^2)}\bigg|_{p=j\omega_i} \qquad (10.13)$$

$$= \frac{P(-\omega_i^2)}{(-2\omega_i^2)Q_1(-\omega_i^2)} > 0$$

where $Q(p^2) = (p^2 + \omega_i^2)Q_1(p^2)$. For the RC network, the residue of $Z|_{RC}$ at a pole $-\sigma_i = -\omega_i^2$ is

$$k_i|_{RC} = (p + \sigma_i)Z(p)|_{p=-\sigma_i}$$

$$= \frac{(p + \sigma_i)P(p)}{p(p + \sigma_i)Q_1(p)}\bigg|_{p=-\sigma_i} \qquad (10.14)$$

$$= \frac{P(-\sigma_i)}{(-\sigma_i)Q_1(-\sigma_i)}$$

Comparing (10.13) and (10.14), one concludes that $k_i > 0$, i.e., that the residues of the input impedance of an RC network are positive.

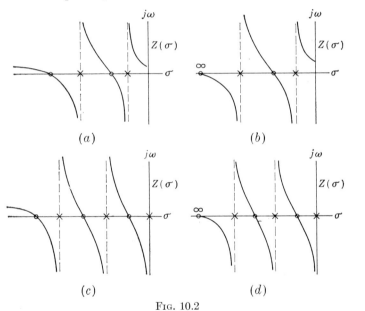

(a)   (b)

(c)   (d)

FIG. 10.2

As a last property, consider the input impedance for the pole-zero plot of Fig. 10.2a. The input impedance has an equal number of finite poles and zeros. For two zeros and two poles

$$Z(p) = H\frac{(p + \sigma_2)(p + \sigma_4)}{(p + \sigma_1)(p + \sigma_3)} \qquad (10.15)$$

where $\sigma_1 < \sigma_2 < \sigma_3 < \sigma_4$. At $p = \infty$

$$Z(\infty) = H \qquad (10.16)$$

At $p = 0$

$$Z(0) = H \left(\frac{\sigma_2}{\sigma_1}\right)\left(\frac{\sigma_4}{\sigma_3}\right) > H \qquad (10.17)$$

Clearly,

$$Z(0) > Z(\infty) \qquad (10.18)$$

From Fig. 10.2, (10.18) is obviously satisfied for all possibilities.

The properties of the driving-point admittance of an RC network can be established in a similar manner. In contrast to the situation for LC networks, the properties of $Y|_{RC}$ are not the same as those of $Z|_{RC}$. Clearly, the poles and zeros of Y lie on the negative σ axis and alternate. However, the critical frequency nearest to or at the origin is a zero, while the critical frequency nearest to or at infinity is a pole. In addition,

$$\frac{dY(\sigma)}{d\sigma} > 0 \qquad (10.19)$$

$$Y(0) < Y(\infty) \qquad (10.20)$$

Finally, the residues of $Y(p)$ at the poles are negative except at the pole at infinity. However, the residues of $Y(p)/p$ at the poles are positive. This becomes clear as one notes that the denominator factor p in $Y(p)/p$ produces a lowest critical frequency which is a pole and a highest critical frequency which is a zero. The alternation of poles and zeros on the negative σ axis is unchanged. Hence $Y(p)/p$ has the same basic properties as $Z(p)|_{RC}$.

10.3 Realization of 1-port RC Networks. The properties developed in the last section are not only necessary but also sufficient. That is, if a function satisfies these properties (either the properties of Z or the properties of Y), a network realization can be found, the driving-point function of which is the given function. In terms of Z, these basic properties are:

(a) Poles and zeros are simple, lie on the negative σ axis, and alternate with each other. The lowest critical frequency is a pole. The highest critical frequency is a zero.

or

(b) Poles are simple and lie on the negative σ axis. The residues of Z at the poles are positive.

In terms of Y, the basic properties are:

(a) Poles and zeros are simple, lie on the negative σ axis, and alternate with each other. The lowest critical frequency is a zero. The highest critical frequency is a pole.

or

(b) Poles are simple and lie on the negative σ axis. The residues of Y/p at the poles are positive.

In this section the sufficiency of these properties is shown. As in the LC cases, four basic or canonical configurations can be developed.

The partial fraction expansion of $Z(p)$ is

$$Z(p) = \frac{k_0}{p} + \frac{k_1}{p + \sigma_1} + \cdots + k_\infty \qquad (10.21)$$

For generality, a pole at the origin and a constant at infinity are included. Since all the residues are positive, each term in (10.21) can be identified as the impedance of a simple RC circuit, as shown in Fig. 10.3. A series connection of these simple circuits is the realization shown in Fig. 10.4. The single capacitance is present if there is a pole at the origin. The single resistance is not present if there is

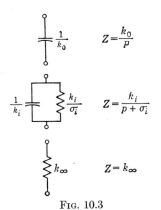

$$Z = \frac{k_0}{p}$$

$$Z = \frac{k_i}{p + \sigma_i}$$

$$Z = k_\infty$$

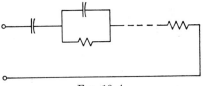

FIG. 10.3   FIG. 10.4

a zero at infinity. An example of the realization is given in the next section.

A partial fraction expansion of $Y(p)$ does not lead to a physical realization, because the residues are not positive. However, a simple manipulation leads to the residues of $Y(p)/p$, which are positive, and this function can be used to obtain another realization. The partial fraction expansion of Y/p has the form

$$\frac{Y}{p} = \frac{k_0}{p} + \frac{k_1}{p + \sigma_1} + \cdots + k_\infty \qquad (10.22)$$

where k_i are the residues of Y/p at the poles. Multiplying through by p, one obtains

$$Y = k_0 + \frac{k_1 p}{p + \sigma_1} + \cdots + k_\infty p \qquad (10.23)$$

$G = k_0 \qquad Y = k_0$

$G = k_i \qquad Y = \dfrac{k_i p}{p + \sigma_i}$

$\dfrac{k_i}{\sigma_i}$

$k_\infty \qquad Y = k_\infty p$

FIG. 10.5

The individual terms in (10.23) can be identified as the admittances of the simple networks shown in Fig. 10.5. The parallel combination of these networks is the realization of (10.23) and is shown in Fig. 10.6. The initial conductance is not present if $Y(0) = 0$.   The last capacitance is not present if $Y(\infty)$ is equal to a constant.

The use of the continued fraction expansions leads to the other two canonical configurations.   The first is obtained by successive removal of

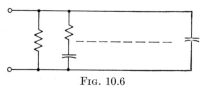

FIG. 10.6

either a constant or a pole at infinity of an impedance or an admittance, respectively.   If an RC impedance function is equal to a constant at infinity, this constant $Z(\infty)$ can be removed as a series resistance.   This is shown in Fig. 10.7a.   The removal of $Z(\infty) = k_\infty$ clearly leaves an RC remainder.   This can be seen from (10.21) and can also be seen from Fig. 10.2a.   Since $Z(\infty) < Z(0)$, the subtraction of $Z(\infty)$ leads to a plot such as Fig. 10.2b.   The remainder function Z' has a zero at infinity; its

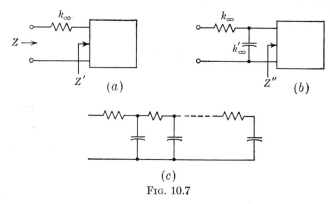

FIG. 10.7

reciprocal $Y' = 1/Z'$ has a pole at infinity.   This pole can be removed as a shunt capacitance having an admittance of $k'_\infty p$, as shown in Fig. 10.7b.   The remainder is an RC admittance function, which can be seen from (10.23).   The reciprocal of the remainder is an RC impedance function having a finite value at infinity.   This completes a cycle which can be continued.   The final configuration is as shown in Fig. 10.7c. The initial resistance is not present if $Z(\infty) = 0$.   The final capacitance is replaced by a short circuit if $Z(0)$ is a constant. $Z(p)$ can be written in terms of a finite continued fraction.

$$Z = R_1 + \cfrac{1}{C_2 p + \cfrac{1}{R_3 + \cfrac{1}{C_4 p + \cdots}}} \qquad (10.24)$$

As in the developments in Chap. 6, a simple numerical procedure consisting of division and inversion can be used to determine the element values.   This is illustrated in the next section.

If attention is centered on the behavior of $Z(p)$ at the origin rather than at infinity, the second configuration resulting from a continued fraction expansion can be developed.   In this case shunt conductances corresponding

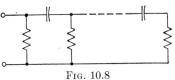

Fig. 10.8

to the value of admittance at zero are removed.   Series capacitances are removed to realize the poles of impedance at the origin.   The network has the configuration shown in Fig. 10.8.   The continued fraction expansion of Z is of the form

$$Z = \cfrac{1}{G_1 + \cfrac{1}{\cfrac{1}{pC_2} + \cfrac{1}{G_3 + \cfrac{1}{\cfrac{1}{pC_4} + \cdots}}}}$$ (10.25)

10.4 Realization Example.   In this section a numerical example is used to illustrate the development of the four canonical configurations. Assume that the given function to be realized is

$$F(p) = \frac{(p + 2)(p + 4)}{(p + 1)(p + 3)}$$ (10.26)

If the function is to be an RC driving-point function, it must satisfy the basic properties listed in Sec. 10.3.

For the given example it is simplest to use property (a), which is clearly satisfied if $F(p)$ is an impedance function.   The two partial fraction expansions are obtained as follows:

$$Z(p) = 1 + \frac{\frac{3}{2}}{p + 1} + \frac{\frac{1}{2}}{p + 3}$$ (10.27)

and

$$\frac{Y(p)}{p} = \frac{(p + 1)(p + 3)}{p(p + 2)(p + 4)} = \frac{\frac{3}{8}}{p} + \frac{\frac{1}{4}}{p + 2} + \frac{\frac{3}{8}}{p + 4}$$

$$Y(p) = \frac{3}{8} + \frac{\frac{1}{4}p}{p + 2} + \frac{\frac{3}{8}p}{p + 4}$$ (10.28)

The two network realizations are shown in Fig. 10.9a and b.

The subtractive or removal process of the continued fraction expansion is accomplished by using successive steps of division and inversion. For the first type, the removal involves k_∞ or $k'_\infty p$. Therefore the division centers on the highest powers of the numerator and the denominator polynomials. For the given example,

$$Z(p) = \frac{p^2 + 6p + 8}{p^2 + 4p + 3} \tag{10.29}$$

$p^2 + 4p + 3 \,\overline{\big)p^2 + 6p + 8}\ |\ 1$—Impedance removal
$\qquad\underline{p^2 + 4p + 3}$
$\qquad\qquad 2p + 5\,\overline{\big)p^2 + 4p + 3}\ |\ \tfrac{1}{2}p$—Admittance removal
$\qquad\qquad\quad\underline{p^2 + \tfrac{5}{2}p}$
$\qquad\qquad\qquad\quad\ \tfrac{3}{2}p + 3\,\overline{\big)2p + 5}\ |\ \tfrac{4}{3}$—Impedance removal
$\qquad\qquad\qquad\qquad\qquad\underline{2p + 4}$
$\qquad\qquad\qquad\qquad\qquad\quad 1\,\overline{\big)\tfrac{3}{2}p + 3}\ |\ \tfrac{3}{2}p$—Admittance removal
$\qquad\qquad\qquad\qquad\qquad\qquad\quad\underline{\tfrac{3}{2}p}$
$\qquad\qquad\qquad\qquad\qquad\qquad\qquad 3\,\overline{\big)1}\ |\ \tfrac{1}{3}$—Impedance removal
$\qquad\qquad\qquad\qquad\qquad\qquad\qquad\quad\underline{1}$
$\qquad\qquad\qquad\qquad\qquad\qquad\qquad\quad 0$—Short-circuit remainder

The network realization is shown in Fig. 10.9c.

To obtain the final configuration, a continued fraction expansion is made that removes either the admittance constant or the impedance pole at the origin. In the division process attention is centered on the lowest

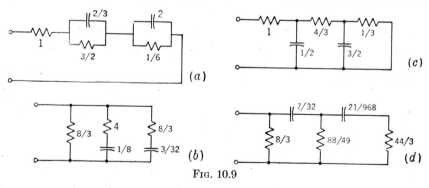

(a)

(b)

(c)

(d)

FIG. 10.9

orders of the numerator and the denominator polynomials. For the example,

$$Y(p) = \frac{3 + 4p + p^2}{8 + 6p + p^2} \tag{10.30}$$

$8 + 6p + p^2 \, \overline{\big)\, 3 + 4p + \quad p^2} \mid \frac{3}{8}$—Admittance removal
$\qquad\quad 3 + \frac{9}{4}p + \frac{3}{8}p^2$

$\qquad\qquad \frac{7}{4}p + \frac{5}{8}p^2 \, \overline{\big)\, 8 + \quad 6p + p^2} \mid \dfrac{32}{7p}$ —Impedance removal
$\qquad\qquad\qquad 8 + \frac{20}{7}p$

$\qquad\qquad\qquad\quad \frac{22}{7}p + p^2 \, \overline{\big)\, \frac{7}{4}p + \quad \frac{5}{8}p^2} \mid \frac{49}{88}$—Admittance removal

$\qquad\qquad\qquad\qquad\qquad \frac{7}{4}p + \frac{49}{88}p^2$

$\frac{3}{44}p^2 \, \overline{\big)\, \frac{22}{7}p + p^2} \mid \dfrac{968}{21p}$ —Impedance removal

$\frac{22}{7}p$

$\qquad\quad p^2 \, \overline{\big)\, \frac{3}{44}p^2} \mid \frac{3}{44}$ —Admittance removal

$\qquad\quad \frac{3}{44}p^2$

$\qquad\qquad \overline{\phantom{\frac{3}{44}p^2}}\; 0 \qquad$ Open-circuit remainder

The network is shown in Fig. 10.9d.
As a check on the arithmetic accuracy, it is useful to determine from the developed networks the zero and infinite frequency behaviors and to compare these with the given function. For each of the networks of Fig. 10.9, the low-frequency behavior is that of a resistance equal to $\frac{8}{3}$ ohms, and the high-frequency behavior is that of a resistance equal to 1 ohm. These results check with (10.26). As a final point, it is not necessary in the realization of $Z(p)$ to follow only one basic procedure. A mixture can be used to obtain other configurations.

10.5   RL 1-port Networks. In the development of the canonical configurations of LC networks in Chap. 6, it should be recognized

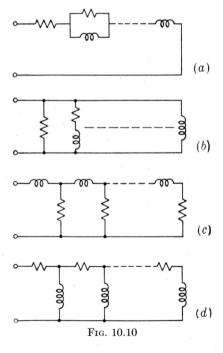

(a)

(b)

(c)

(d)

Fig. 10.10

that the duals of these networks are again LC networks. The duals of RC networks are RL networks. In this section, for completeness, a short discussion is given of RL driving-point impedance or admittance functions.

The development in Sec. 10.2 can be duplicated for RL networks, using a general nodal analysis rather than a mesh analysis. The elements of the determinant and the cofactors for the RL networks have the form ·

$$G_{ij} + \frac{1}{L_{ij}p} = \frac{1}{p}\left(G_{ij}p + \frac{1}{L_{ij}}\right) \qquad (10.31)$$

For the LC network, where the conductances of the RL network are replaced by capacitances of the same numerical value, the corresponding elements of the determinant and the cofactors have the form

$$C_{ij}p + \frac{1}{L_{ij}p} = \frac{1}{p}\left(C_{ij}p^2 + \frac{1}{L_{ij}}\right) \qquad (10.32)$$

Clearly, one can obtain the properties of an RL network from the properties of an LC network. In addition, from a comparison of (10.31) and (10.32), it can be seen that the functional form of an RL impedance function is identical with that of an RC admittance function. Similarly, the functional form of an RL admittance function is identical with that of an RC impedance function. Therefore RL impedance functions have the same basic properties as RC admittance functions, while RL admittance functions have the same basic properties as RC impedance functions. The development of RL canonical configurations, illustrated in Fig. 10.10, therefore follows directly.

PROBLEMS

10.1. Determine which of the following are RC driving-point impedance or admittance functions.

(a) $\dfrac{p + 1}{p + 2}$ (b) $\dfrac{p + 2}{p^2 + p}$ (c) $\dfrac{p^2 + 3p + 2}{p + 4}$ (d) $\dfrac{p^2 + 4p + 3}{p^2 + 2p}$

(e) $\dfrac{p^2 + 2p + 1}{p + 2}$ (f) $\dfrac{p^2 + 6p + 5}{p^2 + 5p + 6}$ (g) $\dfrac{(p + 2)(p + 4)}{(p + 3)(p + 5)}$

10.2. Develop all four canonical forms for each of the realizable functions of Prob. 10.1.

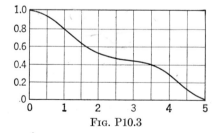

FIG. P10.3

10.3. Using the method of Chap. 3, approximate the magnitude curve in Fig. P10.3 with an RC driving-point impedance function with three poles. Develop one canonical realization.

10.4. Consider a rational function all the poles of which are simple and lie on the negative σ-axis. If a partial fraction expansion is made, some of the residues are positive and some are negative. Under what conditions can the function be realized as the input impedance of the series connection of an RC and an RL network?

10.5. Given a p-r function

$$Z(p) = \frac{(p + 2)(p + 3)}{(p + 1)(p + 4)}$$

realize $Z(p)$ as the driving-point impedance of a series connection of an RL and an RC network.

10.6. If $P(p)$ is a Hurwitz polynomial having all zeros on the negative σ axis, prove that $P(p)/P'(p)$ is the driving-point impedance function of an RL network and $P'(p)/P(p)$ is the driving-point impedance function of an RC network. $P'(p) = dP/dp$.

10.7. If $Z_1(p) = P(p)/Q(p)$ is the driving-point impedance of an RC network, prove that $Z_2(p) = P'(p)/Q'(p)$ can also be realized as the driving-point impedance of an RC network. $P'(p) = dP/dp$ and $Q'(p) = dQ/dp$.

10.8. Given an RC driving-point impedance

$$Z(p) = \frac{(p + 2)(p + 4)}{(p + 1)(p + 3)}$$

realize the two configurations in Fig. P10.8a and b.

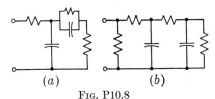

(a)   (b)

FIG. P10.8

CHAPTER 11

SYNTHESIS OF RC 2-PORTS

11.1 Introduction. The discussion in Chap. 10 of the properties and the realization of RC 1-ports is not only valuable in itself, but it also furnishes the tools and techniques necessary in the realization of RC 2-ports. The realization of RC 2-ports is a broad topic. In this chapter a restriction is made to simple RC ladders. The basic realization techniques closely follow those used for LC ladders as developed in Chap. 7. An important distinction to be made, however, is that a resistance-terminated RC ladder, or 2-port, is in itself an RC 2-port. Therefore it is simpler not to consider the terminations separately but to assume their presence in the 2-port. The new 2-port can then be considered as having open- or short-circuit terminations.

As in the LC case, the necessary properties of RC transfer functions, in general, are meager. The poles of the transfer functions are the natural frequencies and must be simple and lie on the negative σ axis. This follows directly from the properties of the 1-port, since the natural frequencies are the poles of either the driving-point impedance or the admittance functions. In certain cases, treated in the next section, restrictions may arise with respect to the presence of a pole at the origin and at infinity. For simple RC ladders having no-node bridging, the location of the transmission zeros is restricted. The zeros occur at the resonances and antiresonances of the shunt and series branches, respectively. A shunt branch is resonant at the poles of its admittance; a series branch is antiresonant at the poles of its impedance. Since the branches are RC 1-ports, the transmission zeros must occur on the negative σ axis. Thus both poles and zeros of an RC ladder must lie on the negative σ axis.

The transmission zeros may, for a general 2-port, lie anywhere in the complex plane with the exception of the positive real axis.[*,†] Complex zeros can be obtained if multiple paths from input to output are provided. This can be accomplished by parallel ladders, bridged-T networks, or twin-T networks[9,16] (see Sec. 12.6).

11.2 Realization of RC Ladders. Irrespective of the presence or absence of finite source and load resistances, the design situation takes

---

* This restriction can be removed if ideal transformers are permitted.

† A. Fialkow and I. Gerst, *Quart. Appl. Math.*, vol. 10, pp. 113–127, July, 1952.

one of the two forms shown in Fig. 11.1. If definite source and load resistances are specified, the design procedure can be such that these resistances are furnished. The desired transfer function, of course, must be compatible with the physical constraints of the resistance terminations. The details of including resistance terminations are given in Sec. 11.4.

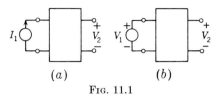

(a)   (b)

Fig. 11.1

For the situation shown in Fig. 11.1a, where the input is a current source and the output is an open circuit, the transfer function is the open-circuit transfer impedance.

$$z_{21} = \frac{V_2}{I_1} \qquad (11.1)$$

For this situation, the specified transfer function cannot have a pole at infinity; because the poles of z_{21} must be included in the poles of z_{11}. The highest critical frequency of z_{11}, in turn, must be a zero.* If the input source is a voltage source, as shown in Fig. 11.1b, the transfer function is the transfer voltage ratio

$$t_V = \frac{V_2}{V_1} = \frac{z_{21}}{z_{11}} = \frac{-y_{21}}{y_{22}} \qquad (11.2)$$

For this situation, the specified transfer function cannot have a pole at both the origin and infinity. The reason is that at d-c and infinity an RC network is purely resistive and an infinite voltage response cannot be obtained from a finite voltage source. Note that in (11.1) only one 2-port parameter is specified by the given transfer function. In (11.2) the ratio of two parameters is specified. Thus a great deal of flexibility exists in the realization, since it should be remembered that any given passive 2-port is completely specified by three parameters.

For either of the situations illustrated in Fig. 11.1, the realization procedure is to establish from the given transfer function two parameters, one a driving-point impedance or admittance, the other a transfer impedance or admittance. As for the LC ladder realization, the driving-point parameter is developed, and the proper transmission zeros are incorporated in the process. For the situation shown in Fig. 11.1a, a z_{11} or a z_{22} with the same poles as z_{21} and zeros that alternate with the poles are chosen. The choice of zeros must be such that the lowest critical frequency is a pole. As is brought out later, z_{11} must be constant at infinity if $z_{21}(\infty)$ is a constant. Naturally, the leading and final elements in the

* By the same reasoning, if the design situation is in terms of y_{21}, poles at the origin are nonrealizable.

development of z_{11} or z_{22} must be shunt elements in order to be compatible with the given current source and the open-circuit load.

The situation shown in Fig. 11.1b is a little more restrictive, since a ratio of two parameters is specified. The numerator polynomial of the given transfer function t_V may be assigned as the numerator of either z_{21} or $-y_{21}$. That is, the zeros of t_V are the zeros of either z_{21} or $-y_{21}$. The denominator polynomial, i.e., the poles, of t_V may then be assigned as the zeros of z_{11} or y_{22}. The poles for either the z_{ij} set or the y_{ij} set are next chosen to alternate with the assigned zeros of z_{11} or y_{22}. In making this last choice, attention must be directed toward satisfying the lowest and highest critical frequency criteria. In the realization the leading element at the input port must be a series element, because of the presence of a voltage source. The final element again must be a shunt element.

11.3   Realization Examples.   As an example, assume that the specified transfer function is

$$z_{21} = \frac{H}{(p+1)(p+3)} \tag{11.3}$$

Both transmission zeros occur at infinity. z_{11} can be chosen to have zeros at -2 and infinity.

$$z_{11} = \frac{(p+2)}{(p+1)(p+3)} \tag{11.4}$$

Clearly, the poles and zeros alternate; the lowest critical frequency is a pole and the highest critical frequency is a zero. Since both transmission zeros are at infinity, it is expected that these zeros are produced by shunt capacitances. Hence the first continued fraction expansion of the last chapter provides the desired realization. The numerical development is as follows:

$$
\begin{array}{r}
p + 2 \,\overline{)\,p^2 + 4p + 3\,}\ \big|\ p \\
\underline{p^2 + 2p} \\
2p + 3\,\overline{)\,p + 2\,}\ \big|\ \tfrac{1}{2} \\
\underline{p + \tfrac{3}{2}} \\
\tfrac{1}{2}\,\overline{)\,2p + 3\,}\ \big|\ 4p + 6 \qquad (11.5) \\
\underline{2p} \\
3 \\
\underline{3} \\
0
\end{array}
$$

The network is shown in Fig. 11.2a. In the last step of the numerical development inversion is not used; instead, the division is continued on the admittance basis. This produces a final shunt resistance and an open-circuit remainder. If it is desired to have the shunt resistance at the input rather than at the output, the 2-port can be turned end to end, as shown in Fig. 11.2b, since reciprocity holds.

By so choosing z_{11} for this problem as to have a zero at infinity, the initial shunt capacitance is assured. If z_{11} had been so chosen as to have two finite zeros, e.g.,

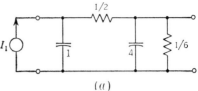

$$z_{11} = \frac{(p+2)(p+4)}{(p+1)(p+3)} \quad (11.6)$$

a configuration with an initial series resistance would have been obtained (see Fig. 10.9c). However, this series resistance is superfluous, because of the input current source. But it should not be implied that a choice of an equal number of poles and zeros is never made. Should z_{21}

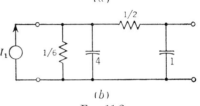

(b)

FIG. 11.2

be equal to a constant at infinity (i.e., should it have an equal number of finite poles and zeros), z_{21} would have no transmission zero at infinity. If z_{11} is chosen in such a way as to have a zero at infinity, somewhere in the ladder development a shunt capacitance is provided. Consequently, a transmission zero at infinity is produced, which indicates that the choice of z_{11} is in error. Therefore $z_{11}(\infty)$ must be a non-zero constant if $z_{21}(\infty)$ is a constant.*

With regard to the constant H in (11.3), any value can be obtained. Once the network has been developed, a resistance normalization can be introduced to obtain any desired value.

For a second example, assume that the specified transfer voltage ratio is

$$t_V = H \frac{(p+1)(p+5)}{(p+2)(p+4)} \quad (11.7)$$

The transmission zeros occur at -1 and -5 and are assigned as the zeros of z_{21}. The poles of t_V are assigned as the zeros of z_{11}. The poles of z_{21} and z_{11} can be chosen to lie at the origin and -3 to alternate with the zeros of z_{11}.

$$z_{21} = H \frac{(p+1)(p+5)}{p(p+3)} \quad (11.8)$$

$$z_{11} = \frac{(p+2)(p+4)}{p(p+3)} \quad (11.9)$$

* This, in essence, guarantees the residue condition for an RC 2-port at infinity. The residue condition states that $k_{11}{}^i k_{22}{}^i - (k_{12}{}^i)^2 \geq 0$, where $k_{11}{}^i$, $k_{22}{}^i$, and $k_{12}{}^i$ are the residues of z_{11}, z_{22}, and z_{12}, respectively, at the pole $p = \sigma_i$. (See Ref. 9.)

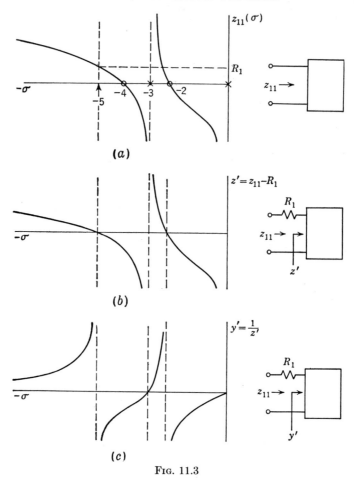

Fig. 11.3

One expects in the development of z_{11} that zero shifting is necessary. As an aid to proper development, successive plots of $z_{11}(\sigma)$ and the remainders are used, as shown in Fig. 11.3. The first element to be removed must be a series element, because of the presence of the voltage source. If this element is a resistance R_1 of value less than $z_{11}(\infty)$, the removal of this element can constitute a zero-shifting step. The zero of z_{11} at -4 can be shifted to -5, the location of one of the transmission zeros. R_1 must have a value of $z_{11}(-5) = \frac{3}{10}$ ohm. It should be noted that in general a partial resistance removal from an impedance shifts the zeros to the left. The maximum value of resistance that can be removed is $z_{11}(\infty)$. The remainder function z', plotted in Fig. 11.3b, clearly is an RC impedance function. The reciprocal function y' has a pole at one of

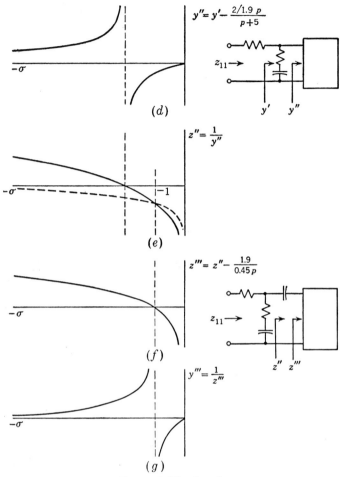

$$y'' = y' - \frac{2/1.9\ p}{p+5}$$

(d)

$$z'' = \frac{1}{y''}$$

(e)

$$z''' = z'' - \frac{1.9}{0.45\,p}$$

(f)

$$y''' = \frac{1}{z'''}$$

(g)

Fig. 11.3 (*Continued*)

the desired transmission zeros, -5. This pole can be removed as a shunt branch through one step of a partial fraction development.

$$z' = \frac{p^2 + 6p + 8}{p^2 + 3p} - \frac{3}{10} = \frac{0.7p^2 + 5.1p + 8}{p^2 + 3p}$$

$$y' = \frac{1}{z'} = \frac{p^2 + 3p}{0.7(p + 5)\left(p + \dfrac{1.6}{0.7}\right)} = \frac{\dfrac{2}{1.9}\,p}{p + 5} + \frac{\dfrac{1}{2.66}\,p}{p + \dfrac{1.6}{0.7}} \qquad (11.10)$$

In this shunt branch the resistance has a value of $1.9/2$ ohms, and the capacitance has a value of $2/9.5$ farad. The remainder function y'' is plotted in Fig. 11.3d.   Neither y'' nor its reciprocal has a pole at the other transmission zero, -1.   In the plot of $z'' = 1/y''$ it can be seen that a partial removal of the pole at the origin with a series capacitance shifts the existing zero to the right.   The correct value of the capacitance is

$$\frac{1}{Cp}\bigg|_{p=-1} = z''(p)\big|_{p=-1}$$

$$C = \frac{0.5}{1.71} \text{ farad} \tag{11.11}$$

The final remainder function is

$$z''' = z'' - \frac{1}{Cp} = 2.66 \frac{p+1}{p} \tag{11.12}$$

$z'''(\sigma)$ is plotted in Fig. 11.3f.   The reciprocal y''' has a pole at -1, which is removed as a shunt branch producing the final transmission zero.

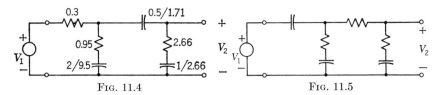

FIG. 11.4   FIG. 11.5

The resistance of this branch has a value of 2.66 ohms, and the capacitance has a value of 1/2.66 farad.   This removal completes the realization, since the final remainder is an open circuit.   The network is shown in Fig. 11.4.

The network evolved is, of course, not unique.   The initial element can be a series capacitance, and the realization can take the form shown in Fig. 11.5.   Alternately, different poles of z_{11} and z_{21} can be chosen. If a pole is chosen at a finite frequency rather than at the origin, an additional resistance is introduced.   There is no advantage in choosing a greater number of finite poles than zeros for z_{11}, because superfluous or redundant elements result.

In the present example one can also work with the short-circuit admittance functions [see Eq. (11.2)].   A suitable choice of the poles of y_{21} and y_{22} are -3 and infinity.

$$-y_{21} = \frac{(p+1)(p+5)}{p+3} \tag{11.13}$$

$$y_{22} = \frac{(p+2)(p+4)}{p+3} \tag{11.14}$$

In the realization, since y_{22} is specified, the first element to be removed must be a shunt element.   If a partial removal of shunt conductance is made, a zero shifting can be accomplished.   The zero-producing step takes the form of a series branch, as shown in Fig. 11.6. The process is then continued, ending with a series branch.

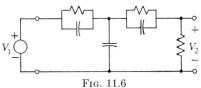

As a final point on zero shifting, the zeros always shift toward the pole being partly removed. If a series resistance is removed from an imped-ance, the zeros shift to the left; and

FIG. 11.6

if a shunt conductance is removed from an admittance, the zeros shift to the right. These statements can be verified by inspection of repre-sentative plots of $Z(\sigma)$ and $Y(\sigma)$.

With regard to the constant H of $t_V(p)$, one cannot obtain any specified value. However, because of the freedom available in choosing the param-eter sets and the techniques of realization, a wide variety of realizable values of H is possible. Obtaining the largest value is a topic that has received much attention,* but it is beyond the scope of this book.

11.4 Resistive Terminations. If an *RC* 2-port is to have a resistive termination at either or both ends, the specified transfer function must have no pole at the origin. (It has already been established that there can be no pole at infinity.) Capacitances in the network are open cir-cuits at zero frequency. Consequently, the terminated 2-port at this fre-quency is a resistive structure, the response of which must be finite.

In the case of z_{21} realization, z_{11} must have the same poles as z_{21}. Therefore it must have no pole at the origin. The finite value of $1/z_{11}(0)$ may be either totally or partially removed as the initial step. In either case, this provides an initial shunt conductance. Except for one situ-ation, complete conductance removal precludes any other shunt con-ductances in the remainder of the network. At each step of the network development after the first, the value of each admittance remainder is zero. Therefore a shunt-conductance removal is impossible. The excep-tion occurs in the case of a total removal, at the origin, of an impedance pole that is used to produce a transmission zero there. After such a removal, the remainder function is finite at the origin. Hence another shunt conductance appears in the development.

In the case of an initial partial conductance removal, the network development can always terminate with a shunt conductance. This statement follows from the reasoning above. Each admittance remain-der is non-zero at the origin. Total conductance removal can be delayed until the last step, which produces the final resistance. Clearly, if only a final shunt conductance rather than the initial conductance is desired, the shunt-conductance removal can be delayed until the last step. Alter-nately, reciprocity can be used for a network developed with an initial

* A. Fialkow and I. Gerst, *op. cit.*

complete conductance removal (see Fig. 11.2). Thus if z_{11} is finite at the origin, a ladder with resistance terminations at either end or at both ends can be realized.

For t_V realization the choice of the proper z_{11} or $1/y_{22}$ follows a similar line of reasoning. If, for example, z_{11} is chosen to be non-zero at infinity, the initial removal may be a series resistance. For a final shunt conductance, $z_{11}(0)$ must be finite.

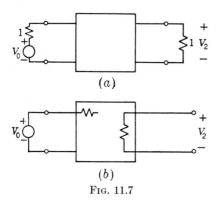

(a)

(b)

Fig. 11.7

As an illustration, assume that the transfer voltage ratio for the situation shown in Fig. 11.7a is

$$\frac{V_2}{V_0} = H \frac{p+1}{(p+3)(p+5)} \quad (11.15)$$

The specified terminations at both ends are to be unit resistances. By absorbing both resistances into the 2-port, as shown in Fig. 11.7b, a t_V realization can be used. Since terminations at both ends are desired, z_{11} should be a non-zero constant at both the origin and infinity. A suitable choice is

$$z_{11} = \frac{(p+3)(p+5)}{(p+2)(p+4)} \quad (11.16)$$

In the development of z_{11}, total pole removals should be made at infinity and $p = -1$ to produce the desired transmission zeros. The impedance and the admittance plots of the development are shown in Fig. 11.8. The first step is the total removal of $z_{11}(\infty)$. This is followed by the removal of the pole of y' at infinity to produce the transmission zero at infinity. Inversion is not used after this step; instead, a zero-shifting partial removal of conductance is made to obtain a zero at $p = -1$. A pole is then removed from the inverted remainder to produce the other transmission zero. Finally, a shunt conductance is removed. The network is shown in Fig. 11.9a. The last resistance is separated into two series resistances to achieve the unit resistance termination as shown in Fig. 11.9(b).

11.5 Active RC Networks. In many low-frequency applications filter-type transfer functions are needed. For example, a transfer function with a low-pass maximally flat magnitude characteristic may be desired. This type of function cannot be achieved by using passive RC networks, because for RC networks the natural frequencies must be negative real. However, if active elements are used in conjunction with RC networks, complex natural frequencies can be obtained. This section illustrates

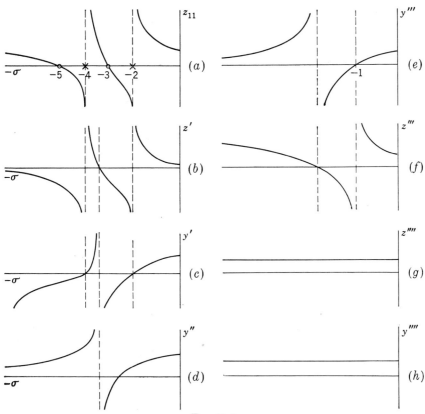

FIG. 11.8

two techniques by which complex poles can be realized with active RC networks. In the examples to follow, transistor amplifiers are used for the active elements. At low frequencies, a common emitter transistor can be approximated with the incremental equivalent circuit shown in Fig. 11.10. The transistor is assumed, for simplicity's sake, to be unilateral. A typical value for R_1 is 1,000 ohms. A typical value of β_0 is 50.

Consider first the feedback amplifier shown in Fig. 11.11. The three-stage transistor amplifier provides an output current which is out of phase

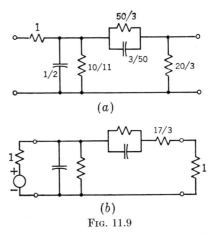

FIG. 11.9

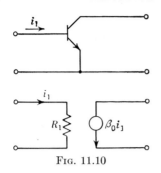

Fig. 11.10

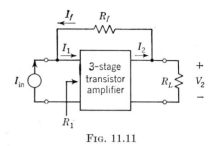

Fig. 11.11

with the input current. Thus any current flowing back through R_f produces negative feedback. From Fig. 11.10, the input impedance of the amplifier without feedback is R_1 and the output impedance is infinity. The input source is assumed to be a current source; its internal impedance is much larger than the input impedance of the feedback amplifier. The three-stage amplifier has a current transfer function $-\mu$.

$$\frac{I_2}{I_1} = -\mu \tag{11.17}$$

The over-all transfer impedance with feedback is easily established.

$$I_1 = I_f + I_{\text{in}} \tag{11.18}$$
$$V_2 = (I_2 - I_f)R_L \tag{11.19}$$
$$V_2 = R_f I_f + I_1 R_1 \tag{11.20}$$

Usually $R_f \gg R_1$ and R_L; therefore the solution of (11.17) through (11.20) leads to

$$Z_{21} = \frac{V_2}{I_{\text{in}}} = \frac{-\mu R_L}{1 + \mu B} \tag{11.21}$$

where

$$B \approx \frac{R_L}{R_f} \tag{11.22}$$

B is the current feedback factor. Equation (11.21) is a familiar feedback amplifier equation. That (11.21) can have complex poles can be seen as follows. Let the current transfer function $-\mu$ have two negative real poles at $-a$ and $-b$.

$$-\mu = \frac{-H}{(p + a)(p + b)} \tag{11.23}$$

Equation (11.21) becomes

$$Z_{21}(p) = \frac{-HR_L}{p^2 + (a + b)p + ab + HB}$$
$$= \frac{-HR_L}{p^2 + \varsigma p + \eta} \tag{11.24}$$

For complex poles

$$\zeta^2 < 4\eta \qquad (11.25)$$

Equation (11.25) can be satisfied by a proper choice of HB. In particular, if a two-pole maximally flat magnitude function is desired, one obtains from Chap. 3:

$$\zeta^2 = 2\eta$$
$$(a + b)^2 = 2(ab + HB)$$

or

$$HB = (a^2 + b^2)/2 \qquad (11.26)$$

Also, it should be remembered that the 3-db radial bandwidth is equal to the radius on which the poles lie, $(a + b)/\sqrt{2}$.

For a design specification of a maximally flat magnitude transfer impedance having a unit radial bandwidth,

$$a + b = \sqrt{2} \qquad (11.27)$$

Either a or b can be chosen independently. Let $a = 1$; thus $b = 0.414$. From (11.26)

$$HB = 0.586 \qquad (11.28)$$

The remaining problems are to realize the desired current transfer function $-\mu$ and the current feedback factor B. The desired two-pole transfer function of (11.23) can be realized simply as shown in Fig. 11.12, where the voltage supply circuitry has been ignored. Most often, d-c coupling is used for low-frequency applications. If R_1, the input impedance of the transistor, is nor-

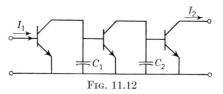

FIG. 11.12

malized to unity, the values of the capacitances should be $C_1 = 1$ farad and $C_2 = 1/0.414$ farad to obtain the desired pole locations $-a$ and $-b$. The current gain of the amplifier of Fig. 11.12 is $\beta_0{}^3$. Thus

$$H = ab\beta_0{}^3 = 0.414\,\beta_0{}^3 \qquad (11.29)$$

From (11.28) and (11.22)

$$B = \frac{0.586}{H} = \frac{0.586}{0.414\,\beta_0{}^3} \qquad (11.30)$$

$$R_f = \frac{R_L}{B} \qquad (11.31)$$

Another basic active RC configuration is shown in Fig. 11.13.* The amplifier is assumed to be unilateral and, for simplicity's sake, to have a

* J. T. Bangert, The Transistor as a Network Element, *Bell System Tech. J.*, vol. 33, pp. 329–352, March, 1954.

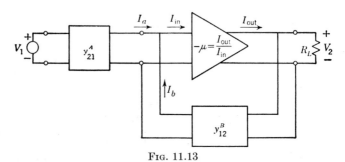

FIG. 11.13

zero input impedance and a zero output admittance. The current gain
of the amplifier is

$$\frac{I_{out}}{I_{in}} = -\mu \qquad (11.32)$$

The input network is described in terms of the short-circuit transfer
admittance

$$\frac{-I_a}{V_1} = y_{21}{}^A \qquad (11.33)$$

The feedback network is also described in terms of the short-circuit
reverse-transfer admittance

$$\frac{-I_b}{V_2} = y_{12}{}^B \qquad (11.34)$$

Noting that

$$I_{in} = I_a + I_b \qquad (11.35)$$

and

$$V_2 = \frac{I_{out}}{\dfrac{1}{R_L} + y_{22}{}^B} = I_{out}Z_L \qquad (11.36)$$

one can solve the above equations to obtain

$$\frac{V_2}{V_1} = \frac{\mu Z_L y_{21}{}^A}{1 - \mu y_{12}{}^B Z_L} \qquad (11.37)$$

Usually μ is sufficiently large so that $|\mu Z_L y_{12}{}^B| \gg 1$. Equation (11.37)
then becomes

$$\frac{V_2}{V_1} \approx -\frac{y_{21}{}^A}{y_{12}{}^B} \qquad (11.38)$$

Note that in (11.38) the zeros of $y_{12}{}^B$ are part of the set of poles of V_2/V_1.
As mentioned previously and as shown in the next chapter, passive RC
2-ports can be realized with complex transmission zeros. Thus V_2/V_1
can have complex poles. The usual design procedure is to choose the

poles of $y_{21}{}^A$ and $y_{12}{}^B$ in such a way that a cancellation occurs in (11.38). For example, let

$$y_{21}{}^A = \frac{H_a}{(p + a)(p + b)} \tag{11.39}$$

$$y_{12}{}^B = \frac{H_b[(p + \sigma_1)^2 + \omega_1{}^2]}{(p + a)(p + b)} \tag{11.40}$$

The pole-zero plots of (11.39) and (11.40) are shown in Fig. 11.14a and b. The over-all transfer voltage ratio is

$$\frac{V_2}{V_1} = \frac{H}{(p + \sigma_1)^2 + \omega_1{}^2} \tag{11.41}$$

The poles of (11.41) are plotted in Fig. 11.14c.

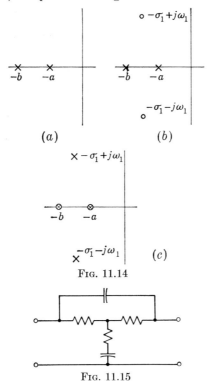

(a)   (b)

(c)

Fig. 11.14

Fig. 11.15

The $y_{21}{}^A$ above can be simply realized as an RC ladder. There remains the problem of finding for the feedback network an RC 2-port which provides the complex transmission zeros. A network that accomplishes this is the bridged-T network shown in Fig. 11.15. It has multiple paths from input to output; hence it is potentially capable of producing complex transmission zeros. A design procedure for this type of network is discussed in the next chapter.

PROBLEMS

11.1. From inspection, determine the transmission zeros of the circuits in Fig. P11.1. Each circuit is driven by a voltage source. If each circuit is terminated in a resistance, what are the transmission zeros?

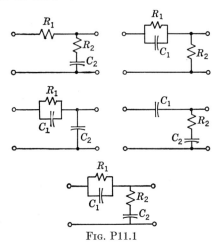

FIG. P11.1

11.2. Realize the following functions as both the open-circuit transfer impedance z_{21} and the unterminated transfer voltage ratio V_2/V_1. For each realization determine the constant H.

$$(a)\ \frac{H}{(p+1)(p+3)} \qquad (b)\ \frac{Hp}{(p+1)(p+3)} \qquad (c)\ \frac{Hp^2}{(p+1)(p+3)}$$

11.3. Repeat Prob. 11.2 for the following functions:

$$(a)\ \frac{H(p+4)(p+5)}{(p+1)(p+2)} \qquad (b)\ \frac{H(p+2)(p+4)}{(p+1)(p+3)}$$

$$(c)\ \frac{H(p+1)(p+4)}{(p+2)(p+3)} \qquad (d)\ \frac{H(p+2)(p+3)}{(p+1)(p+4)}$$

11.4. Realize the functions of Prob. 11.2 as the terminated transfer impedance Z_{21} and as the terminated transfer voltage ratio V_2/V_1. The termination is at the output and is a 1-ohm resistance in each case. Evaluate the constant H for each realization.

11.5. Given the following situation

$$z_{21} = \frac{V_2}{I_1} = \frac{H}{(p+1)(p+2)}$$

which of the following choices for z_{11} are suitable? Explain why

$$(a)\ \frac{p+\frac{3}{2}}{(p+1)(p+2)} \qquad (b)\ \frac{(p+\frac{3}{2})(p+4)}{(p+1)(p+2)}$$

$$(c)\ \frac{(p+\frac{1}{2})(p+\frac{3}{2})}{(p+1)(p+2)} \qquad (d)\ \frac{(p+\frac{1}{2})(p+\frac{3}{2})}{p(p+1)(p+2)}$$

Develop one realization of z_{21} for each suitable case.

11.6. Realize with the configurations shown in Fig. P11.6 the following function as an unterminated transfer voltage ratio:

$$\frac{V_2}{V_1} = \frac{H(p+2)(p+3)}{(p+1)(p+4)}$$

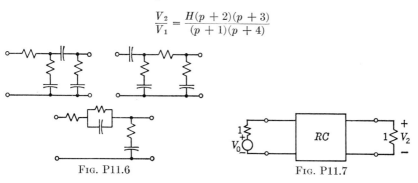

FIG. P11.6   FIG. P11.7

11.7. For the situation shown in Fig. P11.7, realize the following functions as the transfer voltage ratio $\frac{V_2}{V_0}$:

(a) $\dfrac{H}{(p+1)(p+3)}$ (b) $\dfrac{H(p+5)}{(p+1)(p+3)}$

11.8. It is desired to realize the following magnitude characteristic with the cascaded amplifier shown in Fig. P11.8. The presence of the shunt capacitances of the tubes must be included in the realization of RC coupling networks. The input and the output capacitances of the tubes are $10\mu\mu f$ and the transconductance is 0.004 mho.

(a) From the magnitude plot determine a set of poles and zeros of the transfer function.

(b) Realize a suitable set of coupling networks.

(c) Determine the over-all gain of the amplifier. Is this value the maximum obtainable?

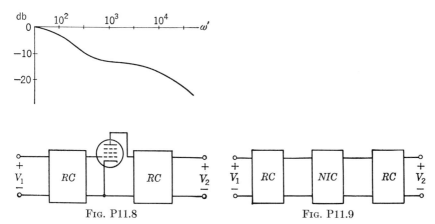

FIG. P11.8   FIG. P11.9

11.9. Calculate the unterminated transfer voltage ratio V_2/V_1 of the circuit in Fig. P11.9 in terms of the parameters of the individual networks. The parameters of the negative impedance converter are described in Prob. 5.13.

11.10. Use the configuration and the result of Prob. 11.9 to realize the following:

$$\frac{V_2}{V_1} = \frac{H(p+1)}{p^2+p+1}$$

11.11. Repeat Probs. 11.9 and 11.10 for a specification of the unterminated transfer impedance z_{21}.

11.12. Determine the transfer admittances and the locations of the transmission zeros of the circuits in Fig. P11.12. Using the method of equating coefficients, realize the following transfer admittances with an appropriate configuration:

(a) $y_{21} = -\dfrac{p^2+p+1}{p+2}$ (b) $y_{21} = -\dfrac{p^2+1}{p+1}$

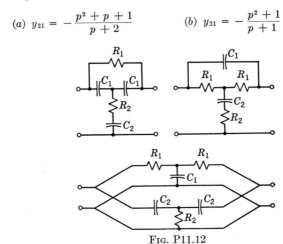

FIG. P11.12

11.13. Using the active RC configuration of Fig. 11.13 realize the following function:

$$\frac{V_2}{V_1} = \frac{p^2+1}{p^2+p+1}$$

CHAPTER 12

SYNTHESIS WITH CASCADED CONSTANT-R 2-PORTS

12.1 The Building-block Technique. The basic realization procedure discussed in the last several chapters can be summarized as follows. Starting from a realizable transfer-function specification, one obtains an input impedance or admittance for the unknown 2-port. The network is developed from this driving-point impedance or admittance, a process in which the presence of the given transmission zeros is taken into account. In this chapter and the ones to follow, another basic realization procedure is developed: the cascaded building-block technique. In this technique the realization takes the form of a cascade of simple and special networks. The over-all transfer function is factored into or built up from simple components, each of which is realized by one of the building blocks.

Clearly, there are restrictions on the properties of the building blocks. A group of isolated 2-ports may be individually developed to realize given transfer functions. The cascade of these 2-ports generally does not provide an over-all transfer function that is the product of the transfer functions of the isolated 2-ports. Inter-action between the cascaded 2-ports takes place. All that can be said for the general case is that the over-all $ABCD$ matrix is the product of the individual $ABCD$ matrices. However, it should be remembered from Chap. 5 that this interaction is eliminated if the cascading includes unilateral, or buffer, 2-ports. If the input and output impedances of the unilateral

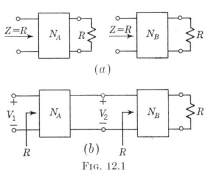

(a)

(b)

FIG. 12.1

2-port are incorporated in the design of the adjacent passive 2-ports, an over-all product-type transfer function can be obtained.

The building-block approach just described can also be accomplished with purely passive 2-ports. Consider the elementary 2-ports shown in Fig. 12.1a. Assume that each 2-port, when terminated in a resistance R, has an input impedance which is also equal to R. If the 2-ports are

177

designed to have the specified transfer voltage ratios t_A and t_B, these transfer voltage ratios of the individual 2-ports are unchanged when the 2-ports are cascaded, as shown in Fig. 12.1b. No interaction occurs to disturb the individual transfer voltage ratio, since each network is still terminated in R. The over-all transfer voltage ratio is simply the product $t_A t_B$.

Networks like these are called constant-R networks. One simple type is the constant-R ladder. Two examples are shown in Fig. 12.2. For either network, the input impedance is R if the branches z_1 and z_2 have the following relation:

$$z_1 z_2 = R^2 \tag{12.1}$$

The voltage transfer function for the circuit of Fig. 12.2a is

$$\frac{V_2}{V_1} = \frac{1}{1 + R/z_2} \tag{12.2}$$

For the circuit of Fig. 12.2b

$$\frac{V_2}{V_1} = \frac{1}{1 + \dfrac{z_2}{R}} \tag{12.3}$$

The realization of these circuits reduces to the design of 1-port networks. Other basic constant-R networks are the constant-R lattice and bridged-T networks. These types of networks receive the most attention in this chapter.

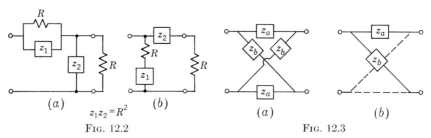

$$(a)$$ $z_1 z_2 = R^2$ $$(b)$$

FIG. 12.2

$$(a)$$ $$(b)$$

FIG. 12.3

In many instances, the specifications do not call for precise synthesis. The need for input impedances that are precisely constant is then not so stringent. For example, an active 2-port may present an input impedance that deviates from a pure resistance only slightly over the band of interest. Constant-R–type cascading can then be used without introducing much interaction distortion.

12.2 The Symmetrical Lattice Network. A symmetrical lattice network has the configuration shown in Fig. 12.3a.[10,13] This network is a balanced structure; i.e., the input and the output do not have a common node. For greater simplicity, the lattice configuration is usually drawn as shown in Fig. 12.3b, where the dashed lines indicate the presence of z_a and z_b. The open-circuit parameters are

$$z_{11} = z_{22} = \frac{z_a + z_b}{2}$$

$$z_{12} = z_{21} = \frac{z_b - z_a}{2} \tag{12.4}$$

If the lattice is terminated in R at the output port, the input impedance is

$$Z_{11} = z_{11} - \frac{z_{12}^2}{z_{22} + R} \tag{12.5}$$

$$= R \frac{z_a + z_b + \dfrac{2z_a z_b}{R}}{z_a + z_b + 2R} \tag{12.6}$$

Equation (12.5) is found directly from the open-circuit equations under the condition $V_2 = -I_2 R$.

If

$$z_a z_b = R^2 \tag{12.7}$$

(12.6) becomes

$$Z_{11} = R \tag{12.8}$$

Since the network is symmetrical, the output impedance is

$$Z_{22} = R \tag{12.9}$$

if the input is terminated in R, i.e., if the source impedance is R. Therefore if (12.7) holds, a symmetrical lattice is a constant-R network.* Equation (12.7) can also be written

$$\frac{z_a}{R} = \frac{R}{z_b} \tag{12.10}$$

Thus the normalized impedance of z_a is equal to the reciprocal of the normalized impedance of z_b. Two networks which have this property are called reciprocal impedance networks. From Chaps. 6 and 10, it should be remembered that if z_a is the realizable impedance of an LC network, z_b is also the impedance of an LC network. If z_a is the impedance of an RC network, z_b is the impedance of an RL network.

The transfer impedance of a symmetrical lattice terminated at the output in R is

$$Z_{21} = \frac{z_{21} R}{z_{22} + R} \tag{12.11}$$

$$= \frac{z_b - z_a}{z_a + z_b + 2R} R \tag{12.12}$$

* It is to be emphasized that, in contrast with the constant-R ladder networks of Fig. 12.2, the symmetrical constant-R lattice has both its input and output impedance equal to R when properly terminated.

For a constant-R lattice, i.e., if (12.7) holds,

$$Z_{21} = R \frac{z_b - R}{z_b + R} \tag{12.13}$$

For the condition shown in Fig. 12.4, where both the source and load impedances are equal to R, the constant-R lattice is said to be resistance-matched. The transfer voltage ratio is simply

$$\frac{V_2}{V_0} = \frac{1}{2} \frac{Z_{21}}{R} = \frac{1}{2} \frac{z_b - R}{z_b + R} \tag{12.14}$$

Since

$$V_0 = 2V_1 \tag{12.15}$$

$$\frac{V_2}{V_1} = \frac{z_b - R}{z_b + R} \tag{12.16}$$

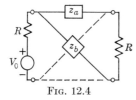

FIG. 12.4

In actual synthesis, the transfer function to be realized usually pertains to (12.16), since the constant-R lattice is part of a cascade. The synthesis procedure is to move from a specification of V_2/V_1 to a specification of z_b. Of course, the resulting z_b must be p-r. The restrictions on V_2/V_1 to ensure a z_b that is p-r can be found as follows. Equation (12.16) is solved for z_b.

$$\frac{z_b}{R} = \frac{1 + V_2/V_1}{1 - V_2/V_1} \tag{12.17}$$

z_b is p-r if z_b is real when p is real and if

$$\text{Re } [z_b] \geq 0 \qquad \text{in the RHP} \tag{12.18}$$

The first condition is clearly satisfied for any realizable V_2/V_1. From (12.17)

$$\begin{aligned}
\text{Re } [z_b/R] &= \text{Re} \left[\frac{1 + \text{Re } V_2/V_1 + j \text{ Im } V_2/V_1}{1 - \text{Re } V_2/V_1 - j \text{ Im } V_2/V_1} \right] \\
&= \frac{1 - (\text{Re } V_2/V_1)^2 - (\text{Im } V_2/V_1)^2}{(1 - \text{Re } V_2/V_1)^2 + (\text{Im } V_2/V_1)^2} \\
&= \frac{1 - |V_2/V_1|^2}{(1 - \text{Re } V_2/V_1)^2 + (\text{Im } V_2/V_1)^2}
\end{aligned} \tag{12.19}$$

To satisfy (12.18), one can see from (12.19) that

$$\left| \frac{V_2}{V_1} \right|^2 \leq 1 \qquad \text{in the RHP} \tag{12.20}$$

The equality in (12.18), and therefore the equality in (12.20), is satisfied for nontrivial cases only on the boundary, i.e., the $j\omega$ axis. Thus, if (12.20) is satisfied, the denominator of (12.17) cannot have a zero in the interior of the right half plane. Hence z_b is analytic in the right half plane. Then it follows from arguments similar to those used in Chap. 6 that (12.20) can be restated as follows:

$$\left| \frac{V_2}{V_1}(j\omega) \right| \leq 1 \qquad (12.21)$$

The validity of (12.21) can also be seen from average-power considerations. The power into the network for sinusoidal excitation is $|V_1|^2/R$. The output power absorbed in the load is $|V_2|^2/R$. Since for a passive structure the output power can at most equal the input power, (12.21) follows. The necessary and sufficient condition to ensure the physical realizability of z_b is that $(V_2/V_1)(p)$ be a stable rational network function for which (12.21) holds. For a given specification of poles and zeros of V_2/V_1, it may be necessary to introduce a constant multiplier to satisfy (12.21). That is, the poles and zeros of V_2/V_1 can be realized but a flat loss may have to be introduced.

12.3 All-pass Constant-R Lattices. In the realizability conditions of the last section no restriction is made on the location of the transmission zeros. That is, the transfer function is not restricted to being minimum phase. Thus a transfer function with zeros anywhere in the complex plane can be realized with a constant-R lattice. This is expected from previous arguments, since multiple paths exist from input to output.

An interesting and important special case arises when z_a and z_b are LC functions. z_b, for example, can then be expressed as

$$\frac{z_b}{R} = \frac{A}{pB} \qquad \text{or} \qquad \frac{pB}{A} \qquad (12.22)$$

where A and B are even polynomials, and $P(p) = A + pB$ is a Hurwitz polynomial. The transfer voltage ratio of the lattice, Eq. (12.16), becomes

$$\frac{V_2}{V_1} = \pm \frac{A - pB}{A + pB} = \pm \frac{P(-p)}{P(p)} \qquad (12.23)$$

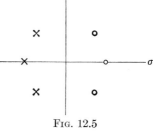

For this special case the zeros all lie in the right half plane and are the negatives of the poles. A representative pole-zero set is shown in Fig. 12.5 and is, as expected, symmetrical about the $j\omega$ axis.

FIG. 12.5

The transfer function for this case is said to be an all-pass function because

$$\left| \frac{V_2}{V_1}(j\omega) \right| = 1 \qquad (12.24)$$

That is, this type of transfer function has a constant magnitude on the $j\omega$ axis and introduces only a phase shift. The phase function is simply expressed in terms of the reactance function $X_b(\omega)$.

$$\frac{z_b(j\omega)}{R} = j\,\frac{X_b(\omega)}{R} \tag{12.25}$$

$$\operatorname{Arg}\frac{V_2}{V_1}(j\omega) = \pi - 2\tan^{-1}\frac{X_b(\omega)}{R} \tag{12.26}$$

A network that has an all-pass transfer function is primarily used for phase equalization and for delay networks.

The realization of the impedance branches of an all-pass lattice is straightforward with use of the techniques of Chap. 6. Usually z_b is determined from a given phase specification, and z_a is then found from (12.10). An example is given in Sec. 12.5.

12.4 Lattice Unbalancing Techniques. The lack of a common input and output node is very often troublesome in practical situations. An unbalanced structure, i.e., one that has a common ground for input and output, is generally preferable, because the source and the load usually have a common ground. In these situations, if a lattice is to be used, ideal (or nearly ideal) isolation transformers are needed. However, in many cases an equivalent unbalanced structure can be found for the lattice. One basic unbalancing technique is discussed in this section.

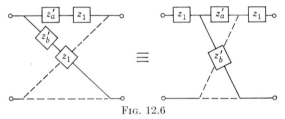

Fig. 12.6

The simplest type of unbalancing technique consists in looking for common impedance elements in z_a and z_b. For example, assume that z_a and z_b have a series impedance z_1 in common.

$$\begin{aligned}
z_a &= z_1 + z_a' \\
z_b &= z_1 + z_b'
\end{aligned} \tag{12.27}$$

z_1 can be pulled out as a series branch external to the lattice, as shown in Fig. 12.6. The two 2-ports are equivalent, since the open-circuit impedances are the same.

$$\begin{aligned}
z_{11} &= \frac{z_a + z_b}{2} = z_1 + \frac{z_a' + z_b'}{2} = z_1 + z_{11}' \\
z_{21} &= \frac{z_b - z_a}{2} = \frac{z_b' - z_a'}{2} = z_{21}'
\end{aligned} \tag{12.28}$$

z'_{11} and z'_{21} pertain to the interior lattice of the right-hand 2-port of Fig. 12.6. The above is, of course, only an initial step in unbalancing. Similarly, if $y_a = 1/z_a$ and $y_b = 1/z_b$ have a parallel admittance y_1 in common, y_1 can be pulled out as a shunt branch external to the lattice. This is shown in Fig. 12.7. The equivalence of the two 2-ports can be seen by an inspection of the short-circuit admittances.

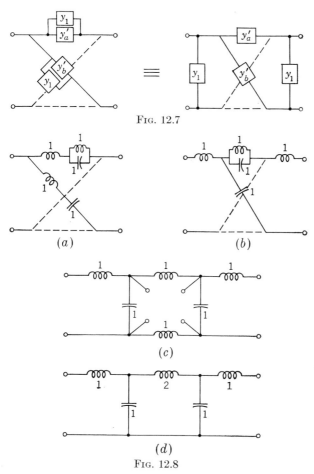

Fig. 12.7

(a)   (b)

(c)

(d)

Fig. 12.8

The two "pulling out" steps, used successively, are sometimes sufficient to unbalance a lattice completely. As an example, consider the lattice shown in Fig. 12.8a. It is first recognized that z_a and z_b have an inductance of value 1 henry in common, which can be removed as a series branch, as shown in 12.8b. The interior lattice of this figure has branches which have a common capacitance in parallel. After a shunt-branch removal, the resulting 2-port is shown in Fig. 12.8c. In this network the remaining unit inductances in the interior of the network can be combined in the top lead as an inductance of value 2 henrys, as shown in Fig. 12.8d. This step is justified because both inductances contribute only to the self-impedance of the interior mesh. Thus in a mesh analysis it is clear that the input and output voltages and currents are unaffected by combining the two inductances.

Unfortunately for the constant-R lattices that are of major interest in this chapter, the above unbalancing technique cannot be used as such. From (12.10), z_a and z_b are reciprocal-impedance networks and do not

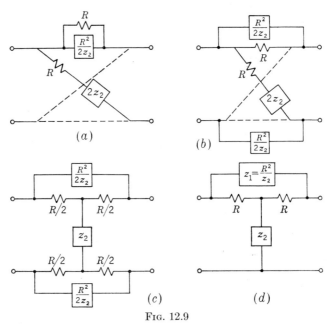

Fig. 12.9

have common series or shunt branches. However, for certain cases, a variation of the technique can be used to achieve unbalancing. Let z_b be restricted to the following form:

$$z_b = R + 2z_2 \tag{12.29}$$

From (12.10)

$$z_a = \frac{R^2}{R + 2z_2} = \frac{1}{1/R + 2z_2/R^2} \tag{12.30}$$

The lattice is shown in Fig. 12.9a and, in an alternate configuration, in Fig. 12.9b. In the latter, attention is centered on the interior lattice, ignoring for the moment the elements $R^2/2z_2$. For the interior lattice, common series resistances can be pulled out, as shown in Fig. 12.9c. It should be noticed that the resistances pulled out are placed in all four exterior leads as resistances of value $R/2$, in contrast with the previous example. This is necessary here, so that the lower branch $R^2/2z_2$ is not shorted out. Finally, the circuit can be drawn in the unbalanced form shown in Fig. 12.9d. This last step is again justified in terms of the mesh equations of the circuit of Fig. 12.9c. Because of symmetry, the currents in the top and bottom meshes are equal. The mutual imped-ances between the top mesh and the input mesh, and between the bottom mesh and the input mesh, are the same. This is also true for the mutual impedances between the output mesh and the top and bottom meshes. Thus the input and output voltages and currents are unchanged if the self- and mutual impedances of the top mesh are doubled and a common ground is connected from the input to the output. The 2-port of Fig. 12.9d is called a constant-R, bridged-T network.

12.5 Bridged-T Networks. In the bridged-T network it is convenient to identify the branch R^2/z_2 as z_1. Thus

$$z_1 z_2 = R^2 \tag{12.31}$$

The voltage transfer ratio of the bridged T from (12.16) and (12.29),

$$\frac{V_2}{V_1} = \frac{1}{1 + z_1/R} \tag{12.32}$$

Certain properties of (12.32) can be immediately established. z_1 is a driving-point impedance function and is therefore p-r. A positive con-stant added to a p-r function does not change the p-r property. Hence $1 + z_1/R$ is p-r. From Chap. 6, the poles and zeros of a p-r function must lie in the left half plane or be simple on the $j\omega$ axis. Consequently, the poles and zeros of $1 + z_1/R$, which are the zeros and poles respec-tively of V_2/V_1, must lie in the left half plane. The transfer function of a bridged-T network stemming from (12.29) is restricted to being mini-mum phase. Should z_1 and z_2 be LC networks, the poles of V_2/V_1 may lie anywhere in the left half plane, while the transmission zeros are restricted to the $j\omega$ axis. It should be noticed that the constant-R ladders of Fig. 12.2 also have the above properties [see (12.2) and (12.3)].

The realization of a constant-R bridged T (or ladder) to achieve a desired transfer-function specification cannot always be accomplished. The properties given above are necessary but not sufficient. If (12.32) is solved for z_1/R, one obtains

$$z_1/R = \frac{1}{V_2/V_1} - 1 \tag{12.33}$$

For a realizable bridged-T network, (12.33) must of course be p-r. As an example, let the desired transfer voltage ratio be

$$\frac{V_2}{V_1} = H \frac{p + \frac{1}{2}}{p^2 + p + 1} \tag{12.34}$$

From (12.33)

$$z_1 = \frac{R}{H} \frac{p^2 + (1 - H)p + 1 - H/2}{p + \frac{1}{2}}$$ (12.35)

Equation (12.35) is p-r if

$$H \leq \tfrac{1}{2}$$ (12.36)

The maximum value of H is chosen to satisfy (12.36), which in turn leads to maximum-gain level. z_1 becomes

$$z_1 = 2R \frac{p^2 + \frac{1}{2}p + \frac{3}{4}}{p + \frac{1}{2}}$$
$$= 2Rp + \frac{\frac{3}{2}R}{p + \frac{1}{2}}$$ (12.37)

This can be recognized as the impedance of the simple network shown in

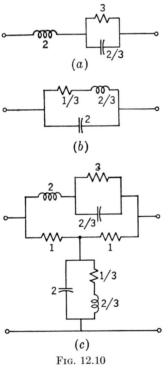

(a)

(b)

(c)

Fig. 12.10

Fig. 12.10a for R normalized to unity. z_2 can be found from (12.31) and leads to the network shown in Fig. 12.10b. The resulting bridged-T network is shown in Fig. 12.10c. If a smaller value of H is chosen, an extra series resistance is added to the network realization of z_1 and an additional shunt resistance is produced in the z_2 configuration.

The above example indicates a practical realization procedure. Starting from a given transfer-function specification, one obtains simple factors, i.e., rational functions, each of which is assigned to one bridged-T structure. If the transfer function of the individual structure is sufficiently simple, not only can a z_1 be found that is p-r but also a physical realization can be simply identified. The actual realization of the networks can usually be obtained through partial-fraction-expansion removal steps. It is to be emphasized that although this realization procedure is basically simple, it suffers from two practical disadvantages. The first is the excessive number of required circuit elements in comparison with requirements for the realization procedures described in previous chapters. The second is the amount of flat loss that is obtained in many instances.

Bridged-T networks with all-pass transfer functions can also be realized. For example, if

$$\frac{V_2}{V_1} = \frac{p^2 - ap + b}{p^2 + ap + b} \tag{12.38}$$

z_a and z_b of a lattice can be found from (12.7) and (12.17). It is assumed for convenience that $R = 1$.

$$z_a = \frac{ap}{p^2 + b} \qquad z_b = \frac{p^2 + b}{ap} \tag{12.39}$$

The corresponding all-pass lattice is shown in Fig. 12.11a. To unbalance this lattice, the procedure given in Sec. 12.4 can be used. The steps in

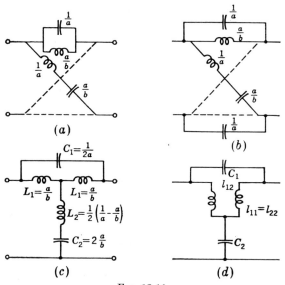

FIG. 12.11

the development are illustrated in Fig. 12.11b and c. The inductance L_2 may be negative; however, this negative inductance can always be realized with coupled coils, as shown in Fig. 12.11d. From Chap. 8

$$l_{11} = l_{22} = L_1 + L_2 = \tfrac{1}{2}\left(\frac{1}{a} + \frac{a}{b}\right) \tag{12.40}$$

$$l_{12} = L_2 = \tfrac{1}{2}\left(\frac{1}{a} - \frac{a}{b}\right)$$

The coefficient of coupling is

$$k = \frac{|1/a - a/b|}{1/a + a/b} < 1 \tag{12.41}$$

Since k is always less than unity for finite a and b, a practical realization is always possible. An alternate procedure to that illustrated in Fig. 12.11 can be followed. This leads to the configuration shown in Fig. 12.12, which is realizable only if

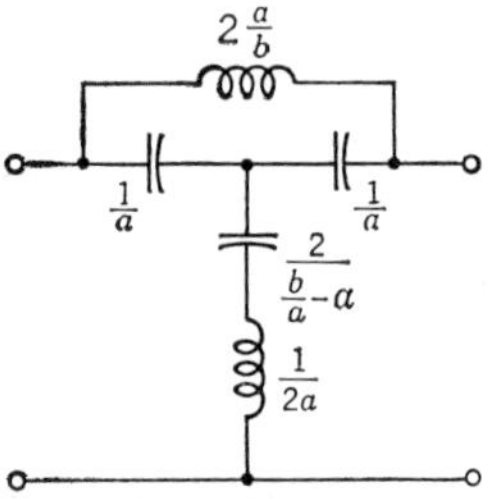

$$b > a^2 \tag{12.42}$$

Fig. 12.12

12.6 Generalization. The constant-R lattice and its derivative form, the bridged-T network, are important for the building-block type of realization. However, this type of symmetrical lattice is only a special case. The general symmetrical lattice where $z_a z_b \neq R^2$ is important in itself in network theory and synthesis.* For example, it is shown in the last chapter that an RC bridged-T network can provide complex transmission zeros. The design of this type of network can follow directly from its lattice equivalent. It is shown below that any symmetrical network has a physical lattice equivalent.

In Chap. 11 the design of an RC 2-port with a short-circuit load and a voltage source is required. The transfer-function specification is then in terms of y_{21}, the short-circuit transfer admittance. From (12.4) it can be shown that

$$y_{21} = \tfrac{1}{2}(y_b - y_a) \tag{12.43}$$

where

$$y_b = \frac{1}{z_b} \qquad y_a = \frac{1}{z_a} \tag{12.44}$$

From the specified y_{21}, y_b and y_a can be found from (12.43). As an illustration, let

$$y_{21} = -\frac{p^2 + p + \tfrac{1}{3}}{p + \tfrac{2}{3}} \tag{12.45}$$

y_{21} is separated into two parts, each of which is the driving-point admittance of an RC network. This can always be accomplished by a partial fraction expansion of y_{21}/p. The components of the partial fraction expansion with positive residues are associated with y_b, and the remaining components are assigned to y_a. For the example,

$$\frac{y_{21}}{p} = \frac{\tfrac{1}{2}}{3p + 2} - 1 - \frac{1}{2p}$$

$$y_{21} = \frac{\tfrac{1}{2}p}{3p + 2} - \left(p + \frac{1}{2}\right) \tag{12.46}$$

$$y_b = \frac{p}{3p + 2} \qquad y_a = 2p + 1$$

---

* The symmetrical lattice is in turn a subclass of a general lattice or a general bridge network having bridge arms z_a, z_b, z_c, and z_d. The general lattice has been found valuable only in special cases, such as situations pertaining to a balanced bridge.

The lattice realization is shown in Fig. 12.13a.   The unbalancing procedure of Sec. 12.5 can now be used to obtain a bridged-T network, as shown in Fig. 12.13b.   This simple example, of course, does not bring out the difficulty that may be encountered in a general problem.   Except in

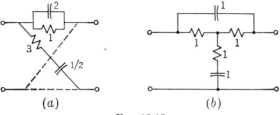

(a)   (b)

FIG. 12.13

simple cases like the above, it may not be possible to ensure a physical unbalanced realization.

The proof that any symmetrical network has a symmetrical lattice equivalent follows from a theorem due to Bartlett.*   This theorem states that any symmetrical passive 2-port has a lattice equivalent which has impedance branches related to special open- and short-circuit impedances of the 2-port.   The development of this theorem follows most easily from an initial consideration of a lattice.   In Fig. 12.14a each impedance branch of a lattice is separated into two equal parts.   If equal voltages $V_1 = V_2$ are applied at the ports, clearly no current will flow in the series arms, and the series arms can be opened without changing the electrical equilibrium.   The crossarms can be shorted together because the potential at the crosspoint is the same for each arm.

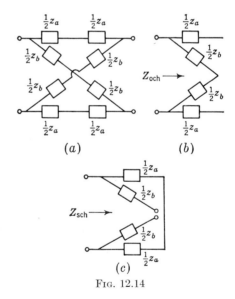

FIG. 12.14

Note that under these conditions the input impedance at either end will be the impedance of the network shown in Fig. 12.14b.

$$Z_{11} = Z_{och} = z_b \qquad (12.47)$$

Next, let the sources at the input and output be such that $V_1 = -V_2$. The currents through the crossarms must then be equal to zero, and the

---

* A. C. Bartlett, "Theory of Electrical Artificial Lines and Filters," John Wiley & Sons, Inc., New York, 1931.

crossarms can be open-circuited without changing the equilibrium. The potentials at the midpoints of the series arms must be equal; and hence the midpoints can be shorted. The input impedance for this situation pertains to the network of Fig. 12.14c.

$$Z_{11} = Z_{sch} = z_a \tag{12.48}$$

Of particular importance is the fact that these two special impedances are equal to the two lattice impedances. Thus, if a similar bisection procedure is followed to find these same special input impedances for any symmetrical 2-port, the equivalent lattice structure is directly obtained. Since for any passive 2-port these special impedances are p-r, the realizability of the lattice is assured. However, it is not true in general that a desired symmetrical configuration can always be found from a physical lattice.

As an example, consider the bridged-T network of Fig. 12.9d. The two special impedances are

$$Z_{och} = R + 2z_2 \tag{12.49}$$

$$Z_{sch} = \frac{1}{1/R + 2/z_1} \tag{12.50}$$

These two impedances are then the impedances z_b and z_a, respectively, of the equivalent lattice [see (12.29) and (12.30)]. For the converse process of finding an equivalent bridged T for a given lattice, z_1 and z_2 must be

$$z_2 = \frac{z_b - R}{2} \tag{12.51}$$

$$\frac{1}{z_1} = \frac{1}{2}\left(\frac{1}{z_a} - \frac{1}{R}\right) \tag{12.52}$$

To be realizable, z_1 and z_2 must be p-r. This is, however, not assured because of the subtraction, even though z_a and z_b are p-r. Clearly, the equivalent bridged T in this form can be obtained if

$$\text{Re}\,[z_b] \geq R \tag{12.53}$$

and
$$\text{Re}\left[\frac{1}{z_a}\right] \geq \frac{1}{R} \tag{12.54}$$

In general, care must be taken in finding the special impedances of a symmetrical 2-port if the 2-port contains crossed branches. In determining Z_{och}, the impedance of half the network under open-circuit conditions, at the line of symmetry the cross branches are shorted together. Similarly, in determining Z_{sch}, the impedance of half the network under short-circuit conditions, at the line of symmetry the crossed branches are open-circuited.

Bartlett's bisection theorem is of particular importance in the analysis of symmetrical 2-ports. The branch impedances z_a and z_b of the equivalent lattice are often easily determined.   From a knowledge of z_a and z_b, the performance of the 2-port can be immediately obtained.

PROBLEMS

12.1. For the situation shown in Fig. P12.1, the load consists of a parallel R and C. The source is purely resistive.   It is desired to develop a 2-port coupling network that will provide a resistance match to the source and incorporate the given load.   The constant-R ladder network of Fig. 12.2a may be used if the load capacitance can be incorporated into z_2.

(a) If V_2/V_0 has the form

$$\frac{V_2}{V_0} = \frac{(p+b)}{p^2 + ap + 1}$$

what constraints on a and b make z_2 p-r?

(b) Show that if (a) is satisfied, a configuration for z_2 is obtained which has a capacitance in the proper location.

(c) Determine the configuration of the network z_1.

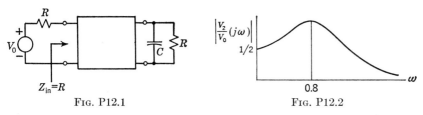

FIG. P12.1   FIG. P12.2

12.2. (a) Determine suitable choices for a and b in Prob. 12.1a in order to obtain an approximation to the curve in Fig. P12.2.

(b) Show that a low-pass maximally flat magnitude response is not realizable and that a peak is always obtained at a finite frequency.

12.3. Show that it is possible to introduce another constant-R section between the source and the constant-R ladder of Prob. 12.1 to obtain an over-all transfer function

$$\frac{V_2}{V_0} = \frac{1}{p^2 + ap + 1}$$

Design the two constant-R ladders to obtain a maximally flat magnitude characteristic with a unit 3-db bandwidth.

12.4. Show that the two structures in Fig. P12.4 are equivalent.   Given the lattice impedances below determine whether the equivalent T network exists.   If so, determine the structure and the element values.

$$z_a = \frac{2p^2 + 4}{p^3 + 4p} \qquad z_b = \frac{4p^4 + 11p^2 + 4}{p^5 + 5p^3 + 4p}$$

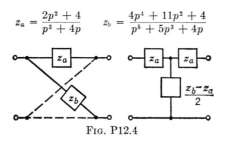

FIG. P12.4

12.5. For a constant-R, bridged-T network for which z_1 and z_2 are LC networks, can the transfer function have all its transmission zeros at infinity?

12.6. Find a constant-R lattice network which has an over-all transfer impedance identical with that of the circuit in Fig. P12.6. Unbalance the lattice, if possible.

12.7. Find a 2-port ladder-network equivalent to the symmetrical lattice in Fig. P12.7.

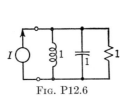

FIG. P12.6

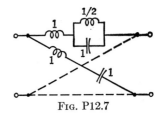

FIG. P12.7

12.8. Determine the maximum value of the constant multiplier of the following transfer function in order that it may be realizable with a constant-R lattice network:

$$\frac{V_2}{V_1} = \frac{H}{p^2 + p + 1}$$

12.9. Realize a constant-R all-pass lattice network that has a maximally flat delay transfer characteristic with two poles and two zeros. Unbalance the structure in bridged-T form.

12.10. Show that the phase function of an all-pass network is a monotonically decreasing function.

12.11. It is desired to linearize the phase of a two-pole maximally flat magnitude transfer function by using an all-pass bridged-T network (shown in Fig. P12.11) with two poles and two zeros. One design procedure is as follows: (a) Plot the phase characteristic of the filter in the passband. (b) Draw a linear phase curve such that the phase difference between the linear curve and the curve of (a) is a monotonically decreasing curve. This difference curve is the ideal phase characteristic to be provided by the all-pass network. (c) Since two degrees of freedom are available, choose two points in the passband to specify the constants of the all-pass transfer function.

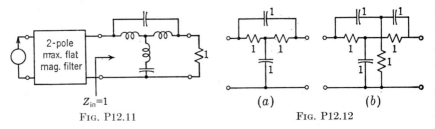

FIG. P12.11   FIG. P12.12

12.12. Use the bisection theorem to determine the transfer function V_2/V_1 of the networks in Fig. P12.12a and b.

12.13. Realize the following function as the transfer voltage ratio of the cascade of two constant-R lattices:

$$\frac{V_2}{V_0} = \frac{H(p + 1)p}{(p + 2)(p^2 + p + 1)}$$

12.14. The following transfer impedance can be realized as shown in Fig. P12.14. Determine and realize z_a and z_b of the lattice from z_{ij}.   Remember that the lattice is symmetrical.

$$Z_{21} = \frac{H(p^2 + 1)}{(p + 1)(p^2 + 2p + 2)}$$

Unbalance the lattice, if possible.

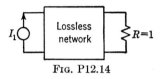

FIG. P12.14

CHAPTER 13

SYNTHESIS WITH IMAGE-MATCHED 2-PORTS

13.1 The Image-match Concept. The building-block synthesis technique introduced in the last chapter depends on the property that there is no interaction between building blocks. The elimination of interaction results from the constant-resistance input impedance (or the input and output impedances) of the terminated 2-ports. If both the input and output impedances are constant-R, the 2-ports are said to be impedance-matched, since at the junction of two 2-ports the impedance is the same in either direction. This impedance-match concept can be generalized to input and output impedances that are not constant resistances. For example, in the cascade connection shown in Fig. 13.1 an impedance match exists at junction 1 if the input impedance of the network N is

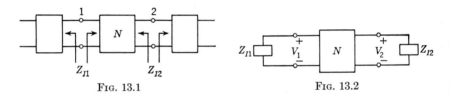

FIG. 13.1   FIG. 13.2

equal to the output impedance of the preceding 2-port. It is commonly stated that an image match exists at the junction, since either 2-port "sees" its virtual image, impedancewise. If an image match also exists at junction 2, the 2-port N is said to be image-matched.

A restriction can be made so that in a cascade of 2-ports, each 2-port is image-matched. Under these conditions, the individual 2-port can be treated separately, as in Fig. 13.2. As in constant-R building-block technique, if an image match is maintained in a cascade, the over-all transfer function is the product of the transfer functions of the individual 2-ports designed in isolation.

13.2 2-port Image Description. From the discussion above, a 2-port is said to be image-matched if the following requirements are satisfied:

$$Z_{11} = Z_{I1}$$
$$Z_{22} = Z_{I2}$$

(13.1)

where Z_{I1} and Z_{I2} are called the *image impedances* of the input and output ports, respectively. The terminated input and output impedances Z_{11} and Z_{22} can be expressed in terms of the open-circuit parameters.

$$Z_{11} = z_{11} - \frac{z_{12}^2}{z_{22} + Z_{I2}}$$

$$Z_{22} = z_{22} - \frac{z_{12}^2}{z_{11} + Z_{I1}} \tag{13.2}$$

The simultaneous solution of (13.1) and (13.2) leads to

$$Z_{I1} = \sqrt{\frac{z_{11}}{y_{11}}}$$

$$Z_{I2} = \sqrt{\frac{z_{22}}{y_{22}}} \tag{13.3}$$

It should be noticed that the image impedances are basic parameters of the 2-port itself. That is, these impedances constitute part of an alternate 2-port description. For a passive reciprocal 2-port, a third parameter is necessary for a complete description. Clearly, this third parameter must be a transfer function. Because of the ultimate application of cascading, it is most convenient to use a transfer voltage or current ratio under the image-matched condition. In particular, a logarithmic measure of the voltage or current ratio is used since, as is brought out later, a logarithmic measure leads to addition rather than multiplication in the calculation of the over-all transfer function of a cascade. The transfer parameter Γ, which is called the *image transfer function*, is defined as follows:*

$$\left.\frac{V_2}{V_1}\right|_{\text{image match}} = \sqrt{\frac{Z_{I2}}{Z_{I1}}} \, e^{-\Gamma}$$

$$\left.\frac{I_2}{I_1}\right|_{\text{image match}} = -\sqrt{\frac{Z_{I1}}{Z_{I2}}} \, e^{-\Gamma} \tag{13.4}$$

Γ can also be simply related to the open- and short-circuit parameters. The transfer voltage ratio under image-matched conditions is found from the following equations

$$V_2 = z_{21}I_1 + z_{22}I_2$$
$$V_1 = Z_{I1}I_1$$
$$V_2 = -Z_{I2}I_2 \tag{13.5}$$
$$\frac{V_2}{V_1} = \frac{z_{21}}{z_{22} + Z_{I2}} \frac{Z_{I2}}{Z_{I1}}$$

* The irrational factor in (13.4) can be identified as the effective impedance transformation of the 2-port. This is brought out in Chap. 14.

From (13.4)

$$\Gamma = -\ln \frac{V_2}{V_1} \sqrt{\frac{Z_{I1}}{Z_{I2}}}$$

$$= -\ln \sqrt{\frac{Z_{I2}}{Z_{I1}}} \frac{z_{21}}{z_{22} + Z_{I2}} \tag{13.6}$$

Equation (13.6) is now manipulated with the use of (13.3), the relationship between the open- and short-circuit parameters, and the identity $\Delta_z = z_{11}z_{22} - z_{12}^2$ to obtain the following result:

$$\Gamma = \ln \frac{\sqrt{z_{11}y_{11}} + 1}{\sqrt{z_{11}y_{11}} - 1} = \ln \frac{\sqrt{z_{11}y_{11}} + 1}{(\sqrt{z_{11}y_{11}} - 1)^{\frac{1}{2}} (\sqrt{z_{11}y_{11}} + 1)^{\frac{1}{2}}}$$

$$= \frac{1}{2} \ln \frac{\sqrt{z_{11}y_{11}} + 1}{\sqrt{z_{11}y_{11}} - 1} \tag{13.7}$$

From an identity of hyberbolic functions, (13.7) can be expressed as

$$\Gamma = \coth^{-1} \sqrt{z_{11}y_{11}} = \coth^{-1} \sqrt{z_{22}y_{22}} \tag{13.8}$$

Consider now the situation of two 2-ports cascaded under image-matched conditions, as shown in Fig. 13.3. At the junction of the

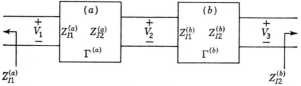

FIG. 13.3

2-ports, $Z_{I1}{}^{(b)} = Z_{I2}{}^{(a)}$. The over-all transfer voltage ratio is

$$\frac{V_3}{V_1} = \frac{V_3}{V_2} \frac{V_2}{V_1} = \left(\sqrt{\frac{Z_{I2}{}^{(b)}}{Z_{I1}{}^{(b)}}} \, e^{-\Gamma_b} \right) \left(\sqrt{\frac{Z_{I2}{}^{(a)}}{Z_{I1}{}^{(a)}}} \, e^{-\Gamma_a} \right)$$

$$= \sqrt{\frac{Z_{I2}{}^{(b)}}{Z_{I1}{}^{(a)}}} \, e^{-(\Gamma_a + \Gamma_b)} \tag{13.9}$$

Note that the over-all image transfer function is equal to the sum of the individual image transfer functions. The over-all 2-port is characterized by the two image impedances $Z_{I1}{}^{(a)}$ and $Z_{I2}{}^{(b)}$ and the image transfer parameter $\Gamma_a + \Gamma_b$. Clearly, if the number of cascaded 2-ports is greater than two, the same conclusion can be drawn.

At this point the disquieting fact should be pointed out that all the image parameters are irrational. In particular, note that for a 2-port consisting of a finite number of lumped elements, Z_{I1} and Z_{I2} are the square roots of rational functions. From Chap. 6, it is obvious that the image impedances are not physically realizable as driving-point imped-ances of finite networks.*   At first glance, then, it appears impossible to obtain an image match with finite networks.   This is true.   Fortunately, however, it is possible to obtain an approximate image match over a given frequency band.

The irrationality of the transfer voltage ratio under image-matched conditions necessitates the use of a new concept for synthesis.   In the preceding chapters the synthesis problem is divided into separate approxi-mation and realization problems.   Take, for example, the constant-R building-block approach of Chap. 12.   The rational function that approximates the specifications is separated into simpler rational func-tions, each of which is realized by a constant-R structure.   If the same approach is adopted for image-matched cascades, the given specifications must be approximated with an irrational function.   This function must then be separated into simpler irrational functions, each of which must be identified as the image transfer function of a simple 2-port.   This pro-cedure is very difficult if not impossible to utilize.   As an alternate procedure, simple finite 2-ports are studied in terms of their image parameters.   From the knowledge of the properties of these basic struc-tures, one can, with experience, synthesize cascaded structures to approxi-mate a given set of specifications.   By and large, this method of synthesis can best be applied to problems of realizing filters and delay networks. The major disadvantage of this image type of synthesis is that one does not have an a priori knowledge of the degree and nature of the approxi-mation to the given specifications.   This is to be compared to the previ-ously described method of synthesis, in which the desired degree of approximation, obtained first, was followed by an exact realization of the approximation.

The above disadvantage of the image type of synthesis is the direct result of inability to obtain a perfect image match.   Any number of 2-ports can be cascaded without interaction if at every junction the two associated 2-ports have the same image impedances.   The cascade of 2-ports which is image-matched at every internal junction can be charac-terized as a single 2-port.   For exact realization of the image transfer function, this over-all 2-port must be image-matched at the source and the load.   As stated earlier, an exact image match at these terminations is not possible if the load and source impedances are rational functions. (Usually the load and the source impedances are resistive.)   Conse-quently, a mismatch occurs at these ports, and error is introduced in the sense that Eqs. (13.4) do not hold.   In the following sections methods of

* It can be shown from artificial transmission line considerations that an image impedance can be realized as the input impedance of an infinite cascade of image-matched structures if a finite amount of loss is present.

minimizing this error are introduced. In the next chapter methods of evaluating the error are developed.

13.3 The Constant-K Image Filters. As indicated in the last section, the image type of synthesis stems from a study of simple basic struc-

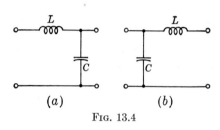

(a)   (b)

FIG. 13.4

tures. The results of these studies are, in essence, catalogued, and the structures are used when appropriate. Only low-pass structures need be studied, since high-pass and bandpass transformations can always be used to extend the range of application. The simplest lossless low-pass structures are the simple L networks shown in Fig. 13.4a and b. For the network of Fig. 13.4a, the image parameters can be found from the following:

$$z_{11} = pL + \frac{1}{pC}$$

$$y_{11} = \frac{1}{pL}$$

$$z_{22} = \frac{1}{pC}$$

$$y_{22} = pC + \frac{1}{pL}$$

(13.10)

$$Z_{I1} = \sqrt{z_{11}/y_{11}} = \sqrt{\frac{L}{C}} \sqrt{p^2LC + 1}$$

(13.11)

$$Z_{I2} = \sqrt{z_{22}/y_{22}} = \sqrt{\frac{L}{C}} \frac{1}{\sqrt{p^2LC + 1}}$$

(13.12)

$$\Gamma = \frac{1}{2} \ln \frac{\sqrt{z_{11}y_{11}} + 1}{\sqrt{z_{11}y_{11}} - 1}$$

$$= \frac{1}{2} \ln \frac{\sqrt{p^2LC + 1} + p \sqrt{LC}}{\sqrt{p^2LC + 1} - p \sqrt{LC}}$$

$$= \ln (\sqrt{p^2LC + 1} + p \sqrt{LC})$$

(13.13)

The appearance of the factors $p \sqrt{LC}$ and $\sqrt{L/C}$ in the above equations suggests the use of the following impedance and frequency normalization factors:

$$\Omega_n = \frac{1}{\sqrt{LC}}$$

$$r_n = \sqrt{\frac{L}{C}}$$

(13.14)

In terms of the normalized element values, the image parameters become

$$Z_{I1} = \sqrt{p^2 + 1} \tag{13.15}$$

$$Z_{I2} = \frac{1}{\sqrt{p^2 + 1}} \tag{13.16}$$

$$\Gamma = \ln (\sqrt{p^2 + 1} + p) \tag{13.17}$$

Clearly, the image impedances of the network shown in Fig. 13.4b are those above, with an interchange of the subscripts 1 and 2. The image transfer functions for both networks are identical. Heretofore functions have been studied in terms of their pole and zero locations and in terms of their behavior for $p = j\omega$. For irrational functions, pole-zero methods are not appropriate and attention is centered on the $j\omega$-axis behavior.

For $p = j\omega$ and $0 \leq \omega \leq 1$, the image impedances are real

$$Z_{I1} = \sqrt{1 - \omega^2} \tag{13.18}$$

$$Z_{I2} = \frac{1}{\sqrt{1 - \omega^2}} \tag{13.19}$$

The image transfer parameter for $p = j\omega$ is conveniently separated into its real and imaginary components.

$$\Gamma(j\omega) = \alpha_I(\omega) + j\beta_I(\omega) \tag{13.20}$$

The real part $\alpha_I(\omega)$ is called the image attenuation or loss function. This definition differs from that of the gain function in Chap. 2, because of the minus sign in the definition of Γ:

$$\frac{V_2}{V_1} = \sqrt{\frac{Z_{I2}}{Z_{I1}}} \, e^{-\Gamma}$$

Thus positive $\alpha_I(\omega)$ in this chapter pertains to attenuation. Similarly, $\beta_I(\omega)$, called the image phase function, is the negative of the usual phase function defined on an output over input basis. For $0 \leq \omega \leq 1$, $\Gamma(j\omega)$ is purely imaginary.

$$\Gamma = \ln (\sqrt{1 - \omega^2} + j\omega)$$

$$= j \tan^{-1} \frac{\omega}{\sqrt{1 - \omega^2}} = j \sin^{-1} \omega \tag{13.21}$$

$$\alpha_I = 0$$

$$\beta_I = \sin^{-1} \omega \tag{13.22}$$

For $\omega \geq 1$, the image impedances are purely imaginary and the image transfer parameter is complex with a constant imaginary part.

$$Z_{I1} = j\sqrt{\omega^2 - 1} \tag{13.23}$$
$$Z_{I2} = -j/\sqrt{\omega^2 - 1} \tag{13.24}$$
$$\Gamma = \ln j\,(\sqrt{\omega^2 - 1} + \omega)$$
$$= \ln(\sqrt{\omega^2 - 1} + \omega) + j\frac{\pi}{2} \tag{13.25}$$
$$\alpha_I = \ln(\sqrt{\omega^2 - 1} + \omega) = \cosh^{-1}\omega$$
$$\beta_I = \frac{\pi}{2} \tag{13.26}$$

The real and imaginary parts of the image impedances and the image transfer parameter are plotted in Fig. 13.5. In the frequency interval $0 \le \omega \le 1$, the image loss function α_I is zero. That is, a signal is transmitted without attenuation in this frequency interval (under image-matched conditions). This interval is thus called the *passband*. Notice, however, that a phase shift is introduced in the passband which is not a linear function of frequency; hence delay distortion is introduced. In the passband the image impedances are real. For $\omega \ge 1$, attenuation is introduced, $\alpha_I > 0$, while the image phase is a constant. This frequency interval is called the *stopband*. In the stopband the image impedances are imaginary. Because of the distinct pass- and stopband properties, these basic structures are useful for filter applications. The frequency where the pass- and stopbands coalesce is called the cutoff frequency.

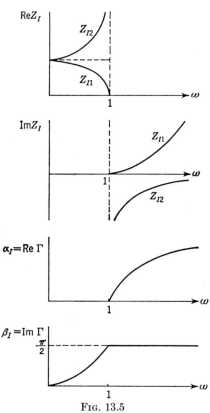

FIG. 13.5

Historically, these basic L sections have been called constant-K sections.* If the impedance of the series branch is called Z_1 and the impedance of the shunt branch is called Z_2, the product is a constant.

$$Z_1 Z_2 = \frac{pL}{pC} = \frac{L}{C} = K^2 \quad \text{(a constant)} \tag{13.27}$$

---

* O. J. Zobel, Theory and Design of Uniform and Composite Electric Wave Filters, *Bell System Tech. J.*, January, 1923.

Because the product of the impedances of the two branches is a constant, the term *constant-K* was coined. Note that if either a high-pass to low-pass or a bandpass to low-pass transformation is made, (13.27) still holds. The resulting networks, shown in Fig. 13.6, are usually referred to as constant-K high-pass sections and constant-K bandpass sections. In general, constant-K refers to any basic section, designed on the image

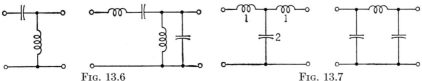

FIG. 13.6   FIG. 13.7

basis, for which the product Z_1Z_2 is a constant. Almost always the over-all image-matched 2-port is used for filter application; therefore Z_1 and Z_2 are the impedances of LC 1-ports. For branches more complicated than those shown in Figs. 13.4 and 13.6, a greater number of alternate pass- and stopbands are obtained.

If two of the low-pass constant-K sections are cascaded under image-matched conditions, either a T network or a π network results, as shown

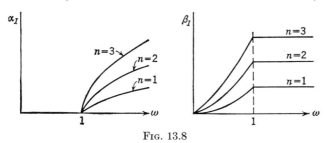

FIG. 13.8

in Fig. 13.7.* To obtain the proper image match, the networks in Fig. 13.4 are cascaded (*a*) to (*b*) or vice versa. For two or more L sections in cascade the over-all image impedances are either the Z_{I1} of (13.18) or the Z_{I2} of (13.19), while the loss and phase functions of each section add arithmetically. Plots of α_I and β_I are shown in Fig. 13.8 with n, the number of L sections in cascade, as a parameter.

$$\alpha_I = 0 \qquad\qquad 0 \le \omega \le 1$$
$$= n \cosh^{-1} \omega \qquad \omega \ge 1$$
$$\beta_I = n \sin^{-1} \omega \qquad 0 \le \omega \le 1 \qquad (13.28)$$
$$= n \frac{\pi}{2} \qquad\qquad \omega \ge 1$$

---

* Commonly, in the literature, the low-pass constant-K T and π networks are used as the basic sections for image design. The parent L sections for these networks have a normalized value of L of $\frac{1}{2}$ and a normalized value of C of $\frac{1}{2}$. Care should be taken in using tabular results, because of the different frequency normalization factor. The passband extends from zero to two for element values of $L = \frac{1}{2}$ and $C = \frac{1}{2}$.

From the plot of α_I, it can be seen that the greater the number of n, the sharper the cutoff of the over-all filter.

As mentioned earlier, the source and load impedances are usually resistive and constant. Since the image impedances, although real in the passband, vary with frequency, a match can be obtained at only one frequency for resistive terminations. The transmission characteristics of Fig. 13.8 can only be approximately realized under these conditions. Fortunately, in many practical situations, the filter specifications are sufficiently nonrestrictive so that the distortion introduced by the mismatch can be tolerated.

As an illustration of image filter design, assume that a low-pass filter is desired. The normalized passband is taken from zero to unity. At a frequency of twice the band-edge frequency, $\omega = 2$, the image attenuation must be equal to or greater than 30 db. From (13.28)

$$\alpha_I(2) = n \cosh^{-1} 2 \geq \frac{30}{8.68} \text{ nepers} \tag{13.29}$$

Since n must be an integer, the smallest value of n is 3. The resulting filter, shown in Fig. 13.9, consists of three L sections. For terminating resistances of unity value, the image match is obtained at d-c. Considerable distortion from ideal performance is expected as the band edge is approached. Often the terminating resistances are chosen to provide a match at some frequency in the passband other than d-c. For example, if the match occurs at $\omega = 1/\sqrt{2}$, the terminating resistances should be $1/\sqrt{2}$ for a port which has an image impedance of (13.18) or $\sqrt{2}$ for a

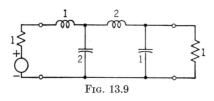

FIG. 13.9

port which has an image impedance of (13.19). This choice of terminating resistances introduces a greater mismatch at lower frequencies, but it reduces the mismatch near the cutoff frequency. If unit terminating resistances are desired, the over-all filter must have an even number of L sections so that the over-all Z_{I1} and Z_{I2} may be equal. Resistance normalization of the 2-port can then be used to obtain the unit resistances.

13.4   The m-Derived Image Filters.* The basic low-pass L structures of Sec. 13.3 provide simple but very useful filter building blocks. However, there exists no freedom to adjust the parameters of the structure. The ratio of L to C is determined by the impedance level normalization, while the product of L and C is determined by the frequency normalization (cutoff frequency normalization). Hence the normalized values of L and C are fixed. If an additional reactive element is introduced in

---

* Zobel, *op. cit.*

the L section, as in Fig. 13.10, a degree of freedom is added.   This degree
of freedom can be used in three ways:

(a) To minimize the mismatch between the image impedances of an
over-all 2-port and a resistive source and load.

(b) To adjust the stopband attenuation characteristic.

(c) To linearize the passband phase characteristic.

An analysis of the circuit of Fig. 13.10a leads to the image impedance

$$Z_{I1} = \sqrt{\frac{L_1}{C_1}} \sqrt{p^2(L_1 + L_2)C_1 + 1} \tag{13.30}$$

Equation (13.30) has the same mathematical form as one of the image
impedances of a constant-K structure, Eq. (13.11).   This means that
this new network can be designed
through a proper choice of L_1, L_2,
and C_1 to provide an image match
with a constant-K filter.   As is
shown below, the other image impedance can be adjusted to provide
a good match with a pure resistance.
The new L section can thus be used
as a terminating matching section.

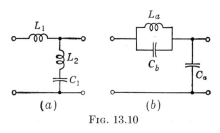

(a)   (b)

FIG. 13.10

The conditions necessary to provide a match with a constant-K structure
are found by equating (13.30) with (13.11).

$$\frac{L_1}{C_1} = \frac{L}{C} = 1$$
$$(L_1 + L_2)C_1 = LC = 1 \tag{13.31}$$

The equality to unity in the above equations is made to introduce the
previous resistance and frequency normalizations.   Since (13.31) constitutes a set of two equations in three unknowns, one possible solution is to
determine L_2 and C_1 in terms of the normalized value of L_1.   Historically,
the normalized value of L_1 has been called m, and this type of L section is
referred to as an *m-derived section*.   In terms of m, the normalized values
are

$$L_1 = m$$
$$C_1 = m$$
$$L_2 = \frac{1 - m^2}{m} \tag{13.32}$$

From the values of (13.32), the other image impedance of the new L section is

$$Z_{I2} = \frac{p^2(1 - m^2) + 1}{\sqrt{p^2 + 1}} \tag{13.33}$$

Notice that (13.33) is a function of the constant m. Hence m can be used to vary the shape of Z_{I2}. For $m = 1, L_2 = 0$, the structure becomes a constant-K network and Z_{I2} is equal to (13.16). The problem now arises as to what value of m should be used to obtain a better match to a resistance than that offered by a constant-K network. One approach is to require that Z_{I2} approximate unity in a maximally flat magnitude sense in the neighborhood of d-c. To accomplish this, (13.33) is expanded by the binomial expansion, as in Chap. 3.

$$Z_{I2} = [p^2(1 - m^2) + 1][1 - \tfrac{1}{2}p^2 + \cdots]$$
$$= 1 + (\tfrac{1}{2} - m^2)p^2 + \cdots \qquad (13.34)$$

For a maximally flat magnitude characteristic, as many successive coefficients of (13.34) are set equal to zero as possible. This leads to

$$m = \frac{1}{\sqrt{2}} \qquad (13.35)$$

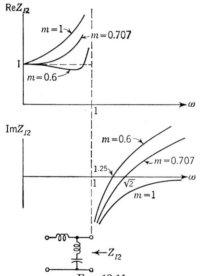

FIG. 13.11

Plots are shown in Fig. 13.11 of the image impedance (13.33) for different values of m. It is seen that the value $m = 0.707$ provides a much better match to unity in the pass-band than the constant-K case. However, an even broader band match can be obtained with smaller values of m. Traditionally, the value 0.6 is used.

The network just studied can be used as a terminating half section only if the constant-K filter presents a series inductance to the termina-tions. This is illustrated in Fig. 13.12. If the initial or final element of a constant-K filter is a shunt capacitance, the network shown in Fig. 13.10b must be used as the terminating section. By means of a develop-ment similar to that used above, the image impedance Z_{I2} is equated to

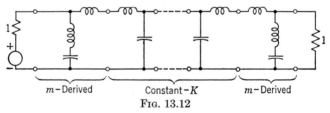

m-Derived　　　　Constant-K　　　　m-Derived

FIG. 13.12

(13.12) to provide a constant-K image match. The constant m is likewise defined in terms of a normalized element value.

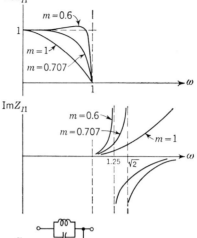

$$C_a = m$$
$$L_a = m$$
$$C_b = \frac{1 - m^2}{m} \qquad (13.36)$$

The image impedances are

$$Z_{I1} = \frac{\sqrt{p^2 + 1}}{(1 - m^2)p^2 + 1} \qquad (13.37)$$

$$Z_{I2} = \frac{1}{\sqrt{p^2 + 1}} \qquad (13.38)$$

Again $m = \dfrac{1}{\sqrt{2}}$ provides a maximally flat magnitude approximation to unity in the passband. However, $m = 0.6$ provides a match which has a broader bandwidth. Plots of Z_{I1}

FIG. 13.13

for several values of m are shown in Fig. 13.13. A constant-K filter with terminating structures of this type is shown in Fig. 13.14. It is to be emphasized that the type of the terminating structure depends on the initial or final element of the constant-K filter. It may be necessary to use one type at one end and the other type at the other end.

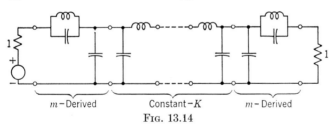

m–Derived   Constant–K   m–Derived
FIG. 13.14

Both types of m-derived sections have the same image transfer function Γ. From (13.7) and either (13.32) or (13.36)

$$\Gamma = \frac{1}{2} \ln \frac{\sqrt{p^2 + 1} + mp}{\sqrt{p^2 + 1} - mp} \qquad (13.39)$$

For $p = j\omega,\ 0 \le \omega \le 1$,

$$\alpha_I = 0$$

$$\beta_I = \tan^{-1} \frac{m\omega}{\sqrt{1 - \omega^2}} \qquad (13.40)$$

Thus the same passband is obtained as for constant-K structures. For $\omega \geq 1$

$$\Gamma(j\omega) = \frac{1}{2} \ln \frac{\sqrt{\omega^2 - 1} + m\omega}{\sqrt{\omega^2 - 1} - m\omega} \tag{13.41}$$

and $\alpha_I = \operatorname{Re} \Gamma(j\omega) \geq 0$ in this interval, which is then the stopband. Notice that for a particular finite value of ω, the ln function in (13.41) becomes infinite.

$$\omega = \omega_\infty = \frac{1}{\sqrt{1 - m^2}} \tag{13.42}$$

Hence an infinite attenuation is produced at this frequency. This is expected, since from either of the networks of Fig. 13.10 a transmission zero is produced at the resonance of L_2 and C_1 or the antiresonance of L_a and C_b.

$$\frac{1}{\sqrt{L_2 C_1}} = \frac{1}{\sqrt{L_a C_b}} = \frac{1}{\sqrt{1 - m^2}} \tag{13.43}$$

The location of the transmission zero separates the stopband into two portions. For $1 \leq \omega \leq \omega_\infty$

$$\alpha_I = \frac{1}{2} \ln \frac{m\omega + \sqrt{\omega^2 - 1}}{m\omega - \sqrt{\omega^2 - 1}}$$
$$\beta_I = \frac{\pi}{2} \tag{13.44}$$

For $\omega \geq \omega_\infty$

$$\alpha_I = \frac{1}{2} \ln \frac{\sqrt{\omega^2 - 1} + m\omega}{\sqrt{\omega^2 - 1} - m\omega}$$
$$\beta_I = 0 \tag{13.45}$$

Plots of α_I and β_I are shown in Fig. 13.15. For m-derived sections there is no transmission zero at infinity. The value of α_I at infinity is finite and equal to

$$\alpha_I(\alpha) = \frac{1}{2} \ln \frac{1 + m}{1 - m} \tag{13.46}$$

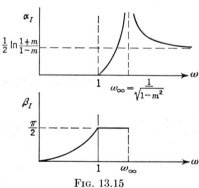

FIG. 13.15

The above m-derived terminating sections have the same pass- and stopbands as the constant-K filter. In addition, the presence of the transmission zero at ω_∞ improves the stopband rejection. Since the transmission zero is dependent on the constant m, m-derived sections can be designed to produce transmission zeros at desired locations. For the terminating m-derived sections, the value of m is confined to a narrow range of values, $0.6 < m < 0.7$, in order to obtain a good match to resistances. The transmission zeros due to these sections lie in the range $1.25 < \omega_\infty < 1.4$. If transmission zeros outside this interval are desired, pairs of m-derived sections can be introduced into the interior of this filter. The use of pairs of m-derived L sections is necessary in order to achieve the proper image matches with the constant-K sections. This is illus-

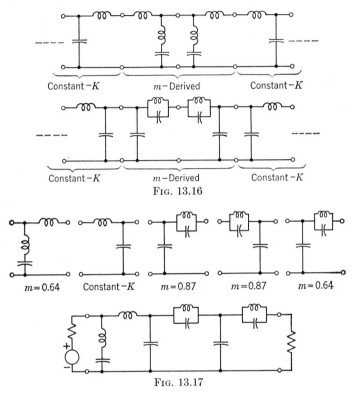

FIG. 13.16

FIG. 13.17

trated in Fig. 13.16. Filters designed so as to have both m-derived and constant-K sections are referred to as *composite* filters.

To illustrate the design of a composite filter, assume that the terminations of the filter at both ends are to be 1 ohm. The passband is from 0 to 1 radian/sec; in the stopband transmission zeros are desired at $\omega = 1.3$, 2, and ∞. To provide the transmission zero at infinity, one constant-K section is needed. The m values corresponding to the finite transmission zeros are $m = 0.64$ and $m = 0.87$. Two m-derived L sections with $m = 0.64$ can be used as the terminating half sections. Two m-derived L sections with $m = 0.87$ are used in the interior of the filter. The reason for using two sections in the latter case is to achieve a necessary constant-K image-impedance matching. One possible design is illustrated in Fig. 13.17. In the over-all filter similar elements in series

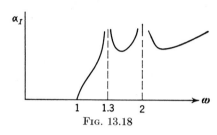

or in shunt are combined. The image-attenuation characteristic of the filter, shown in Fig. 13.18, is the sum of the image-attenuation characteristics of the individual sections. Often the specifications also include at least a minimum attenuation at a given frequency. If the developed filter, as in Fig. 13.17, does not sat-

FIG. 13.18

isfy this type of requirement, additional constant-K or m-derived sections are introduced to make up the deficit.

13.5   The m-Derived Delay Sections.   In Sec. 13.4 it is shown that the degree of freedom in the m-derived sections is used to provide better matching or to introduce transmission zeros in the stopband. This degree of freedom can alternately be used to linearize the passband phase characteristic. Consequently, this new type of m-derived sections can be used advantageously as a network to provide delay.

The delay of an m-derived section is obtained by taking the derivative of the phase function (13.40).

$$\tau_I(\omega) = \frac{d\beta_I}{d\omega} = \frac{m}{(1 - \omega^2 + m^2\omega^2)(1 - \omega^2)^{\frac{1}{2}}} \tag{13.47}$$

In (13.47) a minus sign is not included in $\dfrac{d\beta_I}{d\omega}$, since the image function is defined on the basis of input over output. The parameter m can now be chosen to provide a good delay characteristic. One approach is to require (13.47) to be a maximally flat delay function. In the usual manner, a Taylor's expansion of $\tau_I(\omega)$ is made about $\omega = 0$.

$$\tau_I(\omega) = m[1 + (\tfrac{3}{2} - m^2)\omega^2 + \cdots] \tag{13.48}$$

The coefficient of the ω^2 term is set equal to zero to obtain the maximally flat characteristic. This leads to

$$m = \sqrt{1.5} = 1.225 \tag{13.49}$$

From (13.48) the delay at d-c is equal to m for the normalized case of a passband of unit width. For the denormalized case the d-c delay of the section is m/ω_c, where ω_c is the actual cutoff frequency. For a structure of n sections, the delay is nm/ω_c. Such a structure is often referred to as an m-derived delay line. Referring to (13.32), one can see that for $m > 1$, the inductance L_2 is negative. This negative inductance can be physically realized if two L sections are combined into a T section, as

shown in Fig. 13.19.*   The three inductances of the T section can be
realized as coupled coils with negative mutual inductance.   The self- and
mutual inductances of the coupled coil are

$$l_{11} = l_{22} = \frac{1 + m^2}{2m} L$$
$$l_{12} = \frac{1 - m^2}{2m} L$$

(13.50)

The coefficient of coupling is

$$k = \frac{|l_{12}|}{l_{11}} = \frac{|1 - m^2|}{1 + m^2} < 1$$

(13.51)

Since the coefficient of coupling is always less than unity for $m > 0$, a
physical realization of the coupled coils is possible.   For the maximally
flat delay case, k is equal to $\frac{1}{3}$ and is usually easy to realize.   It must be

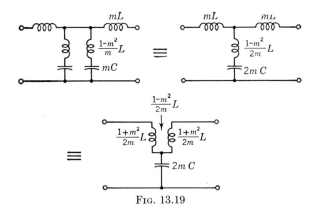

FIG. 13.19

remembered that for the configuration of Fig. 13.19 the delay is twice
that of a basic L section.   The image impedances of the coupled-coil
structure is the constant-K image impedance of (13.18).   Consequently,
m-derived terminating sections are generally used to minimize the mismatch between the image impedance and the resistive terminations.
These terminating sections, however, introduce some delay distortion.
Often this distortion is negligible in comparison with the over-all delay
characteristic.

   In conclusion, it should be noted that the m-derived sections for $m > 1$
produce transmission zeros on the σ axis at $\sigma = \pm 1/\sqrt{m^2 - 1}$.   The
presence of the transmission zero in the right half plane indicates that
these structures are nonminimum phase networks.

   * The same technique cannot be used for the m-derived structure of Fig. 13.10b.
In this structure a negative capacitance is obtained for $m > 1$.

13.6   Lattice Image Filters.   Image filters can also be synthesized by using symmetrical lattice networks as the building-block structures.   In fact, there is a general theory of image filter synthesis based on lattice networks.*   This is the direct result of the general nature of lattice networks.   This section briefly presents the salient features of lattice image filters.   The image impedances are very simply related to the lattice branch impedances z_a and z_b.   From Chap. 12

$$z_{11} = \frac{z_a + z_b}{2} \tag{13.52}$$

$$y_{11} = \frac{z_a + z_b}{2 z_a z_b} \tag{13.53}$$

Because the lattice is symmetrical, the two image impedances are equal.

$$Z_I = \sqrt{\frac{z_{11}}{y_{11}}} = \sqrt{z_a z_b} \tag{13.54}$$

The image transfer function is

$$\Gamma = \tfrac{1}{2} \ln \frac{\sqrt{z_{11} y_{11}} + 1}{\sqrt{z_{11} y_{11}} - 1} = \ln \frac{1 + \sqrt{z_b/z_a}}{1 - \sqrt{z_b/z_a}} \tag{13.55}$$

For filter applications, where specific pass- and stopbands are desired, lossless networks are used in the lattice. z_a and z_b are then LC driving-point impedance functions, and it is convenient to work with the reactance functions X_a and X_b.

$$\begin{aligned} z_a(j\omega) &= jX_a(\omega) \\ z_b(j\omega) &= jX_b(\omega) \end{aligned} \tag{13.56}$$

Equations (13.54) and (13.55) become

$$Z_I(j\omega) = j\sqrt{X_a X_b} \tag{13.57}$$

$$\Gamma(j\omega) = \alpha_I + j\beta_I = \ln \frac{1 + \sqrt{X_b/X_a}}{1 - \sqrt{X_b/X_a}} \tag{13.58}$$

If over a given frequency interval X_a and X_b have different signs, the image impedance is real and the image transfer function is imaginary. Thus this interval is a portion of a passband.   If X_a and X_b have the same signs over a frequency interval, the image impedance is imaginary and the image attenuation function is non-zero.   This interval is then a portion of a stopband. X_a and X_b change signs at the location of either a pole or a zero.   Therefore the presence of either a pole or a zero in one but not the other denotes the boundary between a pass- and a stopband. In Fig. 13.20 the reactance plots of two representative LC networks are

---

* H. W. Bode, A General Theory of Electric Wave Filters, *J. Math. and Phys.*, vol. 13, no. 3, pp. 275–362, November, 1934.

shown.   The stop- and passbands are illustrated if these networks are
the lattice branch networks.   From the above, the two networks do not
have poles or zeros in common at ω_2, ω_3, and ω_5.   These frequencies are
thus the cutoff frequencies.   The sign requirement establishes whether
the intervals between cutoff frequencies are either stop- or passbands.
It should be noted that at the poles and zeros of z_a in the passband (at
the origin, ω_1 and ω_4) z_b has zeros and poles, respectively.   Alternately,
z_a and z_b must have the same poles and zeros in a stopband (at infinity for
the present example).   From (13.58) it is seen that at those frequencies

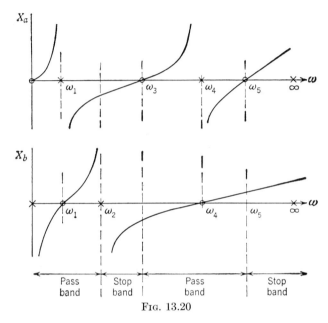

FIG. 13.20

where $X_a = X_b$, the image attenuation is infinite; those are the frequency
locations of transmission zeros.

Because of the simple relationship between the pass- and stopband
intervals and poles and zeros of z_a and z_b, it is very easy to translate a
given specification of an arbitrary number of pass- and stopbands to the
specifications of the LC lattice networks.   In addition to the poles and
zeros needed to define the cutoff frequencies, extra poles and zeros can be
introduced in both the pass- and stopbands by the above rules.   These
extra poles and zeros provide degrees of freedom to obtain desired image-
impedance and image transfer function characteristics.*

* Cauer has shown that this type of filter can be synthesized to provide an image
impedance which is an equal-ripple approximation to a constant in the passband.   In
addition, the filter may have an attenuation characteristic in the stopband which has
equal minima (see Ref. 13).

PROBLEMS

13.1. Determine the image parameters of the networks in Fig. P13.1

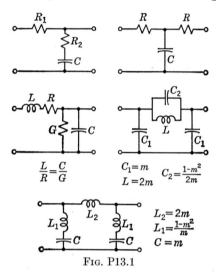

FIG. P13.1

13.2. Calculate the actual transfer voltage ratio V_2/V_0 of a constant-K filter terminated at both ends in 1-ohm resistances and having one and two basic L sections. Plot the magnitude and compare with magnitude characteristics that would be obtained under image-matched conditions.

13.3. Design a low-pass constant-K image filter operating between 300-ohm resistances and having a bandwidth of $100/2\pi$ kc. The attenuation at 30 kc must be at least 40 db. Terminating m sections should be used to minimize the mismatch.

13.4. Design a bandpass image filter which has the following specifications:

> Passband 88 to 108 Mc
> Source and load resistances 300 ohms
> Infinite rejection at 130 Mc
> 60-db attenuation at 60 Mc
> Terminating m sections

Use the conventional low-pass to bandpass transformation.

13.5. A filter with a passband from 4 to 8 Mc is desired. The load and the source are transmission lines that furnish source and load resistances of 200 ohms. The filter, which can be designed on the image basis, must provide transmission zeros at 10 Mc and infinity. A good impedance match between the filter and the lines is desired.

13.6. In practice, the roll-off of the magnitude of the transfer function of an m-derived delay line is primarily due to the dissipation of the inductances. It can be shown that the loss introduced is approximately[*]

$$\alpha \text{ (nepers)} \approx \frac{\omega}{2Q}\tau$$

[*] See Ref. 10, p. 220.

where Q is found from the average Q of the inductances at the cutoff frequency and τ is the delay. Show that the 10 to 90% rise time is

$$t_r \approx \frac{\pi\tau(0)}{2Q}$$

where $\tau(0)$ is the d-c delay.

Design a delay line to satisfy the following specifications:

Amount of delay: 10 μsec
Rise time: at most 1 μsec
Source and load terminations: 300 ohms

Determine the basic delay section, including the Q information, the number of sections needed, and the terminating m sections.

13.7. Determine for an arbitrary reciprocal 2-port the relationship between the parameters of the $ABCD$ matrix and the image parameters.

13.8. Verify the following relationships between the open-circuit impedance parameters and the image parameters:

$$z_{11} = Z_{I1} \coth \Gamma$$
$$z_{22} = Z_{I2} \coth \Gamma$$
$$z_{12} = \sqrt{Z_{I1}Z_{I2}} \operatorname{csch} \Gamma$$

13.9. The results of Prob. 13.8 can be used to analyze the transfer function of a periodic structure. For the configuration in Fig. P13.9, calculate V_2/V_1. Consider the structure as an image-method cascade of simple structures.

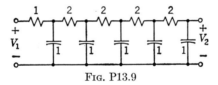

FIG. P13.9

13.10. The following impedances are the branch impedances of a symmetrical lattice:

$$z_a = \frac{p(p^2 + 4)}{(p^2 + 1)(p^2 + 9)} \qquad z_b = \frac{p}{p^2 + 9}$$

Determine and plot the image parameters of the lattice for $p = j\omega$. Indicate the pass- and stopbands.

13.11. The simple constant-K structure can be generalized to that shown in Fig. P13.11, where Z_1 and Z_2 are LC networks and $Z_1Z_2 = 1$. Determine the conditions that define the passband, stopband, and band edges. Design the networks of such a structure with passbands $0 \leq \omega \leq 1$ and $3 \leq \omega \leq 5$.

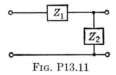

FIG. P13.11

13.12. Design an image lattice filter with the same passbands as those of Prob. 13.11. Unbalance the lattice if possible.

CHAPTER 14

THE SCATTERING MATRIX AND THE EVALUATION
OF MISMATCH DISTORTION

14.1 Introduction. Precise realization of expected performance for a network synthesized on the image-matched basis is obtained only if an image match is maintained at all junctions. However, it can be expected that mismatches always occur at the terminations, because of the non-rational nature of the image impedances. Consequently, distortion is introduced. This distortion can be minimized through the use of special terminating sections. Even though the distortion may be small, it is necessary in precise synthesis work to know the nature and the amount of distortion. The evaluation of the distortion is most simply made through the use of another basic 2-port description, the scattering matrix. The elements of this matrix are called the scattering parameters or the scattering coefficients. These coefficients are introduced in Chap. 9 and, as used there, are commonly referred to as the reflection and the transmission coefficients. In the next two sections a general derivation of the scattering matrix is developed. This is followed by an application of the scattering matrix to the mismatch problem.

14.2 The Scattering Parameter of a 1-port. In all the 2-port descriptions, except for the image description, the parameters are defined on the basis of the actual voltages and currents which exist at the ports, i.e., V_1, V_2, I_1, and I_2. Because the 2-port is linear and superposition holds, each voltage and each current can be considered the sum of two components. For example, the voltage V_1 can be separated into a matched component and a mismatched component. The matched component is the value of V_1 that would exist if the 2-port was image-matched. The mismatched component is taken as the difference between the actual value of V_1 with particular terminations and the above matched component. Similarly, the other voltages and currents of the ports can be separated. One then has a set of eight voltage and current components, although only four are independ-

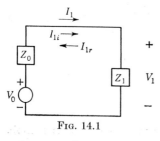

Fig. 14.1

214

ent, as is shown below.   The scattering matrix is defined in terms of these matched and mismatched components.*

The separation of a voltage or current into components is most easily illustrated for a 1-port situation such as that illustrated in Fig. 14.1. The actual current I_1 through Z_1 for the case of a source impedance Z_0 is

$$I_1 = \frac{V_0}{Z_0 + Z_1} \tag{14.1}$$

If the impedance Z_1 is assumed for the moment to be equal to the source impedance Z_0, an image match occurs.   The current under this image-matched condition, which is labeled I_{1i}, is

$$I_{1i} = \frac{V_0}{2Z_0} \tag{14.2}$$

For an arbitrary Z_1, the actual current is considered the algebraic sum of the above component, which would exist under matched conditions, and a mismatch component, which is labeled I_{1r}.

$$I_1 = I_{1i} - I_{1r} \tag{14.3}$$

The matched component can be viewed as an incident wave flowing into the port, as shown in Fig. 14.1.   The mismatched component can be viewed as a wave reflected from the port if a mismatch occurs.   The subscripts i for the matched component and r for the mismatched component represent the incident and reflected components.   Because of these assumed directions, the minus sign appears in (14.3).   An expression for I_{1r} can be obtained from (14.1), (14.2), and (14.3).

$$\begin{aligned} I_{1r} = I_{1i} - I_1 &= \frac{Z_1 - Z_0}{Z_1 + Z_0} \frac{V_0}{2Z_0} \\ &= \frac{Z_1 - Z_0}{Z_1 + Z_0} I_{1i} \end{aligned} \tag{14.4}$$

$$= S_{11}I_{1i} \tag{14.5}$$

In (14.5) the coefficient S_{11}, which is the ratio of the reflected to incident components, i.e., the ratio of the mismatched to matched components, is called the reflection coefficient or the 1-port scattering parameter with respect to the reference Z_0.

$$S_{11} = \frac{I_{1r}}{I_{1i}} = \frac{Z_1 - Z_0}{Z_1 + Z_0} \tag{14.6}$$

---

* The separation of voltages and currents on the above pattern is also used in several other instances.   For example, in distributed systems voltages and currents or the electric and magnetic fields are often separated into incident and reflected components. In multiphase generation and transmission problems, too, use is made of symmetrical and antisymmetrical components.

As expected, if Z_1 is equal to the reference Z_0, $S_{11} = 0$ and an image match exists.

Similarly, the above reflection coefficient can be defined as the ratio of the components of the voltage V_1. If an image match exists, the voltage across $Z_1 = Z_0$ is

$$V_{1i} = \frac{V_0}{2} \tag{14.7}$$

For an arbitrary Z_1, the actual voltage is

$$V_1 = \frac{Z_1}{Z_1 + Z_0} V_0 \tag{14.8}$$

This actual voltage can be considered the sum of a matched component V_{1i} and a mismatched component V_{1r}.

$$V_1 = V_{1i} + V_{1r} \tag{14.9}$$

As in the situation for the components of the current, the voltage components in (14.9) can be treated as incident and reflected components (see Fig. 14.2). A minus sign is not used in (14.9) for the reflected component, because, according to the usual convention, the polarity of a voltage is positive upward. The labeling of the matched and mismatched components agrees with the definitions in distributed systems. In the remainder of the chapter the components of the voltages and currents are referred to as incident and reflected components.

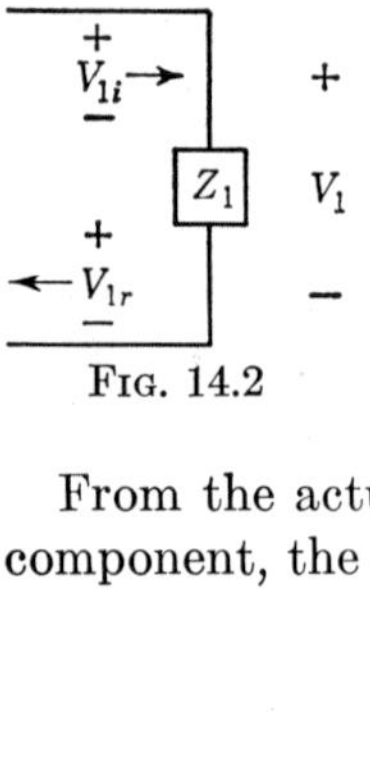

Fig. 14.2

From the actual voltage expression and the definition of the incident component, the reflected component is

$$V_{1r} = V_1 - V_{1i} = \frac{Z_1 - Z_0}{Z_1 + Z_0} \frac{V_0}{2} \tag{14.10}$$

$$= S_{11} V_{1i} \tag{14.11}$$

For both the voltage and the current, the ratio of the reflected component to the incident component is the same reflection coefficient S_{11}. From (14.2) and (14.7) the ratio of the incident voltage component to the incident current component is equal to the reference impedance Z_0.

$$\frac{V_{1i}}{I_{1i}} = Z_0 \tag{14.12}$$

Similarly, from (14.5) and (14.11),

$$\frac{V_{1r}}{I_{1r}} = Z_0 \tag{14.13}$$

14.3 The Scattering Matrix of a 2-port. The voltages and currents of a 2-port can be separated into incident and reflected components, as illustrated in Fig. 14.3. The source and load impedances are arbitrarily chosen impedances Z_{01} and Z_{02}, respectively. These chosen impedances are referred to as the reference impedances. The voltages and currents

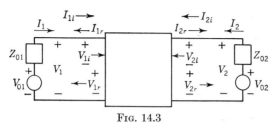

FIG. 14.3

are divided into components by a technique similar to that used with the 1-port. Consider first the voltage at the input port. If the source at the output is assumed for the moment to be absent ($V_{02} = 0$), the incident voltage V_{1i} is defined as the voltage that would exist at the input port if an image match existed. An image match occurs if the input impedance Z_{11} is equal to the reference impedance Z_{01}. (It should be remembered that Z_{11} is the input impedance for the specific load impedance Z_{02}.) Under these conditions

$$V_{1i} = \frac{V_{01}}{2} \tag{14.14}$$

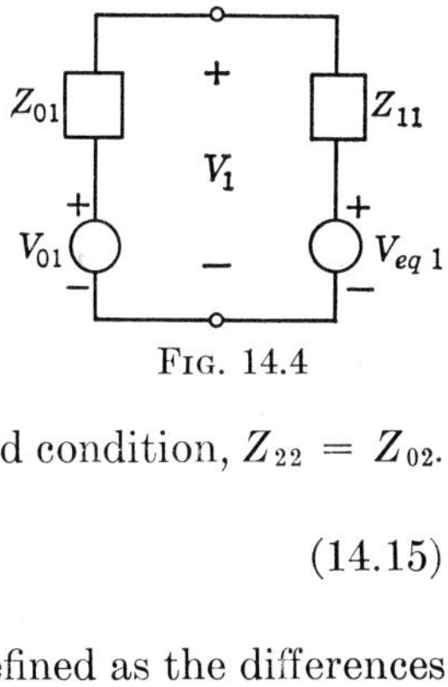

FIG. 14.4

Following the same procedure, one defines the incident component of V_2 on the basis of a source at the output only and for an image-matched condition, $Z_{22} = Z_{02}$.

$$V_{2i} = \frac{V_{02}}{2} \tag{14.15}$$

The reflected components V_{1r} and V_{2r} are again defined as the differences of the actual voltages and the incident components.

$$V_{1r} = V_1 - V_{1i} \tag{14.16}$$
$$V_{2r} = V_2 - V_{2i} \tag{14.17}$$

In general, both V_{01} and V_{02} are present and contribute to the values of V_1 and V_2. An expression for V_1 can be found with the aid of Fig. 14.4, where a Thévenin equivalent is used at the input port. The Thévenin equivalent voltage $V_{eq\,1}$ in terms of the open-circuit parameters of the 2-port and the load impedance is

$$V_{eq\,1} = \frac{z_{12}}{z_{22} + Z_{02}} V_{02} \tag{14.18}$$

From an analysis of the circuit in Fig. 14.4

$$V_1 = \frac{Z_{11}}{Z_{11} + Z_{01}} V_{01} + \frac{Z_{01}}{Z_{11} + Z_{01}} V_{eq\,1} \qquad (14.19)$$

A combination of (14.14), (14.15), (14.16), (14.18), and (14.19) leads to

$$V_{1r} = \left(\frac{Z_{11} - Z_{01}}{Z_{11} + Z_{01}}\right) V_{1i} + \left(\frac{2Z_{01}}{Z_{11} + Z_{01}} \frac{z_{12}}{z_{22} + Z_{02}}\right) V_{2i} \qquad (14.20)$$

In a like manner, the following equation is obtained for the output port:

$$V_{2r} = \left(\frac{2Z_{02}}{Z_{22} + Z_{02}} \frac{z_{21}}{z_{11} + Z_{01}}\right) V_{1i} + \left(\frac{Z_{22} - Z_{02}}{Z_{22} + Z_{02}}\right) V_{2i} \qquad (14.21)$$

The coefficients in (14.20) and (14.21) are called the scattering parameters of the 2-port with respect to the reference impedances Z_{01} and Z_{02}.[*] In terms of these parameters the equations are

$$\begin{aligned} V_{1r} &= S_{11}{}^V V_{1i} + S_{12}{}^V V_{2i} \\ V_{2r} &= S_{21}{}^V V_{1i} + S_{22}{}^V V_{2i} \end{aligned} \qquad (14.22)$$

The physical meaning of the scattering parameters is evident from their definitions in (14.20) and (14.21). For example $S_{11}{}^V$, called the input reflection coefficient, is the ratio of the reflected to incident components of V_1 if the output source is absent (i.e., $V_{2i} = 0$). Under the same condition, $S_{21}{}^V$, called the forward transmission coefficient, is equal to the actual ratio of the load voltage to V_{1i}.

A dual development can be used to derive the relationships between the reflected and incident components of the currents. The resultant scattering equations are of the form

$$\begin{aligned} I_{1r} &= S_{11}{}^I I_{1i} + S_{12}{}^I I_{2i} \\ I_{2r} &= S_{21}{}^I I_{1i} + S_{22}{}^I I_{2i} \end{aligned} \qquad (14.23)$$

The superscripts V and I must be used in (14.22) and (14.23) to identify the basis as voltage or current. It is easily shown that the corresponding reflection coefficients are equal:

$$\begin{aligned} S_{11}{}^V &= S_{11}{}^I \\ S_{22}{}^V &= S_{22}{}^I \end{aligned} \qquad (14.24)$$

However, the corresponding transmission coefficients are not identical unless $Z_{01} = Z_{02}$.

The scattering matrix (i.e., the scattering descriptions) can also be

* C. G. Montgomery, R. H. Dicke, and E. M. Purcell (eds.), "Principles of Microwave Circuits," MIT Radiation Laboratory Series, vol. 8, chap. 5, McGraw-Hill Book Company, Inc., New York, 1948; H. J. Carlin, The Scattering Matrix in Network Theory, *Trans. IRE*, CT-3, no. 2, June, 1956.

obtained in a straightforward manner by using matrix algebra. An advantage of using this approach, as brought out below, is the simple relationship that can be obtained between the scattering matrix, the reference impedances, and the open-circuit impedance matrix or the short-circuit admittance matrix. The actual voltages and currents and their components are written in matrix form as

$$\mathbf{V}] = \mathbf{V}_i] + \mathbf{V}_r] \tag{14.25}$$
$$\mathbf{I}] = \mathbf{I}_i] - \mathbf{I}_r] \tag{14.26}$$

As in (14.12) and (14.13) for the 1-port case, the ratio of the incident components of voltage and current and the ratio of the reflected components of voltage and current are the reference impedances.

$$\frac{V_{1i}}{I_{1i}} = \frac{V_{1r}}{I_{1r}} = Z_{01} \tag{14.27}$$

$$\frac{V_{2i}}{I_{2i}} = \frac{V_{2r}}{I_{2r}} = Z_{02} \tag{14.28}$$

In matrix notation, these equations become

$$\mathbf{V}_i] = [\mathbf{Z}_0] \mathbf{I}_i] \tag{14.29}$$
$$\mathbf{V}_r] = [\mathbf{Z}_0] \mathbf{I}_r] \tag{14.30}$$

where
$$[\mathbf{Z}_0] = \begin{bmatrix} Z_{01} & 0 \\ 0 & Z_{02} \end{bmatrix} \tag{14.31}$$

$[\mathbf{Z}_0]$ is called the reference impedance matrix.

The actual voltages and currents of the 2-port can be related by the open-circuit impedance matrix.

$$\mathbf{V}] = [\mathbf{Z}] \mathbf{I}] \tag{14.32}$$

Equations (14.25) and (14.26) are now introduced into the last equation.

$$\mathbf{V}_i] + \mathbf{V}_r] = [\mathbf{Z}]\{\mathbf{I}_i] - \mathbf{I}_r]\} \tag{14.33}$$

An equation in terms of the current components only is obtained through the use of (14.29) and (14.30).

$$[\mathbf{Z}_0] \mathbf{I}_i] + [\mathbf{Z}_0] \mathbf{I}_r] = [\mathbf{Z}] \mathbf{I}_i] - [\mathbf{Z}] \mathbf{I}_r]$$
$$\{[\mathbf{Z}] + [\mathbf{Z}_0]\} \mathbf{I}_r = \{[\mathbf{Z}] - [\mathbf{Z}_0]\} \mathbf{I}_i]$$
$$\mathbf{I}_r] = \{[\mathbf{Z}] + [\mathbf{Z}_0]\}^{-1}\{[\mathbf{Z}] - [\mathbf{Z}_0]\} \mathbf{I}_i] \tag{14.34}$$

Equation (14.34) can be identified as the current scattering matrix description.

$$\mathbf{I}_r] = [\mathbf{S}^I] \mathbf{I}_i] \tag{14.35}$$

where
$$[\mathbf{S}^I] = \begin{bmatrix} S_{11}^I & S_{12}^I \\ S_{21}^I & S_{22}^I \end{bmatrix} = \{[\mathbf{Z}] + [\mathbf{Z}_0]\}^{-1}\{[\mathbf{Z}] - [\mathbf{Z}_0]\} \tag{14.36}$$

In a similar manner the voltage scattering matrix can be developed. The result is

$$V_r] = [S^V] \, V_i] \tag{14.37}$$

where

$$[S^V] = \begin{bmatrix} S_{11}^V & S_{12}^V \\ S_{21}^V & S_{22}^V \end{bmatrix} = \{[1] + [Z][Z_0]^{-1}\}^{-1}\{[Z][Z_0]^{-1} - [1]\} \tag{14.38}$$

The relationship between the two scattering matrices is obtained from (14.29), (14.30), (14.35), and (14.37).

$$
\begin{aligned}
V_r] &= [Z_0] \, I_r] = [Z_0][S^I] \, I_i] \\
&= [S^V] \, V_i] = [S^V][Z_0] \, I_i] \\
[Z_0][S^I] &= [S^V][Z_0] \\
[S^I] &= [Z_0]^{-1}[S^V][Z_0] \\
[S^V] &= [Z_0][S^I][Z_0]^{-1}
\end{aligned}
\tag{14.39}
$$

Notice for the case where the reference impedances are equal,

$$Z_{01} = Z_{02} = Z_0$$

$$[Z_0] = \begin{bmatrix} Z_0 & 0 \\ 0 & Z_0 \end{bmatrix} = Z_0[1] \tag{14.40}$$

Thus the voltage and the current matrices are identical.

For the general case of unequal reference impedances, it is often inconvenient to have separate voltage and current scattering matrices. A normalized scattering matrix can be introduced which is identical for both the voltage and the current components. This normalized matrix is developed as follows. Normalized voltage and current components can be defined by a manipulation of the relationships of (14.27) and (14.28). For example,

$$V_{1i} = Z_{01} I_{1i}$$

$$V_{1i}^n = \frac{V_{1i}}{\sqrt{Z_{01}}} = I_{1i} \sqrt{Z_{01}} = I_{1i}^n \tag{14.41}$$

The superscript n pertains to the normalized component. Notice that the normalized voltage and current components are equal. In a similar manner, normalized components are defined for the remaining voltage and current components. For the output port the normalization factor is $\sqrt{Z_{02}}$. For example,

$$V_{2i}^n = \frac{V_{2i}}{\sqrt{Z_{02}}} = I_{2i} \sqrt{Z_{02}} = I_{2i}^n \tag{14.42}$$

The scattering equations (14.22) become

$$
\begin{aligned}
V_{1r}^n \sqrt{Z_{01}} &= S_{11}^V V_{1i}^n \sqrt{Z_{01}} + S_{12}^V V_{2i}^n \sqrt{Z_{02}} \\
V_{2r}^n \sqrt{Z_{02}} &= S_{21}^V V_{1i}^n \sqrt{Z_{01}} + S_{22}^V V_{2i}^n \sqrt{Z_{02}}
\end{aligned}
\tag{14.43}
$$

Dividing the first equation in (14.43) by $\sqrt{Z_{01}}$ and the second equation by

$\sqrt{Z_{02}}$, one obtains the normalized scattering matrix in terms of the voltage scattering matrix.

$$\mathbf{V}_r{}^n] = [\mathbf{S}]\ \mathbf{V}_i{}^n] = \begin{bmatrix} S_{11}{}^V & \sqrt{\dfrac{Z_{02}}{Z_{01}}}\ S_{12}{}^V \\ \sqrt{\dfrac{Z_{01}}{Z_{02}}}\ S_{21}{}^V & S_{22}{}^V \end{bmatrix} \mathbf{V}_i{}^n] \qquad (14.44)$$

In a similar manner, the normalized scattering matrix can be expressed in terms of the current scattering matrix.

$$\mathbf{I}_r{}^n] = [\mathbf{S}]\ \mathbf{I}_i{}^n] = \begin{bmatrix} S_{11}{}^I & \sqrt{\dfrac{Z_{01}}{Z_{02}}}\ S_{12}{}^I \\ \sqrt{\dfrac{Z_{02}}{Z_{01}}}\ S_{21}{}^I & S_{22}{}^I \end{bmatrix} \mathbf{I}_i{}^n] \qquad (14.45)$$

The relation between the normalized scattering matrix and the voltage and current matrices can be written in compact form as follows:

$$[\mathbf{S}] = [\mathbf{Z}_0]^{-\frac{1}{2}}[\mathbf{S}^V][\mathbf{Z}_0]^{\frac{1}{2}}$$
$$= [\mathbf{Z}_0]^{\frac{1}{2}}[\mathbf{S}^I][\mathbf{Z}_0]^{-\frac{1}{2}} \qquad (14.46)$$

where $\qquad [\mathbf{Z}_0]^{\frac{1}{2}} = \begin{bmatrix} \sqrt{Z_{01}} & 0 \\ 0 & \sqrt{Z_{02}} \end{bmatrix} \qquad (14.47)$

A physical interpretation can be made concerning the factor $\sqrt{Z_{02}/Z_{01}}$ in the normalized scattering matrix (i.e., the transmission coefficients S_{12} and S_{21}). Consider the scattering matrix of the ideal transformer shown in Fig. 14.5. If the turns ratio of the transformer is equal to $\sqrt{Z_{01}/Z_{02}}$, an image match occurs at both ports.

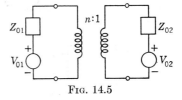

Fig. 14.5

$$n = \sqrt{\dfrac{Z_{01}}{Z_{02}}} \qquad (14.48)$$

$$S^V = \begin{bmatrix} 0 & n \\ \dfrac{1}{n} & 0 \end{bmatrix} \qquad (14.49)$$

$$S^I = \begin{bmatrix} 0 & \dfrac{1}{n} \\ n & 0 \end{bmatrix} \qquad (14.50)$$

The normalized scattering matrix is obtained from (14.46).

$$S = \begin{bmatrix} 0 & 1 \\ 1 & 0 \end{bmatrix} \qquad (14.51)$$

Therefore, if the turns ratio n is set equal to $\sqrt{Z_{01}/Z_{02}}$, the normalized scattering matrix pertains to a direct connection between input and output for the fictitious situation of equal reference impedances. For a general 2-port with unequal terminations, the factor $\sqrt{Z_{02}/Z_{01}}$ in the transmission coefficients can be identified as the effective transformation ratio that is necessary to convert the 2-port to an equal-reference situation. If reciprocity holds for the general 2-port, the normalized scattering matrix is symmetrical ($S_{21} = S_{12}$).

At this point it should be recalled that scattering coefficients are used in Chap. 9 in dealing with power considerations of a lossless 2-port. The scattering coefficients used there are the normalized coefficients. The transmitted power through the 2-port normalized with respect to the maximum power available from the source is equal to $|S_{21}(j\omega)|^2$ and must always be equal to or less than unity. Similarly, the normalized reflected power at the input is equal to $|S_{11}(j\omega)|^2$. For a lossless reciprocal 2-port

$$|S_{11}(j\omega)|^2 + |S_{21}(j\omega)|^2 = |S_{22}(j\omega)|^2 + |S_{21}(j\omega)|^2 = 1 \qquad (14.52)$$

14.4   The Evaluation of Image Filters Using Scattering Matrix.
Image filters are synthesized on the basis of image matches existing at all junctions. In practice, mismatches are always obtained at the source and load terminations. The distortion due to the mismatches can readily be determined through the use of the scattering matrix. The procedure is as follows. The scattering matrix of the filter with ideal terminations is easily found from the image parameters of the over-all filter. From this scattering matrix, the impedance matrix of the over-all 2-port is determined. From this impedance matrix, a scattering matrix can be found with respect to any arbitrary terminations. The transmission coefficient S_{21} of this last matrix is the actual transfer function of interest.

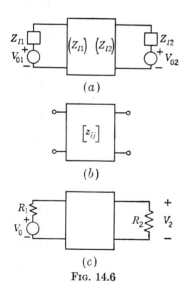

(a)

(b)

(c)

FIG. 14.6

Under image-matched conditions, as in Fig. 14.6a, the input and output reflection coefficients with respect to Z_{I1} and Z_{I2} are zero. The transmission coefficients on a voltage basis are simply related to the image transfer function. From (13.4)

$$S_{21}{}^V = \sqrt{\frac{Z_{I2}}{Z_{I1}}}\, e^{-\Gamma} \qquad (14.53)$$

$$S_{12}{}^V = \sqrt{\frac{Z_{I1}}{Z_{I2}}}\, e^{-\Gamma} \qquad (14.54)$$

The scattering matrix $S_m{}^V$ for the image-impedance reference is

$$[\mathbf{S}_m{}^V] = \begin{bmatrix} 0 & \sqrt{\dfrac{Z_{I1}}{Z_{I2}}}\, e^{-\Gamma} \\ \sqrt{\dfrac{Z_{I2}}{Z_{I1}}}\, e^{-\Gamma} & 0 \end{bmatrix} \tag{14.55}$$

with a reference matrix

$$[\mathbf{Z}_{0m}] = \begin{bmatrix} Z_{I1} & 0 \\ 0 & Z_{I2} \end{bmatrix} \tag{14.56}$$

The open-circuit impedance matrix can be found in terms of the scattering matrix from a manipulation of (14.38).

$$[\mathbf{Z}] = ([\mathbf{1}] + [\mathbf{S}^V])([\mathbf{1}] - [\mathbf{S}^V])^{-1}[\mathbf{Z}_0] \tag{14.57}$$

Substituting (14.55) and (14.56) in the last equation, one obtains the open-circuit impedance matrix of the 2-port.

$$[\mathbf{Z}] = \frac{1}{(1 - e^{-2\Gamma})} \begin{bmatrix} Z_{I1}(1 + e^{-2\Gamma}) & 2\sqrt{Z_{I1}Z_{I2}}\, e^{-\Gamma} \\ 2\sqrt{Z_{I1}Z_{I2}}\, e^{-\Gamma} & Z_{I2}(1 + e^{-2\Gamma}) \end{bmatrix} \tag{14.58}$$

Assume now that the specified terminations are R_1 and R_2. The new reference impedance matrix is

$$[\mathbf{Z}_0] = \begin{bmatrix} R_1 & 0 \\ 0 & R_2 \end{bmatrix} \tag{14.59}$$

The voltage scattering matrix for these references is obtained from (14.38).

$$S^V = \frac{1}{\Delta} \begin{bmatrix} (z_{11} - R_1)(z_{22} + R_2) - z_{12}z_{21} & 2z_{12}R_1 \\ 2z_{21}R_2 & (z_{11} + R_1)(z_{22} - R_2) - z_{12}z_{21} \end{bmatrix} \tag{14.60}$$

where

$$\Delta = (z_{11} + R_1)(z_{22} + R_2) - z_{12}z_{21} \tag{14.61}$$

From (14.60) the actual forward transmission coefficient is

$$S_{21}{}^V = \frac{2z_{21}R_2}{\Delta} \tag{14.62}$$

The z_{ij} in (14.58) are now introduced. After some manipulation the result is

$$S_{21}{}^V = \sqrt{\frac{R_2}{R_1}}\, e^{-\Gamma} \left(\frac{2\sqrt{Z_{I1}R_1}}{Z_{I1} + R_1} \right) \left(\frac{2\sqrt{Z_{I2}R_2}}{Z_{I2} + R_2} \right) \left(\frac{1}{1 - \dfrac{R_1 - Z_{I1}}{R_1 + Z_{I1}}\dfrac{R_2 - Z_{I2}}{R_2 + Z_{I2}} e^{-2\Gamma}} \right) \tag{14.63}$$

A physical interpretation can be made about the different factors of (14.63).[13,14]   The multiplier $\sqrt{R_2/R_1}$ is the effective transformation ratio of the 2-port. The factor $e^{-\Gamma}$ is the image transmission function on the basis of equal image impedances $Z_{I1} = Z_{I2}$. Thus the product $\sqrt{(R_2/R_1)}\, e^{-\Gamma}$ represents the voltage transfer ratio for an image-matched 2-port if image impedances are R_1 and R_2. The three other factors in brackets clearly indicate the distortion terms. The factor $2\sqrt{Z_{I1}R_1}/(Z_{I1} + R_1)$ is a measure of the distortion due to a mismatch at the input only. Similarly, $2\sqrt{Z_{I2}R_2}/(Z_{I2} + R_2)$ is a measure of the distortion due to a mismatch at the output only. They are called the reflection factors at the input and the output. For filter application the following estimates can be made. In the passband the image impedance is purely real. The reflection factor can be more conveniently expressed as follows:

$$\text{Reflection factor} = \frac{2}{\sqrt{Z_I/R} + \sqrt{R/Z_I}} \qquad (14.64)$$

Equation (14.64) is plotted in Fig. 14.7. It is seen that the reflection factor attains a maximum of unity at $Z_I/R = 1$, i.e., the matched situation. For other values of Z_I, the reflection factor is less than unity, and a reflection loss is introduced in the passband.

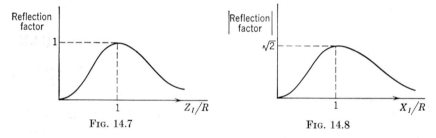

FIG. 14.7   FIG. 14.8

In the stopband the image impedance is purely imaginary, and the magnitude of the reflection factor can be expressed as

$$|\text{Reflection factor}| = \left| \frac{2}{\sqrt{jX_I/R} + \sqrt{R/jX_I}} \right| \qquad (14.65)$$

in which $Z_I = jX_I$. Equation (14.65) has been plotted in Fig. 14.8.

It is seen that the magnitude of the reflection factor attains a maximum of $\sqrt{2}$ at $X_I/R = 1$. Thus the mismatch in the stopband can actually introduce a reflection gain of at most 3 db at a port. A total of 6-db reflection gain is possible in the stopband because of the mismatch at the input and the output. In the design of image filter, care must be taken to allow an extra 6-db attenuation loss beyond the specified loss.

The last factor in (14.63) is called the interaction term. It arises because of multiple reflections at the input and the output for the components that are transmitted through the 2-port. For an illustration, refer to Fig. 14.9. Of the transmitted component a from input to output, part is reflected back toward the input as component b. This reflection is due to the mismatch between Z_{I2} and R_2. At the input another mismatch occurs, and component c is reflected back toward the output. Viewed in this manner, these internal reflections continue ad infinitum. That is, the internal path $abac$ is a closed-loop feedback path and contributes to distortion.

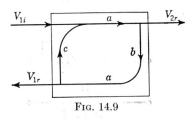

Fig. 14.9

Using the familiar feedback formula, one can justify the interaction term in (14.63). For filter application, the contribution due to interaction is usually small if the matching is fairly good in the passband and the image attenuation is high in the stopband.

PROBLEMS

14.1. Determine the scattering matrices of the situations illustrated in Fig. P14.1. The reference impedances are 1-ohm resistances.

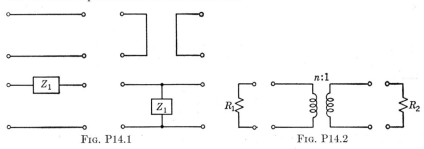

Fig. P14.1   Fig. P14.2

14.2. Determine the voltage and current scattering matrices of the situation shown in Fig. P14.2. R_1 and R_2 are the reference impedances. Show that if $n = \sqrt{R_1/R_2}$ the scattering matrices reduce to (14.49) and (14.50).

14.3. Determine the scattering coefficients of the networks shown in Fig. P14.3. From the scattering matrix of each, determine the open-circuit impedance matrices.

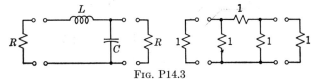

Fig. P14.3

14.4. Equations (14.36) and (14.38) express the current and voltage scattering matrices in terms of the open-circuit impedance matrix and the reference impedance matrix. Prove the following formulas which relate the open-circuit impedance matrix and the short-circuit admittance matrix to the scattering matrices.

$$[Z] = [Z_0]\{[1] + [S^I]\}\{[1] - [S^I]\}^{-1}$$
$$[Y] = [Y_0]\{[1] - [S^V]\}\{[1] + [S^V]\}^{-1}$$
where $\qquad [Y] = [Z]^{-1} \qquad$ and $\qquad [Y_0] = [Z_0]^{-1}$

14.5. Determine the scattering matrix of the 2-port in Fig. P14.5 with respect to unit resistance terminations. Start from the short-circuit parameters.

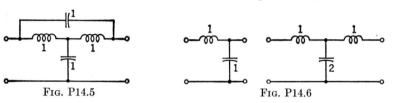

FIG. P14.5   FIG. P14.6

14.6. Determine the forward transmission coefficient of one- and two-section low-pass constant-K filters terminated in 1-ohm resistances (Fig. P14.6). Plot the various magnitude distortion terms of (14.63).

14.7. Repeat Prob. 14.6 with a two-section m-derived low-pass filter, shown in Fig. P14.7.

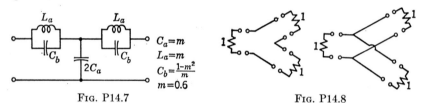

$$C_a = m$$
$$L_a = m$$
$$C_b = \frac{1-m^2}{m}$$
$$m = 0.6$$

FIG. P14.7   FIG. P14.8

14.8. Determine the scattering matrices of the 3-port networks in Fig. P14.8.

14.9. A resistive two-way splitting network, shown in Fig. P14.9, has the scattering matrix

$$[S] = \begin{bmatrix} 0 & t & t \\ t & 0 & 0 \\ t & 0 & 0 \end{bmatrix}$$

The network is matched at all three ports. The transmission coefficient from port 2

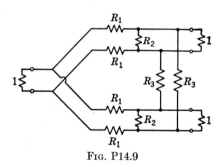

FIG. P14.9

to port 3 is zero, and the transmission coefficients from port 1 to port 2 and port 3 are equal.

(a) Determine the short-circuit admittance matrix from the specified [S], using the result of Prob. 14.4.

(b) Determine the short-circuit admittance matrix from the network in terms of R_1, R_2, and R_3.

(c) Compare the results of (a) and (b).   Determine R_1, R_2, R_3, and the transmission coefficient t.

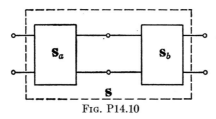

FIG. P14.10

14.10. The scattering matrix of the cascade of two 2-ports shown in Fig. P14.10 can be expressed in terms of the scattering matrices of the individual 2-ports. Prove the following:

$$S_{11} = S_{11a} + S_{12a}S_{11b}(1 - S_{22a}S_{11b})^{-1}S_{21a}$$
$$S_{22} = S_{22b} + S_{21b}(1 - S_{22a}S_{11b})^{-1}S_{22a}S_{12b}$$
$$S_{21} = S_{21b}(1 - S_{22a}S_{11b})^{-1}S_{21a}$$
$$S_{12} = S_{12a}(1 - S_{11b}S_{22a})^{-1}S_{12b}$$

The reference impedances are 1-ohm resistances.

APPENDIX 1

SIMPLE CONTINUANTS

The network functions of simple ladder networks can be expressed in terms of special determinants called simple continuants. These mathematical forms have simple expansion and recursion rules which make for subsequent ease in the development of the network functions. In this appendix simple continuants are introduced, and the relationship to the network functions is derived.

For the simple ladder network shown in Fig. A1.1, it is assumed for the moment that the first and the last branches are shunt branches.* The

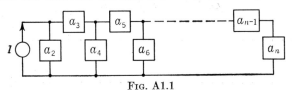

FIG. A1.1

source is a current source, and the load, if any, is included in the final shunt branch. The branches a_i are passive 1-port networks of any complexity. The a's with even subscripts denote the admittances of the successive shunt branches. The a's with odd subscripts denote the impedances of the successive series branches. From a conventional nodal analysis, the determinant of the equations can be written as follows:

$$\Delta = \begin{vmatrix} \left(a_2 + \dfrac{1}{a_3}\right) & -\dfrac{1}{a_3} & 0 & \cdots \cdots \cdots \cdots \\[2ex] -\dfrac{1}{a_3} & \left(\dfrac{1}{a_3} + a_4 + \dfrac{1}{a_5}\right) & -\dfrac{1}{a_5} & 0 \cdots \cdots \cdots \\[2ex] 0 & -\dfrac{1}{a_5} & & \cdots \cdots \cdots \cdots \\[2ex] \cdots \cdots \cdots \cdots \cdots \cdots \cdots \cdots & & -\dfrac{1}{a_{n-1}} \\[2ex] \cdots \cdots \cdots \cdots \cdots \cdots \cdots \cdots & -\dfrac{1}{a_{n-1}} & \left(\dfrac{1}{a_{n-1}} + a_n\right) \end{vmatrix} \quad \text{(A1.1)}$$

* It should be remembered that a simple ladder has no-node bridging.

229

In (A1.1) the only non-zero elements lie on the principal diagonal and on the two adjacent diagonals. This type of determinant is known as a *general continuant*. In addition, the determinant (A1.1) is symmetric. It can now be shown that a symmetric general continuant can be expressed in simpler form as a simple continuant.

For the assumption above, n is always even and the determinant has an order of $n/2$ (i.e., $n/2$ rows and $n/2$ columns). From the theory of determinants a general continuant of order $n/2$ can always be written in expanded form as another general continuant of order $n - 1$.* From this theorem, (A1.1) becomes

$$\Delta = \begin{vmatrix} a_2 + \dfrac{2}{a_3} & -\dfrac{1}{a_3} & 0 & \cdots \cdots \cdots \cdots \\ -1 & 1 & -\dfrac{1}{a_3} & 0 \cdots \cdots \cdots \\ 0 & -1 & \left(\dfrac{2}{a_3} + a_4 + \dfrac{2}{a_5}\right) & -\dfrac{1}{a_5} & \cdots \cdots \cdots \\ \cdots \cdots \cdots \cdots \cdots \cdots \cdots & 1 & -\dfrac{1}{a_{n-1}} \\ \cdots \cdots \cdots \cdots \cdots \cdots & -1 & \left(\dfrac{2}{a_{n-1}} + a_n\right) \end{vmatrix} \quad \text{(A1.2)}$$

(A1.2) is now manipulated by the following rules:
  (a) Add twice [column $2k$] to [column $2k - 1$], $k = 1, 2, \ldots , n - 1$.
  (b) Add twice [row $2k$] to row [$2k + 1$], $k = 1, 2, \ldots , n - 1$.
At this point the determinant has the form

$$\Delta = \begin{vmatrix} a_2 & -\dfrac{1}{a_3} & 0 & \cdots \cdots \cdots \\ 1 & 1 & -\dfrac{1}{a_3} & 0 \cdots \cdots \\ 0 & 1 & a_4 & -\dfrac{1}{a_5} & \cdots \cdots \\ \cdots \cdots \cdots \cdots \cdots \cdots & -\dfrac{1}{a_{n-1}} \\ \cdots \cdots \cdots \cdots \cdots & 1 & a_n \end{vmatrix} \quad \text{(A1.3)}$$

* T. Muir and W. H. Metzler, "A Treatise on the Theory of Determinants," George Banta Publishing Company (The Collegiate Press), Menasha, Wis., 1930.

The manipulation proceeds by

(c) Multiplying:

All rows 1, 2, . . . , $n - 2$ by a_{n-1}
All columns 1, 2, . . . , $n - 2$ by $1/a_{n-1}$
Column $n - 2$ by a_{n-1}
The determinant by $1/a_{n-1}$

(d) Repeating the operations of (c) for a_{n-3}, starting with row $n - 4$
(e) Continuing the process, completing the sequence with row 2, column 2.

The determinant becomes

$$\Delta = \frac{1}{a_3 a_5 \cdots a_{n-1}} \begin{vmatrix} a_2 & 1 & 0 & & & & \cdots \\ -1 & a_3 & 1 & 0 & & & \cdots \\ & & \cdots & & & & \cdots \\ & & \cdots & & & & \cdots \\ & & \cdots & & -1 & a_{n-1} & 1 \\ & & \cdots & & 0 & -1 & a_n \end{vmatrix} \qquad (A1.4)$$

The actual determinant of the right-hand side of (A1.4) is a *simple continuant* and has the special notation

$$K(a_2, a_3, \ldots, a_n) = \begin{vmatrix} a_2 & 1 & \cdots \\ -1 & a_3 & 1 & \cdots \\ & & \cdots & a_n \end{vmatrix} \qquad (A1.5)$$

The determinant of (A1.4) can thus be written

$$\Delta = \frac{K(a_2, a_3, \ldots, a_n)}{a_3 a_5 \ldots a_{n-1}} \qquad (A1.6)$$

The recursion formulas can be developed by the Laplace expansion of the simple continuant of (A1.5).

$$K(a_2,a_3, \ldots ,a_n) = a_2 \begin{vmatrix} a_3 & 1 & \cdot & \cdot & \cdot & \cdot & \cdot \\ -1 & a_4 & \cdot & \cdot & \cdot & \cdot & \cdot \\ \cdot & \cdot & \cdot & \cdot & \cdot & \cdot & 1 \\ \cdot & \cdot & \cdot & \cdot & -1 & a_n \end{vmatrix}$$

$$- 1 \begin{vmatrix} -1 & 1 & \cdot & \cdot & \cdot & \cdot \\ 0 & a_5 & 1 & \cdot & \cdot \\ \cdot & \cdot & \cdot & \cdot & \cdot & a_n \end{vmatrix}$$

$$= a_2 K(a_3,a_4, \ldots ,a_n) + K(a_5, \ldots ,a_n) \quad (A1.7)$$

By definition, $K(0) = 1$. Similarly, if one started from the lower right corner of the determinant in (A1.5), the following could be obtained:

$$K(a_2,a_3, \ldots ,a_n) = a_n K(a_2, \ldots ,a_{n-1}) + K(a_2, \ldots ,a_{n-2}) \quad (A1.8)$$

Successive use of (A1.7) leads to an expansion technique which is illustrated with $K(a_1,a_2, \ldots ,a_5)$. The element a_1 is included for generality. The expansion takes the form of a sum of products of the elements. This first term is the product of all the a's.

$$a_1 a_2 a_3 a_4 a_5 \quad (A1.9)$$

The next several terms are obtained from (A1.9) by removing each possible successive pair of elements and retaining the remainders. The remainders for the example are

$$a_3 a_4 a_5 \qquad a_1 a_4 a_5 \qquad a_1 a_2 a_5 \qquad a_1 a_2 a_3 \quad (A1.10)$$

This is followed by the remainders after the removal from (A1.9) of pairs of successive pairs. The remainders for this step are

$$a_1 \qquad a_3 \qquad a_5 \quad (A1.11)$$

This completes the expansion for the example; the value of the determinant is equal to

$$K(a_1,a_2, \ldots ,a_5) = a_1 a_2 a_3 a_4 a_5 + a_3 a_4 a_5$$
$$+ a_1 a_4 a_5 + a_1 a_2 a_5 + a_1 a_2 a_3 + a_1 + a_3 + a_5 \quad (A1.12)$$

For a more general case, one would continue to remove a greater number of pairs at each step. It should be noted that in the case of an even number of elements, the final step would be the removal of all elements. Unity is then added to the expansion, since $K(0) = 1$.

If the network function of interest is the input impedance, the numerator cofactor can also be expressed in terms of simple continuants.

$$Z_{11} = \frac{\Delta_{11}}{\Delta} \quad (A1.13)$$

From the similarity of the form Δ_{11} to Δ, Δ_{11} can be written immediately as

$$\Delta_{11} = \begin{vmatrix} \left(\dfrac{1}{a_3} + a_4\right) & +1 & & \cdots\cdots \\ -1 & a_5 & +1 & \cdots\cdots \\ \cdots\cdots\cdots\cdots & & -1 & a_n \end{vmatrix}$$

$$= \frac{K[(1/a_3 + a_4), a_5, \ldots, a_n]}{a_5 a_7 \cdots a_{n-1}} \tag{A1.14}$$

By repeated use of (A1.7), (A1.14) becomes

$$\Delta_{11} = \frac{K(a_3, \ldots, a_n)}{a_3 a_5 \cdots a_{n-1}} \tag{A1.15}$$

The input impedance is

$$Z_{11} = \frac{K(a_3, a_4, \ldots, a_n)}{K(a_2, a_3, \ldots, a_n)} \tag{A1.16}$$

For the over-all transfer impedance

$$Z_{21} = \frac{\Delta_{1n}}{\Delta} \tag{A1.17}$$

The cofactor Δ_{1n} is obtained directly from (A1.1).

$$\Delta_{1n} = (-1)\left(-\frac{1}{a_3}\right)\left(-\frac{1}{a_5}\right)\cdots\left(-\frac{1}{a_{n-1}}\right)$$

$$= \frac{1}{a_3 a_5 \cdots a_{n-1}} \tag{A1.18}$$

The transfer impedance then is

$$Z_{21} = \frac{1}{K(a_2, a_3, \ldots, a_n)} \tag{A1.19}$$

If a series element of impedance a_1 is present at the input, the transfer impedance of (A1.19) is not affected, because a_1 is in series with the current source. However, the input impedance is changed.

$$Z_{11} = a_1 + \frac{K(a_3, \ldots, a_n)}{K(a_2, \ldots, a_n)} = \frac{K(a_1, a_2, \ldots, a_n)}{K(a_2, \ldots, a_n)} \tag{A1.20}$$

The right-hand expression of (A1.20) follows from the recursion formula (A1.7).

If the input is a voltage source and the element a_1 is present, the transfer voltage ratio can be obtained in the following manner. First, the voltage source and the series impedance a_1 are converted to a current source V_1/a_1 and a shunt admittance $1/a_1$. The admittances $1/a_1$

and a_2 are combined to give $a_2' = 1/a_1 + a_2$. From (A1.19) the transfer impedance is

$$\frac{V_2}{V_1/a_1} = \frac{1}{K(a_2', a_3, \, \ldots \, , a_n)} \qquad (A1.21)$$

Hence the transfer voltage ratio is

$$\frac{V_2}{V_1} = \frac{1}{a_1 K(1/a_1 + a_2, a_3, \, \ldots \, , a_n)} = \frac{1}{K(a_1, a_2, \, \ldots \, , a_n)} \qquad (A1.22)$$

The second form of (A1.22) follows from a repeated use of the recursion formula.

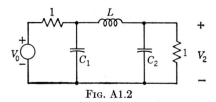

FIG. A1.2

To illustrate the use of simple continuants, the transfer voltage ratio of Fig. A1.2 is determined. For this circuit

$$a_1 = 1 \qquad a_2 = pC_1 \qquad a_3 = pL \qquad a_4 = pC_2 + 1 \qquad (A1.23)$$

Using (A1.22), one obtains

$$\begin{aligned}
t_V &= \frac{1}{(1)(pC_1)(pL)(pC_2 + 1) + (pL)(pC_2 + 1) + (pC_2 + 1) + pC_1 + 1} \\
&= \frac{1/LC_1C_2}{p^3 + \dfrac{C_1 + C_2}{C_1C_2}p^2 + \left(\dfrac{1}{C_1C_2} + \dfrac{C_1 + C_2}{LC_1C_2}\right)p + \dfrac{2}{LC_1C_2}} \qquad (A1.24)
\end{aligned}$$

POWER AND ENERGY IN 1-PORT NETWORKS

In Chap. 6 the properties of a passive 1-port network are derived on the basis of (1) stability, (2) the fact that the sinusoidal average power into the network is nonnegative, and (3) certain theorems from complex function theory. The result of the development is that the impedance of a passive lumped 1-port is a positive real rational function. In the text this basic property is shown to be sufficient for networks containing only two kinds of elements. An alternate method of showing the necessity of the positive real criterion is based on the energy storage in and the instantaneous power flow into the 1-port. By and large, the latter method involves a greater amount of manipulation than the former and,

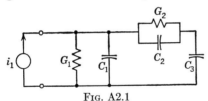

FIG. A2.1

in addition, requires a knowledge of quadratic forms. A complete development of this method has been made by Bode, Guillemin, Tuttle, and others. For illustrative purposes, it is developed for networks containing only resistances and capacitances.

Initially, the network shown in Fig. A2.1 is used as a focal point. The equilibrium equations on the node basis in the time domain are

$$i_1 = (G_1 + G_2)v_1 + (C_1 + C_2)\frac{dv_1}{dt} + \left(-G_2v_2 - C_2\frac{dv_2}{dt}\right)$$

$$0 = \left(-G_2v_1 - C_2\frac{dv_1}{dt}\right) + G_2v_2 + C_2\frac{dv_2}{dt} + C_3\frac{dv_2}{dt}$$

(A2.1)

These equations can be more easily dealt with in terms of the self- and mutual conductances and capacitances.

$$i_1 = G_{11}v_1 + C_{11}\frac{dv_1}{dt} + G_{12}v_2 + C_{12}\frac{dv_2}{dt}$$

$$0 = G_{21}v_1 + C_{21}\frac{dv_1}{dt} + G_{22}v_2 + C_{22}\frac{dv_2}{dt}$$

(A2.2)

If the first equation is multiplied by v_1, the second equation by v_2, and the two equations are added, an expression for the instantaneous power into the network is obtained.

$$P_{in}(t) = G_{11}v_1^2 + G_{12}v_1v_2 + G_{21}v_1v_2 + G_{22}v_2^2$$
$$+ C_{11}v_1 \frac{dv_1}{dt} + C_{12}v_1 \frac{dv_2}{dt} + C_{21}v_2 \frac{dv_1}{dt} + C_{22}v_2 \frac{dv_2}{dt} \quad \text{(A2.3)}$$

For the general case this can be compactly written by using a double-summation notation.

$$P_{in} = \sum_{i=1}^{n} \sum_{j=1}^{n} G_{ij}v_iv_j + \sum_{i=1}^{n} \sum_{j=1}^{n} C_{ij}v_i \frac{dv_j}{dt} \quad \text{(A2.4)}$$

The upper limits of the summations have been written as n rather than 2, since (A2.4) is valid for any RC network which has no internal sources.

The two components of (A2.4) can be interpreted as the instantaneous dissipation in the conductances F and as the instantaneous time rate of change of stored electric energy in the capacitances $(d/dt)E$.

$$P_{in} = F + \frac{d}{dt} E \quad \text{(A2.5)}$$

where

$$F = \sum_{i=1}^{n} \sum_{j=1}^{n} G_{ij}v_iv_j \quad \text{(A2.6)}$$

$$\frac{d}{dt} E = \sum_{i=1}^{n} \sum_{j=1}^{n} C_{ij}v_i \frac{dv_j}{dt} \quad \text{(A2.7)}$$

To amplify (A2.7), consider the stored energy in a single capacitance:

$$E = \int_0^t vi \, dt = \int_0^t vC \frac{dv}{dt} dt = \frac{1}{2} Cv^2 \quad \text{(A2.8)}$$

The time rate of change of this quantity is of the same form in (A2.4). In general, for any number of capacitances the instantaneous stored energy is

$$E = \frac{1}{2} \sum_{i=1}^{n} \sum_{j=1}^{n} C_{ij}v_iv_j \quad \text{(A2.9)}$$

The derivative of (A2.9) with respect to time is

$$\frac{dE}{dt} = \frac{1}{2} \sum \sum C_{ij}v_i \frac{dv_j}{dt} + \frac{1}{2} \sum \sum C_{ij}v_j \frac{dv_i}{dt} \quad \text{(A2.10)}$$

Since $C_{ij} = C_{ji}$

$$\frac{dE}{dt} = \sum_{i=1}^{n} \sum_{j=1}^{n} C_{ij} v_i \frac{dv_j}{dt} \qquad \text{(A2.11)}$$

Quantities F and E are known mathematically as quadratic forms.[6] From physical arguments, the values of F and E must always be positive irrespective of the value of the variables $v_i(t)$, $v_j(t)$, because both the instantaneous dissipation and the instantaneous stored energy must be positive. The positive property of these quadratic forms is thus a function of only the coefficients of the form, i.e., G_{ij} and C_{ij}, and not of the variables. These types of quadratic forms are called positive definite.

The next step is to duplicate the above process in the complex-frequency domain. In the step corresponding to (A2.3), the equations are multiplied by the conjugate of the voltages in conformance with the definition of power in the frequency domain. The final expression for a general network is

$$I_1 \bar{V}_1 = F_0 + pE_0 \qquad \text{(A2.12)}$$

where

$$F_0 = \sum_{i=1}^{n} \sum_{j=1}^{n} G_{ij} V_i \bar{V}_j \qquad \text{(A2.13)}$$

$$E_0 = \frac{1}{2} \sum_{i=1}^{n} \sum_{j=1}^{n} C_{ij} V_i \bar{V}_j \qquad \text{(A2.14)}$$

The quadratic forms F_0 and E_0 clearly have the same coefficients as the quadratic forms F and E.* Although the variables of the quadratic forms are complex, F_0 and E_0 are real. This is seen by considering the pairs of terms involving G_{ij} and G_{ji} or C_{ij} and C_{ji}, where it is to be noted that $G_{ij} = G_{ji}$, $C_{ij} = C_{ji}$. For example,

$$C_{ij} V_i \bar{V}_j + C_{ji} V_j \bar{V}_i = C_{ij}(V_i \bar{V}_j + V_j \bar{V}_i) = 2C_{ij} \, \text{Re} \, [V_i \bar{V}_j] = \text{real} \quad \text{(A2.15)}$$

Since the coefficients of F_0 are equal to the coefficients of F, and the coefficients of E_0 are equal to the coefficients of E, F_0 and E_0 are also positive definite quadratic forms.

A dual procedure can also be followed, starting from a general mesh analysis. The final result corresponding to (A2.12) is

$$V_1 \bar{I}_1 = F_0^* + \frac{E_0^*}{p} \qquad \text{(A2.16)}$$

where

$$F_0^* = \sum_{i=1}^{n} \sum_{j=1}^{n} R_{ij} I_i \bar{I}_j \qquad \text{(A2.17)}$$

$$E_0^* = \frac{1}{2} \sum_{i=1}^{n} \sum_{j=1}^{n} S_{ij} I_i \bar{I}_j \qquad \text{(A2.18)}$$

* Properly, F_0 and E_0 are hermitian forms, since the variables of the forms are $V_i(p)$, $V_j(p)$, which are functions of complex variables.

In (A2.18), S_{ij} are the self- or mutual elastances of the meshes (reciprocal capacitances).

Expressions for the input admittance and the input impedance are found by dividing (A2.12) and (A2.16) by $|V_1|^2$ and $|I_1|^2$, respectively.

$$Y(p) = \frac{I_1}{V_1} = \frac{1}{|V_1|^2}(F_0 + pE_0) \tag{A2.19}$$

$$Z(p) = \frac{V_1}{I_1} = \frac{1}{|I_1|^2}\left(F_0^* + \frac{E_0^*}{p}\right) \tag{A2.20}$$

From the real positive definite natures of the quadratic forms it can be shown directly that $Y(p)$ and $Z(p)$ are positive real functions. For example, (A2.20) is clearly real when p is real. For $p = \sigma + j\omega$

$$\operatorname{Re}\left[Z(\sigma + j\omega)\right] = \frac{1}{|I_1|^2}\left(F_0^* + \frac{\sigma E_0^*}{\sigma^2 + \omega^2}\right) \geq 0 \qquad \text{for } \sigma \geq 0 \quad \text{(A2.21)}$$

The subsidiary properties of RC 1-port networks, as developed in Chap. 10, can be derived from (A2.19) and (A2.20).

An identical procedure can be followed for networks containing R, L, and C. From the nodal analysis the results in the time domain are

$$P_{\text{in}}(t) = F + \frac{d}{dt}(E + T) \tag{A2.22}$$

where F and E are given in (A2.6) and (A2.9), and

$$T = \frac{1}{2}\sum_{i=1}^{n}\sum_{j=1}^{n}\Gamma_{ij}\psi_i\psi_j \tag{A2.23}$$

In (A2.23), Γ_{ij} are the self- and mutual reciprocal inductances and ψ_i is the instantaneous flux linkage associated with the ith mesh. T constitutes the instantaneous magnetic energy stored in the inductances of the network. In the frequency domain

$$I_1\bar{V}_1 = F_0 + pE_0 + \frac{T_0}{p} \tag{A2.24}$$

where

$$T_0 = \frac{1}{2}\sum_{i=1}^{n}\sum_{j=1}^{n}\Gamma_{ij}V_i\bar{V}_j \tag{A2.25}$$

The input admittance can be written as

$$Y(p) = \frac{1}{|V_1|^2}\left(F_0 + pE_0 + \frac{T_0}{p}\right) \tag{A2.26}$$

Again because the quadratic forms are real and positive definite, it is easily shown that $Y(p)$ is positive real.

SELECTED BIBLIOGRAPHY

Several writers have compiled extensive bibliographies in network theory (see Weber's and Tuttle's books cited below). Valuable bibliographies are found in the *IRE Transactions on Circuit Theory:*

On the approximation problem—

Winkler, S.: "The Approximation Problem of Network Synthesis," *Trans. IRE*, CT-1, no. 3, September, 1954.

On the realization problem—

Darlington, S.: "A Survey of Network Realization Techniques," *Trans. IRE*, CT-2, no. 4, December, 1955.

Below a selected number of books are cited (1) to aid the reader in obtaining information or extending his knowledge about the basic aspects of circuit analysis and the requisite mathematics and (2) to help him further his studies in network synthesis.

CIRCUIT ANALYSIS AND MATHEMATICS

1. Guillemin, E. A.: "Introductory Circuit Theory," John Wiley & Sons, Inc., New York, 1953. An introduction to the basic aspects of circuit analysis in both the time and the frequency domains. Treatment covers power and energy in passive circuits and relationships to the driving-point impedance functions.
2. Van Valkenburg, M. E.: "Network Analysis," Prentice-Hall, Inc., Englewood Cliffs, N.J., 1955. Circuit analysis in the time domain by both the classical and the Laplace transform methods.
3. Gardner, M. F., and Barnes, J. L.: "Transients in Linear Systems," vol. I, John Wiley & Sons, Inc., New York, 1942. Both this book and Ref. 4 deal with linear system analysis by the Laplace transform methods. Properties and theorems of the Laplace transform are included.
4. Goldman, S.: "Transformation Calculus and Electrical Transients," Prentice-Hall, Inc., Englewood Cliffs, N.J., 1949.
5. Weber, E.: "Linear Transient Analysis," vols. I and II, John Wiley & Sons, Inc., New York, 1954. A comprehensive work on linear circuit analysis; intensive development of network theory.
6. Guillemin, E. A.: "The Mathematics of Circuit Analysis," Technology Press, M.I.T., Cambridge, Mass., and John Wiley & Sons, Inc., New York, 1949. A comprehensive treatment of determinants, matrix algebra, Fourier analysis, and complex function theory (including Hurwitz polynomials, stability, and positive real functions).

7. Churchill, R. V.: "Introduction to Complex Variables and Applications," McGraw-Hill Book Company, Inc., New York, 1948. An excellent first book on complex function theory.

NETWORK THEORY AND SYNTHESIS

8. Tuttle, D. F., Jr.: "Network Synthesis," vol. I, John Wiley & Sons, Inc., New York, 1958. A painstaking, definitive treatment of the properties and synthesis of 1-port passive networks. Mathematics developed as needed.
9. Guillemin, E. A.: "Synthesis of Passive Networks," John Wiley & Sons, Inc., New York, 1957. A complete treatment at the graduate level of 1- and 2-port realization methods.
10. Bode, H. W.: "Network Analysis and Feedback Amplifier Design," D. Van Nostrand Company, Inc., Princeton, N.J., 1945. A classical book on network theory, in which the relationships between parts of network functions are of particular importance. Of primary interest to network theorists.
11. Cauer, W.: "Theorie der linearen Wechselstromschaltungen," 2d ed., Akademie-Verlag, G.m.b.H., Berlin, 1954. "Synthesis of Linear Communication Networks," vols. I and II, McGraw-Hill Book Company, Inc., New York, 1958. Another classical work on network theory, primarily for the specialist in filter synthesis.
12. Belevitch, V.: "Théorie des circuits de télécommunication," Librairie universitaire, Louvain, Belgium, 1957. A modern book on network theory and synthesis; extensive use of scattering parameters.
13. Guillemin, E. A.: "Communication Networks," vol. II, John Wiley & Sons, Inc., New York, 1935. A classical work on communication networks, 2-port characterization, and image theory.
14. Reed, M. B.: "Electric Network Synthesis," Prentice-Hall, Inc., Englewood Cliffs, N.J., 1955. An extensive work on image filter design; many design charts.
15. Balabanian, N.: "Network Synthesis," Prentice-Hall, Inc., Englewood Cliffs, N.J., 1958.

APPLICATION

16. Truxal, J. G.: "Automatic Feedback Control System Synthesis," McGraw Hill Book Company, Inc., New York, 1955. Application of network synthesis to control systems. Chapter on RC network synthesis should be particularly noted.
17. Stewart, J. L.: "Circuit Theory and Design," John Wiley & Sons, Inc., New York, 1956. Modern network theory developed and applied to linear electronic circuit analysis and design.

INDEX

241